The Real Estate Manager's Technical Glossary

Editorial Consultants
Jack C. Cornachio, CPM®
Louis A. Danzico, CPM®
James S. Peacock, CPM®
David C. Parks

Robert S. Solorio
Curriculum and Publishing Project Manager

Caroline Scoulas
Senior Editor

Daniel Lohmann
Graphic Designer

The Real Estate Manager's Technical Glossary

Thomas J. Griffin, CPM®

IREM Institute of Real Estate Management

CHICAGO

Library of Congress Cataloging-in-Publication Data

Griffin, Thomas J., 1961-
    The real estate manager's technical glossary / Thomas J. Griffin.
       p.   cm.
    Includes index.
    ISBN 1-57203-030-5 (pbk.)
    1. Buildings--Mechanical equipment--Dictionaries.   I. Title.
  TH6010.G65 1998
    690'.0--dc21   98-42454
                                                                      CIP

Printed in the United States of America

1 2 3 4 5 6 7 8 9 10 Printing / Year 08 07 06 05 04 03 02 01 00 99

To my wife, Karen, and our son, Tom Chase.

Preface

Every facet of real estate management is affected by technical issues. The value of a real estate asset can vary significantly in response to how well the real estate manager understands, and deals with, these technical concerns. Whether the challenge is dealing with a tenant construction project deadline, deregulation of the utility industry, or a change to an existing fire code, a fundamental understanding of a property s technical issues is paramount. Properties whose managers effectively communicate with the property engineer, the construction manager, the architect, service providers, and other technical representatives are the ones where the property s value will be maximized.

In order to communicate effectively with those who provide products and services to the properties they manage, real estate professionals need an understanding of the terminologies other professionals use. While several dictionaries of real estate terms have been published, the real estate professional would have to consult a variety of other separate publications to find definitions and explanations of technical terms used by architects, contractors, service providers, and those in the building trades. There has been no single source for this type of information until now. *The Real Estate Manager's Technical Glossary* has been created to fill that need by compiling selected lists of frequently encountered technical terms into a single volume. Approximately 2,000 terms have been collected into nine separate, industry-specific glossaries.

Basic Engineering and Building Mechanical Systems terms are specific to the physical principles that underlie the operations of many building systems. This glossary includes general information about engineering theory, weights and measures, and piping and pumping systems, as well as specifics related to pneumatic and plumbing systems, heat exchangers, valves, and actuators. *Life Safety and Fire Protection Systems* compiles definitions specific to fire alarm and detection systems, sprinklers and other extinguishing systems, emergency procedures, and other life safety concerns.

Heating, Ventilating, Air Conditioning (HVAC) and Refrigeration Systems includes terms related to climate, design issues, and the materials and equipment used in these systems. (It does not cover indoor air quality issues, which are addressed in a separate glossary.) **Boilers** includes equipment for generating heat and hot water and the fuels used to do this. **Water Treatment, Water Chemistry** definitions are specific to water supplies, waste water, and the treatment of water used in HVAC and boiler systems.

Electrical, Lighting, Data, and Telecommunications Systems includes the principles of electricity as well as wiring, motors, control devices, and computer and telecommunications networks. **Elevators and Escalators** includes emergency elevator operations as well as terms for components and operations of these types of equipment.

Architecture, Construction, and Project Management defines building materials and components, construction techniques, and design principles, as well as many of the legalities of contracting. **Environmental Management and Indoor Air Quality** compiles terms related to environmental regulations that affect the management of real estate. Indoor air quality is included here because it is the focus of increased attention by regulators at the U.S. EPA.

The goal of *The Real Estate Manager's Technical Glossary* is to provide a quick reference to pertinent technical information in an easy-to-read, easy-to-access format. To accomplish this goal, the most easily recognized term is defined within a glossary, and other names for the same thing or other uses of the same term are cross-referenced to it. In some instances, a definition will be more comprehensive, including related or derivative terms that have been cited individually with cross-references. Italics are used within definitions and applications to highlight alternate names, indicate terms that have been cross-referenced to them, or identify relevant terms that are defined separately.

In addition to substantive descriptions written in everyday language, more than one fourth of the definitions include real estate application information that provides additional background and context, and nearly 100 are accompanied by line drawings. Many illustrations are related to more than one term and are cross-referenced accordingly. To help you find a specific term, a comprehensive index has been included. There is also a list of sources for additional, more-detailed, technical information.

Acknowledgments

The definitions in this book are based on research into a variety of published sources as well as related personal experience. The following publications and printed materials proved invaluable to my understanding (see Additional Resources for publication details):

Dictionary of Architecture and Construction published by McGraw-Hill, Inc.

Environmental Management for Real Estate Professionals published by the Institute of Real Estate Management.

RPA Designation Study Course from Building Owners and Managers Institute.

Refrigeration and Air-Conditioning presented by the Air-Conditioning and Refrigeration Institute and published by Prentice-Hall, Inc.

Carrier System Design Manual from Carrier Corporation.

Anixter Wiring System Catalog from Anixter Brothers, Inc.

Several individuals contributed significantly in transforming the initial concept of a compendium of helpful technical terms into *The Real Estate Manager's Technical Glossary.* Sincere appreciation to the following real estate managers who served as editorial consultants and provided invaluable professional expertise in the validation, clarification, and input of specific industry applications from a diverse geographical perspective: Jack C. Cornachio, CPM®, Vice President of Boston Financial Group in Boston, Massachusetts; Louis A. Danzico, CPM®, President of Management Enterprises, Inc., in Scranton, Pennsylvania; James S. Peacock, CPM®, Senior Vice President of Peacock Construction, Incorporated, in Lafayette, California; and David C. Parks, Managing Director of Joe Adame MANAGEMENT, INC., in Corpus Christi, Texas.

From an author's perspective, the all-encompassing guidance provided by IREM's senior editor, Caroline Scoulas, throughout the various stages of the manuscript development was critical to the successful completion of this publication. Her ability to interpret, reformat, and present a broad range of technical information with clarity and readability was exceptional. Also special thanks to Dan Lohmann for the creative computer-generated illustrations, book cover design, and typesetting.

Thomas J. Griffin, CPM®

Contents

Basic Engineering and Building Mechanical Systems

absolute pressure   One of the two general methods of quantifying pressure, the other being *gauge pressure* (which see). The pressure exerted by the weight of the atmosphere. At sea level, the average pressure of the atmosphere is sufficient to hold a column of mercury at a height of 29.92 inches. This pressure is equivalent to 14.7 pounds per square inch (psi), referred to as 14.7 *pounds per square inch absolute (psia)*.

> REAL ESTATE APPLICATION: When measuring the pressure of a system in absolute pressure, atmospheric pressure (14.7 psi) is added to the measured (gauge) pressure. Gauge pressure rather than absolute pressure is used almost exclusively in pressure measurements of all types of systems.

accumulator   A device that acts as a hydraulic flywheel by storing an amount of pressurized liquid (e.g., hydraulic fluid) and releasing it during periods of demand; also called *hydraulic accumulator*.

acetylene   See *welding*.

actuator   A device that controls the position of a mechanical component (valve, damper, etc.). The control can be either two position (open/closed) or modulating (multi-position). Small motors often serve as the drive mechanism for valve and damper actuators.

agitator   A device used to induce motion in a confined fluid.

air bound   See *vapor lock*.

air break   In a drainage system, a piping arrangement in which a drain from a fixture discharges into the open air and then into another receptacle (drain) in order to prevent fluid backflow.

air compressor   A machine, usually motor-driven, that compresses air for use in automatic controls or air-operated tools, charging water-pressure tanks, starting diesel engines, etc.; the main operating component of a pneumatic system. Air compressor discharge pressures for general use applications range from 80 to 125 psi.

air dryer   Situated on the discharge side of an air compressor, a vital component of a pneumatic system that lowers the temperature of and removes moisture from air for use in various pneumatic controls. Pneumatic controls rely on clean, moisture-free air for proper operation.

air gap   An unobstructed vertical distance between the lowest point of a faucet opening, which provides water to a sink or tank below it, and the level at which water will overflow from a sink or tank. (See also diagram at *trap*.)

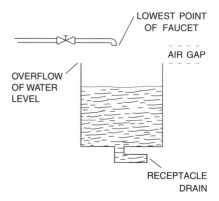

> REAL STATE APPLICATION: An air gap is required by various municipal plumbing and health codes.

air lock   See *vapor lock*.

air-operated pilot valve   An assembly consisting of a pressure control regulator and an air-operated valve used in pressure-control applications. The pressure control pilot receives pneumatic air from an air supply (e.g., air compressor), regulates the air pressure, and sends an air control signal to a diaphragm control valve. An air-operated pilot valve assembly can be recognized from the pilot controller, which is in the shape of a box with a spring on top. On the face of the box are two pressure gauges, the left gauge normally indicating the supply air pressure and the right gauge normally indicating the control air pressure (air pressure to the diaphragm valve). The diaphragm valve is easily recognized by the pancake-shaped *diaphragm* contained in a painted metal enclosure on the top of the valve.

air vent   A vent installed at the high point of a hot-water system in order to facilitate elimination (allow the escape) of air from the system.

American Society of Mechanical Engineers (ASME)   Technical association of mechanical engineers that conducts research and develops boiler, pressure vessel, and power test codes. ASME also develops safety codes and standards for equipment (e.g., for elevators).

American Society of Plumbing Engineers (ASPE)   Organization of consulting engineers involved in design and specification of plumbing systems. ASPE code committees examine pertinent regulatory codes and submit proposed revisions to code-writing authorities to simplify, standardize, and modernize codes pertaining to plumbing.

angle valve   A valve, similar in construction to a globe valve, used in piping systems when it is necessary to make a 90-degree turn. (See also *globe valve*.)

approach   In a heat exchanger system, the difference between the temperature of the primary fluid entering the system (the fluid absorbing heat from or adding heat to another fluid) and the discharge temperature of the secondary fluid (to which the heat has been transferred or from which the heat has been absorbed).

> REAL ESTATE APPLICATION: A plate-and-frame-type heat exchanger with a condenser water (primary fluid) inlet temperature of 50°F and a chill water (secondary fluid) discharge temperature of 52°F has a 2-degree approach. If the heat exchanger surfaces become fouled or dirty, the approach temperature will increase as a result of the reduction in heat transfer efficiency. The difference in temperature between the relatively cool condenser water leaving a cooling tower and the ambient wet-bulb temperature of the air is also referred to as the approach.

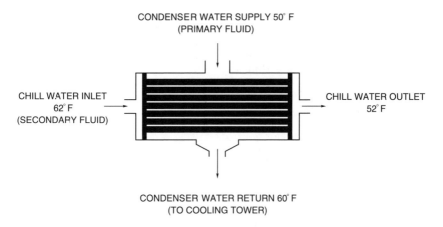

CONDENSER WATER SUPPLY 50° F
(PRIMARY FLUID)

CHILL WATER INLET
62° F
(SECONDARY FLUID)

CHILL WATER OUTLET
52° F

CONDENSER WATER RETURN 60° F
(TO COOLING TOWER)

shell and tube heat exchanger with a 2° approach
(primary fluid inlet temperature [50°F] minus secondary fluid outlet temperature [52°F])

arc welding   See *welding.*

automatic regulator   A device that measures the value of an amount or condition that is subject to change over time (pressure, temperature, etc.) and operates to maintain this value within specified limits.

axial force   A force that acts parallel to a machine's rotating axis (turbine rotor, pump shaft, fan shaft, etc.) and may be inherent in the design and operation of the equipment; also called *axial load.* The axial movement of a rotor, shaft, or other component may be due to the force of the working fluid (steam, water, air, etc.) on the equipment's rotary components (e.g., impeller, turbine blades). Bearings are designed and installed on equipment for the specific purpose of carrying this axial load.

PUMP SHAFT OR TURBINE ROTOR

AXIAL FORCE (ALONG THE AXIS)

axial load

babbitt   A tin-based metal alloy used as the bearing surface of larger bearings. The babbitt lining concept is based on the fusing of this thinner layer of bearing material to a bronze or steel sheet, thereby improving the fatigue life of the bearing material. The softer (lower strength) babbitt metal serves to yield at higher temperatures and heavy loads, thus protecting the primary rotating components (e.g., rotor, shaft) that the bearing is supporting. (The term is often capitalized and sometimes spelled babbit.)

backflow   Flow of water or other liquids into the piping of a potable water system in the direction opposite of its normal flow.

backflow preventer   A check valve or similar device that prevents liquids from an unintended source (e.g., sewage) from entering a potable water system. In many applications, the use of such devices is mandated by federal or state laws or local building codes.

REAL ESTATE APPLICATION: The main supply piping that provides water to a building's potable water system typically provides water to various other systems within a building as well (e.g., HVAC and sprinkler systems). This "common piping" method is very cost-effective and preferred over installing separate piping mains for each respective building system. However, backflow preventer devices are required at each connection point to these nonpotable branch lines to prevent cross-contamination of the potable system.

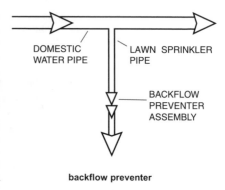

backflow preventer

back pressure   Pressure of a fluid (liquid or gas) developed in opposition to the flow of a fluid in a pipe or duct due to gravity, friction, or other restriction of flow.

baffle   A fixed, plate-shaped barrier for directing or controlling the movement of a liquid or a gas within a confined area, as in a chiller machine or a boiler.

balancing   Rotating machines such as pumps, air handlers, motors, and turbines are required to be balanced in order to ensure smooth operation under a full range of loads and speeds. Since the effect of an imbalance is magnified by rotation, it is important to ensure the balancing of the machine accounts for both static and dynamic conditions, particularly for high-speed machines (e.g, turbines). Proper balancing is achieved through the addition or removal of correcting weight (welding and grinding).

balancing valve   A valve designed so that its resistance to flow may be varied (adjusted). Balancing valves are used in parallel piping circuits (e.g., two parallel hot water pipes that serve two different portions of a floor) in order to balance the pressure drops and provide relatively similar water pressure to the receptacles served by each circuit.

ball valve   A valve that uses a movable ball-shaped device fitted into a spherical seat to regulate the flow of fluids. A *ball check valve* permits the flow of fluid in one direction only.

barometer   An instrument for measuring atmospheric pressure outdoors; barometric pressure is usually expressed in inches of mercury. The earth is surrounded by a blanket of air extending approximately 50 miles above sea level. This air has weight (atmosphere pressure) that varies with changes in its water content and temperature as a result of the weather.

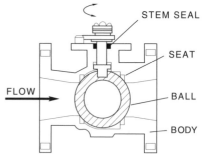

ball valve

bearing   A device installed on rotating machinery components in order to permit relative motion between two machined elements. A bearing supports and aligns a moving part. Two basic types of relative motion are possible—rolling or sliding—and bearings are therefore classified into two general types: rolling-contact and sliding-contact. Both of these types of bearings can be designed to accommodate axial and radial loads. Bearings, which are vital components for the proper operation of rotating machinery, are installed on all types of rotating equipment, including turbines, blowers and air handlers, engines, pumps, motors, and generators. The inner race of the bearing fits tightly around the rotating shaft of the equipment, and the outer race of the bearing is affixed to the inside surface of the bearing housing. There are many variations of rolling-contact and sliding-contact bearings. Some of these bearings must be lubricated by an outside source and others are self-lubricating.

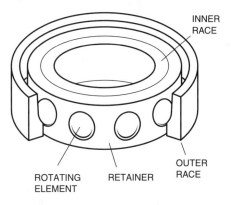

single-row angular-contact ball bearing

belt A drive mechanism (cable), usually comprised of hard rubber material, that is fitted around a prime mover (motor) pulley or sheave and the driven equipment (air handler fan) pulley or sheave in order to transmit rotary motion of the prime mover to the driven equipment. Equipment operated by belts is said to have a belt drive arrangement. Rubber belting is usually purchased in standard sizes in endless form (circular) or can be made endless by splicing. Rotating belts are typically protected by belt guards in order to prevent injuries to operators and maintenance personnel. The traction surface of a belt is grooved in belt-sheave applications.

blending valve A three-way valve that permits a liquid entering it to be mixed with the liquid that recirculates through the valve in order to maintain a desired temperature.

blower A heavy-duty fan.

boiling point The temperature at which a given liquid begins to change from a liquid state to a vapor state at a given pressure (e.g., steam in the case of water; refrigerant gas in the case of liquid refrigerant); also called *boiling temperature*. Water boils at 212°F (100°C) at atmospheric pressure.

booster A fan or pump used to increase or maintain the pressure of the working fluid (air, water, etc.) in a system; also called *booster fan* or *booster pump*. Booster pumps and fans are sometimes used in an auxiliary mode to supplement main pumps and fans, especially to move water or heat longer distances down a pathway.

brake horsepower (bhp) The useful mechanical power provided by an engine, motor, or other device as determined by a friction brake or similar measuring device applied to the shaft.

branch line The portion or section of a piping system that connects the main supply piping (circuit) to the terminal units.

brazing   A process of joining metals with nonferrous filler material, usually in rod or wire form, using heat between 800°F and the melting point of the base metal.

British thermal unit (Btu)   A widely accepted unit of measurement for heat. One Btu is the amount of heat required to raise the temperature of one pound of water 1°F at atmospheric pressure.

REAL ESTATE APPLICATION: Amounts of the various forms of energy used in buildings (electricity, steam, fuel, etc.) can be converted to Btu's as a common unit of energy measurement (i.e., 1 kilowatt of electricity equals 3,413 Btu).

Energy Source	Unit of Measurement	Btu Equivalent
Electricity	Kilowatt	3,413
No. 2 Fuel Oil	Gallon	143,000
Natural Gas	Cubic Feet	1,000
Steam (low pressure)	Pound	1,200

Calculating total Btu's per rentable square foot per year is useful in comparing one property's energy consumption to that of another, particularly if the properties use different energy sources.

bushing   A pipe fitting used to connect runs of straight pipe in which the diameter of one pipe is smaller than the diameter of the other.

butterfly valve   A device for controlling fluids whose opening/closing mechanism is a straight lever handle that is rotated a quarter of a turn (90 degrees) to open or close the valve. (This mechanism is what distinguishes it from other valves.) The butterfly valve is widely used because it offers the advantages of throttling, positive shutoff, and quick opening and closing (automatic or manual). Its construction is sturdy yet simple: It consists of a body, a resilient seat, a butterfly-shaped disk, a valve stem, packing, a notched position plate, and a handle.

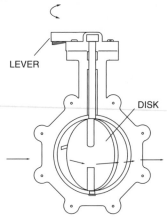

butterfly valve

REAL ESTATE APPLICATION: Butterfly valves are used extensively in automatic applications because of the limited movement (one quarter turn) required to open and close the valve, which makes it easy for a motor-and-linkage-type operator to stroke the valve open or closed.

bypass   Any device such as a pipe, duct, or electrical conduit and its associated valves, dampers, and/or switching devices used to direct the flow of a liquid, gas, or electricity around an element instead of through it.

REAL ESTATE APPLICATION: A bypass circuit may be utilized in order to isolate and make repairs to a piece of equipment in the primary flow

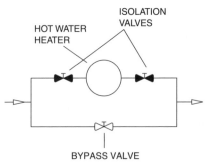

circuit. A bypass circuit may also be utilized as a warm up or pressure equalizing circuit in steam or water systems.

calibrate The process of comparing one measuring instrument (thermostat, pressure gauge, etc.) with another instrument of higher accuracy in order to ensure the first instrument is accurate within specified limits throughout its entire range.

REAL ESTATE APPLICATION: Operators, engineers, and other technicians sometimes measure a substance whose temperature is known (e.g., ice at 32°F) with a temperature sensor in order to verify the sensor's accuracy at that temperature. This procedure serves as a quick field check at that temperature but is not an approved calibration method.

camshaft One of the principal components of an internal-combustion (e.g., diesel) engine, consisting of a shaft with systematically arranged eccentric projections (referred to as cams) designed to control the operation of fuel oil valves, air inlet and exhaust valves, etc. The camshaft is driven by the engine's crankshaft.

cap A device (also called pipe fitting) that fits over and seals the end of a pipe. The seal is provided by threads, solder, or other means.

REAL ESTATE APPLICATION: Abandoned copper piping, which once served a kitchen in a tenant space that is now vacated, should be cut and capped at the junction where the horizontal pipe run meets the pipe riser near the pipe chase (shaft).

casing The peripheral housing of a pump, turbine, fan, gear unit, or other equipment, which serves to enclose, contain, and direct the flow of the liquid (water) or vapor (air or steam) from the inlet to the discharge point. A pump casing is provided with suction, discharge, drain, and vent connections. The suction connection is designed to guide the fluid to the eye of the impeller, where it is then forced (pumped) to the periphery of the impeller and discharged to the outer part of the pump casing (referred to as the volute).

casting Producing metal products by pouring liquid metal into a mold; also called *founding*. Pump casings, impellers, etc., are typically produced off site in a foundry.

cavitation The collapse of bubbles in flowing liquid, particularly at the impeller and suction areas of a centrifugal pump. Cavitation can be detected by a crackling noise during pump operation and can result in pitting damage (also called cavitation) to a pump's impeller. Cavitation will most often occur when the liquid being pumped is close to its flash point (vaporization).

REAL ESTATE APPLICATION: Pumping hot water from a drainage pit with a centrifugal pump operating at a slight negative pressure (vacuum) could cause cavitation at the pump's suction connection.

Celsius A metric system of temperature measurement based on the interval between two standard points being 100 degrees, abbreviated °C; also called *centigrade*. The standards are the freezing point and boiling point of water, which are, respectively, 0° and 100° Celsius. One Celsius degree is equal to 1.8 (⁹/₅) Fahrenheit degrees (see diagram on next page). The centigrade scale has replaced the Fahrenheit scale as the internationally accepted form of temperature measurement. (See also *Fahrenheit*.)

REAL ESTATE APPLICATION: The freezing point of water (0°C) is equal to 32°F and the boiling point of water (100°C) is equal to 212°F. The formula for converting from Fahrenheit to Celsius is: $C = \frac{5}{9} \times (°F - 32)$. The conversion of Celsius to Fahrenheit uses the formula: $F = \frac{9}{5} \times (°C + 32)$.

centrifugal force   The force exerted on an object that is moving in a circular path about a fixed point (center), causing it to move outward in a straight line or "fly off at a tangent." An overspeed governor and a centrifugal pump operate on the principle of centrifugal force.

REAL ESTATE APPLICATION: Centrifugal pumps, which utilize the throwing force of a high-speed impeller, are widely used in pumping applications. Liquid is pulled in at the eye of the impeller and discharged at a high velocity at the outer rim of the impeller. The movement of the liquid is then slowed as it flows through the volute (discharge side of the casing). As the velocity decreases, the pressure (potential energy) of the liquid increases. At this point, the velocity head (force of movement) of the liquid is converted to static pressure (also called *static head*.)

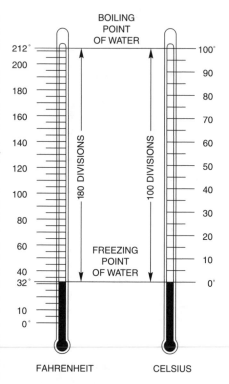

Fahrenheit/Celsius conversion

Centrifugal pumps are non-positive displacement, but they can overheat if operated at zero capacity for prolonged periods.

check valve   A valve installed in a piping system to permit the flow of a fluid in only one direction. Check valves are automatically controlled by the movement of the fluid itself—a reverse in flow of the fluid closes the check valve, thereby stopping the flow. The intended direction of fluid flow through a check valve is indicated by an arrow symbol typically located on the side of the valve body.

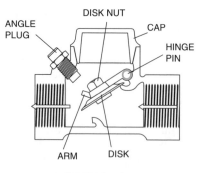

swing check valve

circuit   An independent, continuous, circular path of piping, valves, heat exchangers, fittings, and/or other components through which a working fluid (e.g., water) flows; also called *loop*.

REAL ESTATE APPLICATION: The paths of movement of condenser water and chilled water are examples of circuits or loops encountered in commercial HVAC systems.

circulating pump   An electric motor-driven device used to mechanically circulate water in a system; also called *circulator.*

REAL ESTATE APPLICATION: Small circulating pumps are very common in domestic water plumbing systems, particularly in larger buildings. Circulating pumps maintain a continuous flow of water through the hot water heating tanks in order to maintain a fairly constant hot water supply temperature at the various sinks, kitchen areas, and other outlets. Without circulating pumps, remote water discharge points located at relatively long distances from the hot water source could experience a substantial drop in the water temperature, particularly at night and under light demand (usage) conditions.

cleanout   A strategically located removable plug or cap that provides access to a piping or plumbing system for inspection or so that debris (a cause of water stoppage) can be removed by maintenance personnel.

clearance   The distance separating one fixed or moving component from another, as the distance between a pump shaft and the pump casing, usually expressed as a minimum or maximum distance (e.g., minimum clearance of 0.005 inches); sometimes also called *tolerance* (which see).

close-coupled   A term referring to the proximity of a pump to its prime mover or driving unit (e.g., motor, turbine). In close-coupled applications, the shaft of the motor or turbine is extended through the pump casing and secured directly to the impeller. The pump casing is bolted to the end bell of the motor. (No couplings are required in close-coupled pump applications.) Other design criteria must be considered in order to prevent water leakage from the pump into the motor.

REAL ESTATE APPLICATION: Close-coupled pumps are used in compact layout situations.

closed circuit   See *closed recirculating system* in Water Treatment, Water Chemistry.

coefficient of expansion   A measure of the change in length (or volume) per unit of length (or volume) per unit change in temperature (usually measured in °F).

REAL ESTATE APPLICATION: A fuel oil's coefficient of expansion can be vital information when filling a storage tank because of the potential for expansion of the fuel, particularly if the tank is subject to warmer temperatures.

coefficient of performance (COP)   The ratio of work performed or energy applied as compared to the energy consumed or expended. Coefficient of performance is expressed in simple numerical format with no units (e.g., 12.95, 9.6).

REAL ESTATE APPLICATION: Coefficient of performance information is common in air conditioning and refrigeration applications.

cogeneration   A process of providing electricity to a property through employment of a steam turbine electric generator operated by the property and extracting steam from the turbine exhaust in order to provide building heat or hot water. In some municipalities, excess electric power generated by the turbine generator may be sold to the utility.

compound   A term meaning two (2). For example, compound pumps, turbines, and meters employ working fluids (water, steam, etc.) which can flow in two distinct directions. A compound gauge indicates pressure both above and below atmospheric pressure.

compressor   A machine of the reciprocating or rotary type for compressing air or other gases (e.g., refrigerant gas).

condensable   Characteristic of a gas or vapor which can easily change in state to a liquid by either lowering its temperature or increasing its pressure or both.

condensation   The process of changing the state of a substance from a vapor to a liquid *(condensate)*. This change of state is accomplished by removing the latent heat of vaporization. In condensers (heat exchangers), the vapor flows across copper tubes, through which relatively cool water is flowing, in order to lower the temperature of the vapor, changing it to a liquid. This operating concept is fundamental to all condensers. The liquid condensate collects at the bottom of the condenser shell and is pumped out by a condensate pump. Condensers often operate under a vacuum in order to increase the efficiency of steam flow across the tubes.

conduction   One of the three modes of heat transfer (see also *convection; radiation*). Heat transfer by conduction is accomplished when there is physical contact between the heat source and the receiver. Heat is transferred (conducted) from molecule to molecule along the surface of the materials. An example is the immersion of a relatively cool metal plate in boiling water. The amount of heat transferred from the water to the metal plate depends on the cross-sectional area of the material (plate), the temperature difference between the water and the plate, the thermal conductivity of the plate material, and the time of heat flow.

constant   Referring to a condition, as of pressure, temperature, load, etc., which does not vary appreciably over time (e.g., constant load, constant pressure).

control valve   A device that regulates the flow of a fluid which affects the controlled process. The valve is controlled by a signal from a pneumatic, electric, electronic, or other device.

convection   One of the three modes of heat transfer (see also *conduction; radiation*); the mechanical movement of a mass of fluid (liquid or gas). Convection, by itself, does not technically transfer heat; rather, it moves portions of a liquid or gas from one place to another, providing an opportunity for heat transfer to occur. There are two basic types of convection: *Natural convection* occurs due to a difference in temperature, hence, a change in the density of a fluid. *Forced convection* is accomplished by means of a fan, blower, pump, or other mechanical device.

converter   A heat exchanger, usually of the shell and tube type, designed to transfer heat from one distributing system to another. A converter may be either a steam to water or a water to water heat exchanger.

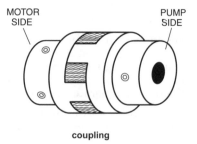

MOTOR SIDE

PUMP SIDE

coupling

coupling   A metal device used to connect the shaft of a centrifugal pump to the shaft of its prime mover (motor). There are many variations of couplings. The two general classifications are rigid and flexible. Rigid couplings connect the two shafts solidly, and flexible couplings allow for minor misalignment (angular, parallel, or a combination of the two). A short cylindrical pipe sleeve used for joining straight runs of pipe of the same size is also called a coupling.

cracking   Used in reference to opening a valve part way (e.g., one-quarter to one-half turn).

crankshaft   One of the largest and most important moving parts of an internal-combustion (e.g., diesel) engine, the component that converts the reciprocating movement of the pistons and connecting rods into the rotary-type motion required to drive reduction gears, electric generators, pumps, and the like. The crankshaft is typically fabricated in one piece and is subject to all of the forces developed in an engine. Along with serving as the principal component in the engine's power transmission, the crankshaft drives the camshaft which, in turn, controls the operation of all of the engine's fuel and air combustion valves.

critical speed   The rate of speed of a rotating machine at which excessive vibration (caused by a shifting of the center of gravity due to the effects of centrifugal force) ceases. As the rate of rotation increases, a motor or turbine can reach a specific speed that causes vibration; however, if the speed is increased further, the vibration will normally cease.

REAL ESTATE APPLICATION: With the increasing use of variable-speed drive motors, it is important to determine a machine's critical speed during the commissioning and testing process immediately following installation. The variable-speed drive controller can then be programmed to quickly increase (ramp up) or decrease (ramp down) the speed of the motor through the critical speed zone.

cross-connection   A connecting point between two piping systems in which one contains potable water and the other contains nonpotable (possibly contaminated) water for use in an air-conditioning cooling system or a sprinkler system.

REAL ESTATE APPLICATION: The installation of backflow preventers is required at cross-connection points in piping systems.

cut-in/cut-out   A temperature or pressure control device that opens (cut-in) or closes (cut-out) a control circuit.

REAL ESTATE APPLICATION: A refrigeration unit typically has high- and low-pressure cut-out devices that shut down the unit (compressor) at predetermined values.

cycle   A series of events that repeat in the same order.

REAL ESTATE APPLICATION: In a large building, the central HVAC system condenser water cycle refers to a circuit in which condenser water flows through piping from component to component repeatedly—e.g., from chiller to condenser water pump to cooling tower and back to the chiller.

cylinder   The barrel (bore) in which an engine piston moves up and down. The *cylinder assembly* serves to confine and release the gases of combustion. (See also *diesel engine.*)

decibel   A standard unit of measurement of the loudness of sound.

degree   The standard unit of measurement of the temperature of a system or fluid.

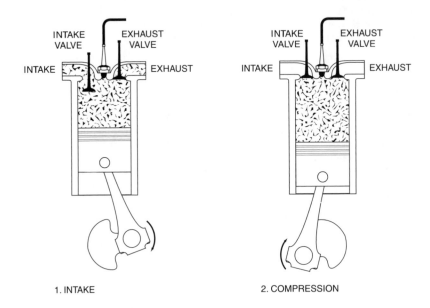

1. INTAKE   2. COMPRESSION

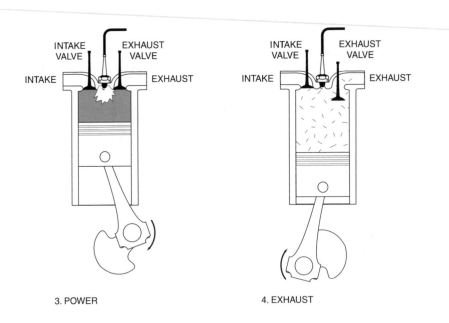

3. POWER   4. EXHAUST

four-cycle internal-combustion engine

delta See *differential.*

demand The load on a system—i.e., how much it is expected to produce or to be used, often measured over a specified time period—expressed in gallons per hour, kilovolt-amperes, etc.

> REAL ESTATE APPLICATION: Anticipated future demand is an important criterion in regard to the design of a building system.

density The weight of a given substance per unit volume, usually expressed in pounds per cubic inch, pounds per cubic foot, or grams per cubic centimeter. For many substances, volume varies slightly with changes in temperature, and as a result, the density changes.

> REAL ESTATE APPLICATION: Cool air is denser (heavier) than warm air and can lead to substantial stack effects in a high-rise structure by displacing warmer air at the entrance to the building, particularly in cold weather conditions.

design pressure The highest operating pressure for which a system or component was designed. The design pressure of a system usually consists of the operating pressure plus a safety factor.

> REAL ESTATE APPLICATION: The required design pressure of a hot water system is vital to the selection of system materials, sizing, etc.

dewater To remove water, as from a flooded space or excavation site, usually by pumping.

dewpoint The temperature at which vapor (moist air, steam) at 100 percent humidity begins to condense and deposit as a liquid.

diaphragm A component within a pressure-sensing device (valve operator or pressure gauge) that responds to changes in the pressure of a system, converting the pressure to a linear motion and subsequent movement of a valve, pressure gauge, or other device.

diesel engine An internal-combustion engine (facing page) frequently used in building emergency power and drive applications. (See also *cylinder.*)

> REAL ESTATE APPLICATION: A diesel engine is the preferred method of emergency power generation. Because the diesel engine has its own source of fuel for combustion, thus operating independently from a property's normal source of power, its performance has proven reliable in power-loss situations. (Natural gas is also sometimes used for emergency power generation because of potential hazards related to diesel fuel storage tanks.)

differential Commonly referred to as *delta,* the difference between two values—e.g., a heat exchanger's fluid inlet and outlet temperatures or cut-in and cut-out temperature settings *(differential temperature);* also *differential pressure.* (See diagram on next page.)

direct drive The connection of a driven piece of equipment (pump, generator, etc.) directly to its prime mover (e.g., motor or engine) as opposed to connection via reduction gears, pulleys, or sheaves.

discharge The outlet side of a pump, nozzle, or other device. The piping connected to the discharge side of a pump is referred to as the discharge piping.

diverter A three-way valve, typically motorized and automatically operated, positioned at the junction of a piping tee to direct fluid flow from one pipe

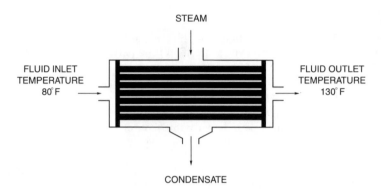

STEAM

FLUID INLET
TEMPERATURE
80° F

FLUID OUTLET
TEMPERATURE
130° F

CONDENSATE

fluid temperature differential of 50°F (130°F minus 80°F)

to another. A *diverting valve* differs from a blending valve in that it directs all of the fluid to one location or the other, whereas a *blending valve* directs the fluid to two locations.

REAL ESTATE APPLICATION: Three-way valves are commonly used in condenser water systems and cooling tower applications to divert condenser water away from the cooling tower during chiller plant start up and low load applications.

domestic water   Water used for domestic purposes such as laundry, showers, dishwashing, etc.; also referred to as *potable water.*

domestic water pump   A pump that provides domestic water at a sufficient pressure, particularly in high-rise buildings when the pressure available from the municipal water supply is insufficient.

down-feed system   A hydronic (heating or cooling, water or steam) or similar pumping system in which the main piping is situated above the branch lines and terminal units. Water or steam flows to the units in the down direction and returns in the up direction.

draft   A current of air moved through a flue, heater, or other space as a result of a pressure difference (difference in density due to temperature differences).

drain tank   A tank for receiving waste water from various systems such as boiler drains, condensate drains, and the like.

dryer   See *air dryer.*

duty cycling   An electrical power demand control strategy that involves automatic cycling (turning equipment off and on repeatedly) when full-time (continuous) operation is unnecessary.

REAL ESTATE APPLICATION: Minimum on and off times need to be established to prevent additional wear and tear or damage to equipment or equipment controllers as a result of excessive cycling. Cost savings and additional wear on the equipment should be evaluated prior to executing a duty cycling program.

eddy current test   A nondestructive type of electrical test performed on heat exchanger (e.g., chiller) tubes in order to determine the physical condition of the tube with respect to wear, corrosion, and other deterioration.

eductor   An ejector-type pump used in the rapid dewatering (pumping out) of an open space such as a severely flooded basement. Water provided from another source (e.g., a fire hose) serves as the motive force and is pumped into the eductor along with the water from the flooded space.

ejector   A jet-type pumping apparatus used for removing fluids. The ejector entrains the fluid in the flow of a primary fluid supplied from another source (e.g., a stream of high-pressure water or steam). Ejectors differ from eductors in that they typically remove a fluid or gas from a system, such as a large steam condenser, whereas an eductor removes liquid from a space.

elbow   A pipe, conduit, or sheet metal fitting used to join two pipes or ducts that connect to one another at an angle. The four angles provided by elbows are 22½°, 45°, 60°, and 90°.

energy   The capacity to do work. It can be in the form of heat, mechanical, electrical, chemical, etc. No form of energy can be expended or produced without expending or producing a like amount of some other form of energy.

energy audit   A methodical review of energy sources and uses performed for the purpose of identifying existing or potential problems at a property and for consideration of building and mechanical upgrades, equipment replacement, or equipment and system operational modifications.

> REAL ESTATE APPLICATION: An energy audit is usually a review of energy used and the cost of energy to operate systems and equipment; such an audit is also included in payback analysis when considering replacements.

enthalpy   The internal heat energy of a substance such as air at a given temperature and pressure, quantified as a unit of heat per unit of weight (e.g., Btu/lb). Enthalpy is a measure of the total heat (sensible heat plus latent heat) of a substance.

> REAL ESTATE APPLICATION: Outside air at 76°F and 50% relative humidity contains more moisture and has a higher latent (absorbed) heat content and a higher value of enthalpy than outdoor air at 76°F and 10% relative humidity. Large central automated HVAC systems often compare indoor air enthalpy (air being returned from the occupied spaces to the central air handlers) to the outside air enthalpy in order to determine which source of air (indoor or outdoor) to select for tempering (heating or cooling) a building.

equalizer   A device consisting of a pipe and isolation valves and used to maintain equal pressure or equal liquid levels between two containers or systems; also called *equalizer valve* or *equalizer tube*.

evaporation   The changing of a liquid to a gas. Heat is absorbed in the process. A cooling tower operates on the concept of evaporation.

exhaust steam   Steam that has been expended (served its useful purpose) in a steam turbine or steam engine cylinder.

> REAL ESTATE APPLICATION: Exhaust steam can be a tremendous loss of energy in an operating plant unless it is re-used—e.g., to heat other fluids such as domestic water or boiler feedwater (as waste heat) or to operate low-pressure machinery. In some situations, exhaust steam flows across a condenser (carrying cool water in its tubes) and is converted into liquid condensate.

expansion See *thermal expansion.*

expansion tank A closed vessel for supplying additional water to a heating/cooling system, connected to a pumping system in such a manner that, when the system is initially filled with water, air is trapped in the top portion of the tank. When the temperature of the system is increased, the water expands (increases in volume) and compresses the air in the tank (which must be vented), thus providing space for the extra volume of water without creating over-pressurization.

Fahrenheit A temperature measurement scale commonly used in the United States but replaced internationally with the metric system's Celsius temperature scale; abbreviated °F. Fahrenheit degrees are smaller than Celsius degrees. One Fahrenheit degree is equal to 0.55 (5/9) of a Celsius degree. The freezing point of water is equal to 32°F (0°C) and the boiling point of water is equal to 212°F (100°C). (See also *Celsius* for conversion formulas and comparison diagram.)

feasibility analysis A study (due diligence) of a potential recommended system or equipment modification (e.g., an energy conservation measure) in order to determine the means and cost of implementation, payback period, etc., prior to proceeding with the modification.

fitting Any of a variety of accessories for providing flexibility in the installation and use of piping; often called *pipe fitting*. Pipes are connected to pipe fittings via flanges or threads, or they are joined by welding, soldering, or brazing. Pipe fittings are designed in accordance with the nominal pipe size for which they are intended. The following fittings are frequently used in piping installations: elbows, couplings, bushings, unions, flanges, plugs, and caps.

REAL ESTATE APPLICATION: Various shapes of fittings—e.g., tee (T), wye (Y), cross (+)—are used in connecting lengths of pipe together. When selecting fittings, it is important to ensure that their allowable working pressure is equal to or greater than that of the pipe to which they are connected. Vitrified clay and polyvinyl chloride (PVC) pipes and fittings are used for sewage and drainage systems; water mains are usually ductile iron, while interior water distribution may be copper or plastic (polybutylene or polyethylene) tubing with cast iron used for drains and sanitary lines.

flange A flat edge projecting perpendicular to the end of a metal pipe or other component used as a means of connecting (and disconnecting) one component of a system with another (e.g., a pipe to a valve). The size of the opposing flanges and the size, number, and location of their connection holes match one another. The flange is actually a part of the valve body or the connecting end of a pipe. Flanges permit the removal of piping and other equipment for cleaning, repair, or replacement.

flash point The temperature at which an oil or other flammable liquid will give off sufficient vapor to support a flash flame but not support continuous combustion.

REAL ESTATE APPLICATION: The flash point of a fuel is typically indicated on specification documents in order to ensure proper burning characteristics for its proposed use. Flash point information is also included in material safety data sheets (MSDSs) for various liquid chemicals and products.

float   A device, usually spherical in shape and having a substantial surface area, that floats on the surface of a liquid and controls the liquid flow by actuating a valve; also called *float control* or *float valve*.

REAL ESTATE APPLICATION: A float valve is used to control the flow of make-up feed water and subsequently to regulate the liquid level. Float valves are also used in tank-type toilets.

flowmeter   An instrument used to measure the velocity (speed) or volume of fluid movement.

flow switch   A device that senses the movement of fluid through a system (pipe, chiller tubes, etc.) and is actuated (produces an output) when the fluid flow reaches a predetermined value.

REAL ESTATE APPLICATION: Flow switches are used on chiller machines as freeze protection safety devices in order to ensure adequate flow of chill water or condenser water through a chiller.

fluid   A gas or liquid that will flow and take the shape of its container.

fluid dynamics   The characteristics of fluids (liquids and gases) based on their physical properties—e.g., temperature, pressure, volume, and state (condition).

flush valve   A commonly used plumbing valve designed to provide a fixed volume of water for flushing purposes, as in a toilet or urinal; also known by the name Flushometer, which is a trademark.

foot-pound   A unit of measure of mechanical work equal to the effort expended in moving (lifting) one pound of mass a distance (height) of one foot, abbreviated ft-lb; 33,000 ft-lbs per minute is equal to one horsepower (hp).

forced convection   See *convection*.

freezing point   The temperature at which a liquid changes to a solid at a given pressure due to a decrease in temperature or removal of heat. Water at sea level (atmospheric pressure) freezes at 32°F (0°C).

friction   The resistance to motion of objects in contact with one another. There are three definite types of friction: rolling friction (a wheel rolling on a track), sliding friction (a piston moving in a cylinder or a shaft turning in a bearing), and fluid friction (water moving through a pipe). Friction results in wear and power (energy) losses.

fusible   Capable of being melted. A fusible plug is a safety device that melts at a predetermined (high) temperature to prevent a vessel or container from bursting. A similar device may be used to actuate a sprinkler system.

gasket   A ring of resilient (flexible) material used at a joint between two mating surfaces to provide a leakproof seal.

REAL ESTATE APPLICATION: Gaskets are applied between valve flanges and pipe flanges in mechanical systems.

gas welding   See *welding*.

gate valve   A valve used to control the flow of a fluid in a straight line when a minimum amount of restriction is required. The shapes of the gate valve body and internal components allow for a relatively smooth (laminar) flow of a fluid when the valve gate is in the fully open (raised) position. Gate valves do not provide laminar flow during throttling (modulation). Gate valves should be installed in system applications where their position will be either fully open or fully closed.

gauge pressure One of the two general methods of quantifying pressure, the other being *absolute pressure* (which see). The pressure actually shown on a dial or readout of a gauge that registers pressure at or above atmospheric pressure.

> REAL ESTATE APPLICATION: Gauge pressure, expressed in *pounds per square inch gauge (psig)*, is used almost exclusively in the measurement of system pressure. A pressure gauge with a reading of 0 psi indicates there is no pressure in excess of atmospheric pressure.

gear See *reduction gear.*

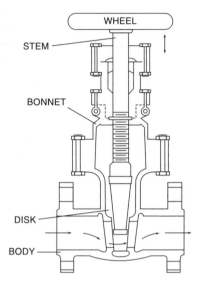

gate valve

gland seal A soft, pliable ring or other device which, when compressed (as between a pipe and a fitting) forms a seal. Specifically, the fitting of a centrifugal pump shaft packing gland or stuffing box with a water-sealed lantern ring, thereby maintaining slight positive pressure in order to prevent air from entering the pump casing. The gland seal creates a slight outward leak of water rather than an inward leak of water or air into the pump. The gland seal prevents leakage between the pump's fixed parts (the shaft sleeves) and movable part (the shaft). Aside from providing a seal and, thus, preventing a vacuum, the cooling water supply to the gland seal provides cooling and flushes the seal in order to prevent grit and other material from entering the seal. The water to the gland seal is typically provided by a connection to the pump casing (under pressure) through tubing to the seal.

globe valve A widely used device that is capable of varying (throttling) the flow of a fluid in a piping system; also called *globe stop valve*. A globe valve regulates fluid flow by raising or lowering a threaded spindle to which a disk is attached. As the disk is raised or lowered, the opening between the disk and the fixed seat is enlarged or reduced, thereby increasing or decreasing the flow of fluid. The body and internal components (disk and seat) of the valve are fabricated and shaped to permit relatively smooth (laminar) flow of the fluid through the different throttling ranges.

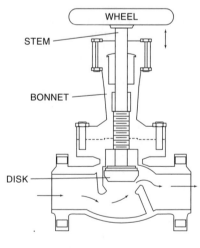

globe valve

governor   A device used to control the speed of machinery (e.g., electric generator turbine, diesel engine, elevator). Used in the course of normal operation of a prime mover, it is referred to as a *constant-speed governor* or *speed-regulating governor*. When used exclusively as a safety device for equipment, it is referred to as an *overspeed governor*. The basic operating concept of a governor applies the theory of centrifugal force, using weights attached to a tensioned flywheel-type arrangement. The weights move outward as the speed of the equipment increases, resulting in subsequent mechanical action that will either slow the equipment (speed-regulating governor) or shut it down (overspeed governor).

gravity feed   A water system (e.g., domestic water, fire protection) in which the source of water (storage tank) is positioned at a level higher than the fixtures being served; also called *gravity water system*. A domestic water gravity storage tank provides the minimum required pressure for the system and also provides additional storage capacity, particularly during peak consumption periods.

grease   A lubricating mixture consisting primarily of a fluid lubricant, a thickener (usually a mixture of soaps), and other materials added to impart specific properties. Greases are intended for the lubrication of bearings in certain types of equipment where oil lubrication is not economically feasible or satisfactory for a particular mechanical design.

grease trap   A baffle or similar device installed in a drain or waste water pipe to prevent grease from entering the sewer. The device allows liquid fat to cool and solidify so the grease can separate from the liquid and float to the top of the trap for removal.

   REAL ESTATE APPLICATION: Grease traps are very common in building cafeteria kitchens, coffee shops, and any area where food is prepared or served. Periodically the traps need to be opened, cleaned, and serviced.

head   The force or pressure exerted by a liquid in a pumping system as a result of such factors as (1) the vertical distance a pump is required to move (lift) the liquid on the discharge side, (2) the total friction encountered in a piping system, or (3) the total vertical distance of the liquid from the pump suction (positive or negative). Various factors must be considered in the design of a pumping system in order to ensure the effective transfer of fluids at the required rate in gallons per minute. All of the negative and positive friction and head losses and gains make up a system's net positive suction head (NPSH).

header   A relatively large diameter section of pipe, short in length, to which a number of branch outlets are connected.

heat   A form of energy that is transferred from one fluid or solid to another by means of the temperature difference between the two substances. Heat always transfers from the warmer to the cooler substance.

heat exchanger   A device designed to readily permit the flow of thermal energy from one fluid (liquid or gas) to another. Heat is transferred from the warmer fluid to the cooler fluid due to the physical properties of the fluids, which are exchanging thermal energy, and the physical properties of the heat transfer surfaces (metal plates, tubes, etc.) of the heat exchanger. (See also *shell-and-tube heat exchanger* and accompanying diagram.)

REAL ESTATE APPLICATION: There are many different types of heat exchangers encountered in building systems. Some examples are: shell-and-tube heat exchanger, plate-and-frame heat exchanger, cooling tower, induction unit, and condensing unit. There are two general classifications of heat exchangers: In *counter-flow heat exchangers,* the flow of the two fluids is parallel and in opposite directions. *In cross-flow heat exchangers,* one fluid flows at right angles to the other.

heating medium   A term commonly used to describe the substance (fluid) used to convey heat from the heat source to the point of use. Air, water and steam are three examples of heating mediums.

heat sink   An area of relatively low temperature to which heat flows from an area of higher temperature. A steam turbine condenser and a building on a warm summer night are examples of heat sinks.

heat transfer   The flow of thermal energy from one substance, body, or system to another. Heat is always transferred from an area of higher temperature to one of lower temperature. Conduction, radiation, and convection are the three modes of heat transfer.

hood exhaust system   A stainless steel cover positioned over a fryer or grill in a restaurant to move smoke, odors, and heat into a dedicated duct and out of the building. A hood exhaust system is normally furnished with an exhaust fan, grease filter, fire-extinguishing system, and light fixture.

REAL ESTATE APPLICATION: Kitchen hood exhaust systems should be cleaned and inspected periodically (e.g., every six months). Ductwork should meet applicable fire resistance code requirements (e.g., one-hour rating).

horsepower   A standard unit of measure of the work or power output from motors, engines, boilers, turbines, and other machines, abbreviated hp or HP. One horsepower is equivalent to 33,000 ft-lb/min or 746 watts (.746 kilowatts). A 100-hp motor operating at full load consumes approximately 74.6 kilowatts per hour (100 hp × 746 w = 74,600 w = 74.6 kwh).

hot water heater   Packaged equipment designed for domestic hot water production comprising a tank, heating elements, and temperature and feed water controls; also called *domestic hot water heater.* Water is heated to a predetermined set point temperature using electrical resistance elements, steam coils, or natural gas.

hot water storage tank   A tank for the storage of hot water, which meets specific code requirements that vary depending on the size of the tank and the pressure of the system.

REAL ESTATE APPLICATION: Hot water storage tanks heat water using electric heating elements, steam coils, or gas.

house system   A term used in reference to a central building mechanical system (e.g., HVAC), as opposed to a smaller tenant mechanical system.

REAL ESTATE APPLICATION: A tenant in an office building who requires condenser water for an auxiliary HVAC unit might connect the HVAC unit into the house system of the building rather than install a separate condenser water system.

hydrostatic test   A water-pressure test conducted on pressure vessels (boilers, tanks, etc.) and piping after initial installation or following major overhauls and repairs. A hydrostatic test consists of filling a system with water, closing off all outlets to valves, gauges, and other devices, and applying a predetermined hydrostatic pressure to the system by means of a small hydraulic-type pump.

ignition temperature   The minimum temperature at which combustion of a substance (e.g., fuel oil) can be started.

impeller   The rotating component of a centrifugal pump. The impeller is attached to the pump shaft, where it is balanced and rotates within the pump casing. The impeller rotates the liquid mass with the peripheral speed of its vane tips, thereby producing the pump working pressure (head). Impellers can be of the straight-vane or curved-vane type. The impeller design can yield radial flow and/or axial flow.

straight-vane single-suction
closed impeller

inches of mercury column   A term referring to a device used in measuring pressure; there is also an *inches of water column*. The system pressure being measured will exert a force on a column of liquid (e.g., mercury or water), pushing the liquid upward a specific distance corresponding to the pressure in the system.

indicator   A device that displays the position, status, temperature or pressure setting, liquid level, or other parameter of a fluid in a system or a piece of equipment. For example, a valve position indicator (indicator valve) will show whether the valve is open or closed or positioned somewhere in between.

infrared (IR)   A region immediately above the visible spectrum in which radiant energy (light) is emitted. *Infrared radiation* is produced naturally by all materials at all temperatures above absolute zero. The intensity of the radiation will vary depending on the temperature and surface characteristics of the material. A *passive infrared system* detects the natural radiation of a material. An *active infrared system* heats the surface of a material which then radiates infrared energy to a detector.

> REAL ESTATE APPLICATION: A nondestructive method of testing materials, infrared is a popular means of testing the integrity of a roof and the presence of moisture.

instantaneous load   A demand on a hot water, electrical, or other system that occurs quickly, with no advance warning or indications.

instantaneous water heater   A water-heating device designed to operate without a hot water storage tank in the system; also called *tankless water heater*. Instantaneous water heaters are more common in smaller size, domestic hot water heating systems.

instrument   A term used to designate a device used to measure, record, indicate, or control equipment.

insulation   Any substance or technique that limits the transfer of heat, cold, moisture, sound, or electricity or provides protection against fire. *Thermal insulation* is a material applied to the outsides of ducts and pipes to retard the transfer of heat from one object to another (e.g., from cool water in a pipe to the surrounding air). Insulating effectiveness is based on a material's thermal conductivity.

interlock   A device that prevents a specific part of a system from operating when another part (or parts) of the system is not operating. Interlock devices typically are operated by electricity and serve primarily as safety devices.

intermittent   The unsystematic and unpredictable occurrence of system or component fluctuations, alarms, or status changes. Intermittent problems or flaws in engineered systems are more difficult to troubleshoot than those that occur consistently.

internal-combustion engine   See *diesel engine.*

International Standards Organization (ISO)   An entity that promotes the development of worldwide industry standards and publishes these standards. There are a variety of ISO requirements and designations specific to respective manufacturing and service industries.

international system of units   See *standard international (SI) units.*

labyrinth seal   A packing system consisting of a series of rows of metallic strips used to seal a working fluid (e.g., steam) between a moving part (rotor or shaft) and a fixed part (casing); sometimes called simply *labyrinth.* Labyrinth seals are common in steam turbine seal applications.

lagging   Thermal insulation for large pipes, ducts, tanks, and the like.

laminar flow   Streamline movement of a fluid (liquid or gas) through a conduit (pipe or duct) in which the flow is smooth, and the molecules comprising the fluid move in layers parallel to each other. In laminar-flow conditions, heat is transferred by molecular conduction (as opposed to convection) within the fluid from layer to layer. Laminar-flow conditions yield lower heat transfer rates than turbulent-flow conditions. (See also *turbulent flow.*)

latent heat   See definition in Heating, Ventilating, Air Conditioning (HVAC) and Refrigeration Systems.

leaching   A process of separating a liquid from a solid (waste water) by percolation into the surrounding soil (e.g., a leaching cesspool).

life cycle   The total number of years of operation of a system or piece of equipment from its installation (commissioning) to replacement or removal; also known as *operating life cycle.*

   REAL ESTATE APPLICATION: The life-cycle costs of a system include the initial purchase price as well as the total maintenance and operating costs throughout its lifetime. The life-cycle costs of building systems should be evaluated prior to purchase.

limit control   A device used to open or close electric circuits as predetermined high and low limits of temperature, pressure, or fluid levels are reached.

loop   See *circuit.*

lubrication   A process of providing oils or greases to surfaces exposed to mechanical contact (friction) and wear (e.g., a bearing and shaft) in order to separate the two surfaces with a thin fluid film. Lubrication occurs when the pressures developed in the fluid film are sufficient to support the bearing load. There are several methods of applying lubricants to ensure proper lubrication, including constant-level lubricators, ring-oiled bearings, grease caps, gravity-feed oilers, and forced-feed (pressurized) lubricators. The choice of lubrication method is as important as the selection of the lubricant itself.

main   In a piping system, the principal (central) pipe to which branch piping is connected.

makeup water   See definition in Water Treatment, Water Chemistry.

manifold   Several valves, usually both suction and discharge, arranged in a group for the convenience of opening and closing in a single location, particularly when taking by suction from and discharging to several different sources or receptacles (e.g., fuel oil tanks); referred to specifically as a *valve manifold*. Also, a section of duct or pipe with a number of branches that are close together.

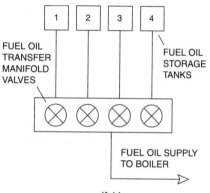

manifold
(fuel oil transfer manifold,
from fuel oil storage tanks to boiler)

manometer   An instrument for measuring pressure consisting of a U-shaped glass partially filled with water or mercury, with one side connected to the pressure source.

mechanical seal   A sealing method in which two highly polished sealing surfaces, running adjacently, are positioned in a plane perpendicular to the shaft, with one surface connected to the shaft and the other to the stationary portion of the pump. Complete sealing is accomplished at the fixed members. A slight leakage (flow) of liquid past the seal surfaces is required in the mechanical seal method. (While there are many variations of mechanical seal design, all operate on this principle.) This relatively new method has effectively replaced prior methods (e.g., stuffing box shaft seal) in most centrifugal pump applications.

mercury   A heavy, silver-colored metallic element (chemical symbol: Hg), which exhibits the unique physical characteristics of (1) being a liquid at room temperature and (2) expanding and contracting in volume with slight variations of temperature. Because of these properties, mercury is frequently used in thermometers and other temperature-measuring devices. It is also used in measuring pressure of fluids (reported as inches of mercury).

meter   A device for measuring the amount of a substance (e.g., a liquid, gas, electricity) as it flows. Also, a unit of measure in the *metric system* (which see).

metric system   An internationally recognized system of measures and weights, based on the meter (length) and the gram (weight), which utilizes base units and factors (multiples and submultiples) of ten. These units (meter and gram) are also accepted and used in the internationally recognized standard international (SI) unit system of measurement. (See *standard interna-tional [SI] units* for sample meter and gram conversion factors.) The metric system measures temperature in degrees Celsius and measures heat energy (heating and cooling) in watts and kilowatts.

REAL ESTATE APPLICATION: To encourage use of the metric system in the United States, the government passed two acts. The Metric Conversion Act was promulgated in 1975 and the Omnibus Trade and Competitiveness Act in 1988. These Acts established that metric measures would be used in all federal procurement, grants, and business-related activities by September 30, 1992. The goal of these Acts was to make the United States more com-petitive in international trade. Compliance is voluntary, however.

Many federal agencies have made the shift to metric, including the General Services Agency (GSA), which oversees all federal building con-struction and management. It is expected that the shift to metric will con-tinue with private sector companies, including the real estate industry.

mixing valve   A valve that mixes liquids, either automatically or manually, to maintain a desired temperature.

REAL ESTATE APPLICATION: Mixing valves are common in domestic water pip-ing systems.

modulator   A type of controlling device that adjusts in relatively small in-crements rather than by either fully open (on) or fully closed (off) positioning.

REAL ESTATE APPLICATION: Ventilation dampers are modulating devices.

nameplate data   The design and operating specifications for a piece of equipment (e.g., a motor) that are stamped on a thin metal plate and physi-cally attached to the equipment. The accompanying diagram shows how the types of data for an induction motor might be displayed.

REAL ESTATE APPLICATION: Nameplate data can be very helpful to building operators and managers, particularly if the technical manual for the equip-ment is not immediately available. (If they can be located, manufacturers may be able to provide specification and warranty data.)

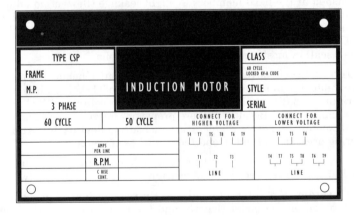

nameplate data (induction motor)

natural convection   A form of heat transfer occurring because of a difference in density between different parts of a fluid (liquid, gas).

> REAL ESTATE APPLICATION: An example of this phenomenon occurs in a natural convection boiler. Because relatively cool feed water entering the boiler is more dense than the heated water, it travels to the lowest heating surfaces of the system. As this water is heated, it becomes less dense and moves upward to the top of the boiler. Cooler water continues to move down to the lowest portion of the boiler displacing the warmer water and continuing the cycle.

neoprene seal   A synthetic, resilient, soft rubber seal, common in HVAC and refrigeration components, which is resistant to hydrocarbon oil and gas.

nominal dimension   The identifying size of a pipe or other opening (e.g., valve, pump suction, discharge); also called *nominal pipe size*. Nominal dimensions are close to, but not necessarily identical with, the actual measured dimensions. A pipe with a nominal pipe size of 3 inches may have an actual measured outside diameter of 3½ inches.

nondestructive testing   Testing of materials or components (e.g., pipes, roofs) using methods that do not result in damage to the materials being tested.

> REAL ESTATE APPLICATION: Ultrasound and infrared are two examples of nondestructive testing methods. Cutting out a section of roofing and examining it for moisture is an example of a testing method that is *destructive*.

nozzle   An opening (passageway) or a row of openings (nozzle block) arranged in such a way as to direct high-pressure steam onto a set of turbine blades. The nozzle block of a turbine is where the thermal energy of steam is converted to mechanical kinetic energy at the turbine blades.

oil analysis   The removal, inspection, and testing of the lubricating oil of a machine.

> REAL ESTATE APPLICATION: Oil analysis is performed to ensure that internal metal components of equipment (chiller compressor, reduction gear unit, or other machinery) are not wearing (grinding), as well as measure indicators of the condition and composition of the oil itself.

open circuit   See *open recirculating system* in Water Treatment, Water Chemistry.

orifice   A relatively small, accurate-sized (precision cut) opening for controlling the flow of fluid.

overload   A load in excess of the load for which the equipment or system was designed.

override   A manual command input signal into an automated control system, which replaces (supersedes) an existing program or setting (time schedule, temperature set point) either temporarily or on a permanent basis.

> REAL ESTATE APPLICATION: A building HVAC operator may be required to input a temporary override command in order to extend the operation of an air handler for a tenant function between the hours of 6:00 P.M. and 9:00 P.M.

overspeed trip   An emergency safety device to prevent a turbine, elevator, or other machinery from overspeeding, typically set at a predetermined percentage above the equipment's operating speed (e.g., 110%). The overspeed trip employs a weight (plunger) and compressed spring arrangement and uses centrifugal force to trip a safety latch or throttle valve (steam turbine).

oxyacetylene welding   See *welding.*

packing   Material pressed into a void to prevent fluid leakage; more specifically, successive rings of flexible, resilient, impervious-type material pressed into a circular void (packing gland) around a shaft or valve stem to prevent fluid leakage from the system side of the packing.

parallel connection   In any mechanical or electrical system, an arrangement in which two or more components are physically situated side-by-side as opposed to one in front of the other—i.e., *series connection* (which see). Parallel arrangements are frequently used in mechanical systems to provide redundancy and flexibility in operation of the system.

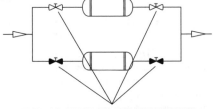

FUEL OIL STRAINER ISOLATION VALVES

parallel connection
(flow through one of two fuel oil strainers)

pass   A term referring to the number of times one fluid passes another fluid in a heat exchanger. A heat exchanger in which the two fluids pass each other once is called a single-pass heat exchanger. If each fluid passes the other more than once, the unit is a multipass heat exchanger and is typically referred to by the number of passes (e.g., two-pass or three-pass heat exchanger).

peak load   The maximum load carried by a machine or system over a designated period of time.

performance curve   A graphic representation of an operating characteristic of a piece of equipment, such as a fan or a pump. The graphic display points show how an operating characteristic varies as a function of a single parameter (e.g., air volume flow rate vs. fan speed).

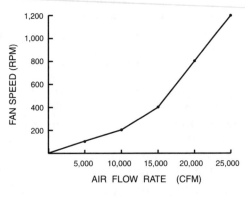

performance curve

permeability   A measure of the ability of a material to be penetrated by water vapor; the ratio of water vapor (moisture) flow to the vapor pressure between two surfaces; also called *permeance.* Permeability is measured in perms (1 *perm* = 1 grain of water vapor per square foot hour per inch of mercury vapor pressure difference).

REAL ESTATE APPLICATION: A material with a relatively high perm rating is less waterproof than one with a lower perm rating.

petcock   A very small valve installed in a piping system or related equipment to allow drainage of water or release of air from the system. A petcock turn handle piece is typically the size of a small key and can be opened with two fingers by turning it 90°.

pilot positioner   See *air-operated pilot valve.*

pinion   A relatively small, lightweight, high-speed, machined-steel rotating shaft with a toothed surface for driving a larger-size gear. Pinions are common in turbine drives that employ reduction gears.

pipe fitting   See *fitting.*

pipe grade   Iron and steel pipe is made in three grades (weights) known as standard (schedule 40), extra strong (schedule 80), and double extra strong (schedule 180).

pipe riser   See *riser.*

piping   A fabricated continuous pipe or tube, with flanges and *fittings* (which also see) attached, for use in the transport of liquids and vapors. Typical piping materials are iron, steel, copper, and polyvinyl chloride (PVC).

piston   A key component of an internal-combustion (e.g., diesel) engine which, through its movement, compresses air in its respective cylinder and reverses direction upon ignition and expansion of the air, resulting in the rotary movement of a shaft. Pistons must be designed light enough to minimize the inertia loads on related engine parts, yet made of materials that will withstand the extreme heat and pressure of combustion.

pitch   The slope or inclination of a horizontal pipe when it is installed in a piping (e.g., plumbing, heating) system.

plate-and-frame heat exchanger   A type of heat exchanger consisting of a frame, an inlet and outlet header, a series of metal plates (having excellent heat transfer properties), and miscellaneous fittings, gaskets, gauges, and other components; also called *plate heat exchanger.*

REAL ESTATE APPLICATION: Plate-and-frame heat exchangers are usually used in building HVAC applications. In the heat exchanger, cool condenser water removes heat from building chill water and then returns to a cooling tower to eject heat to the atmosphere, thereby lowering its temperature for subsequent use in the heat exchanger.

pneumatic   Moved or driven by air pressure; air compressed at a predetermined pressure and temperature and used to operate tools and equipment or control systems (e.g., HVAC valves). Pneumatic air is provided by a building's air compressors. Compressed air represents a storage of energy. Work is done on the working fluid (air) in order for the air to perform work on another system.

REAL ESTATE APPLICATION: Proper maintenance of air compressors and associated equipment (filters, dryers, coolers) is important to ensure effective operation of all the components the pneumatic system serves. Excessive moisture entrained in a pneumatic system can result in damage to the various components served by the air.

point   A software site identified by a specific unique address, which senses or controls an element or device as part of a direct digital-controlled *energy management system.* Various components to be sensed, controlled, or trended are assigned a specific address so that they can each be identified as a point.

REAL ESTATE APPLICATION: A cooling tower fan controlled by an energy management system could be assigned a point identified as CTF1 so an operator could scan a computer monitor for this point to verify the status (on or off) of the particular fan.

positioner   A control component, usually electrically operated (by a small motor), used for moving (positioning) dampers, vanes, valves, and the like, frequently used in the control of HVAC components.

positive-displacement pump   Typically a gear-type rotary pump that traps liquid on the suction side of the pump casing and forces it to the discharge side of the pump. The liquid is trapped in the tight clearances between the gear teeth and the pump casing. A reciprocating pump is another type of positive-displacement pump. (See diagram at *rotary pump.*)

> REAL ESTATE APPLICATION: Positive-displacement pumps operate at low-to-moderate speeds and are almost always used in pumping fuel oils and lubricating oils. Since positive-displacement pumps discharge a given amount of fluid as the gears rotate (due to very tight clearances), it is vital for the pump discharge valve to always be open during operation in order to avoid unsafe high pressures, pump and discharge piping damage, or operator injury.

potable water   See *domestic water.*

pounds per square inch absolute (psia)   See *absolute pressure.*

pounds per square inch gauge (psig)   See *gauge pressure.*

pour point   The lowest temperature at which a substance (e.g., oil) will flow. The pour point of an oil will depend on its viscosity or thickness—oils with relatively higher viscosities normally have higher pour points.

power   A measure of work over a period of time, usually expressed as horsepower (hp); one horsepower is equal to 33,000 ft-lb of work per hour.

pressure   Force per unit area, typically represented as pounds per square inch (psi) of area. Pressure is also expressed as inches of water (in. H_2O) or inches of mercury (in. Hg), meaning the force required to support a column of water or mercury so many inches high. Even if a pressure is expressed as inches of water or mercury, it actually represents and can be converted to pounds per square inch (psi).

pressure drop   The difference in pressure between the inlet and outlet of a filter, heat exchanger, or other equipment. All components having resistance to flow will have a pressure drop. The pressure of the fluid will be higher at the inlet side and lower at the outlet side.

> REAL ESTATE APPLICATION: A pressure drop in various mechanical systems and components is inherent and unavoidable. Calculated pressure drops need to be incorporated into the design of mechanical pumping systems. Over time (between maintenance, cleaning and replacement of filters, etc.), the pressure drop through heat exchangers and the like will increase.

pressure-reducing valve   An automatic device that lowers and maintains a constant pressure of a fluid (e.g., water); also called *pressure-regulating valve* or *pressure regulator.* A reducing valve can be adjusted to any pressure setting within the design limits of the valve; it should then maintain a constant discharge pressure, regardless of variations in the supply pressure, as long as the supply pressure is as high as or higher than the desired discharge pressure. There are various types of pressure-reducing valves but most types are spring operated.

pressure relief valve   See *relief valve.*

prime mover   A machine that converts fuel, steam, or electricity into mechanical energy. Electric motors, steam and gas turbines, and diesel engines are examples of prime movers.

priming   The process of removing air or vapor from a pump casing, particularly in a centrifugal pump application with *suction lift* (no positive suction head available).

> REAL ESTATE APPLICATION: The concept of suction lift applies when a centrifugal pump is used to evacuate a tank or sump with the suction line below the pump itself. When the suction lift is great, a check valve may be installed in the suction line, below the liquid level, in order to maintain a volume of fluid (prime) in the suction line and the pump and, thus, enable flow to start. A priming system for a centrifugal pump is often automated by using an air pump, air ejector, gland sealing, or other devices.

pump   A device that uses an external source of power (electric motor) as a prime mover to apply a force to a fluid such as water in order to move the fluid from one place to another. There are numerous types and sizes of pumps for various systems applications. Pumps are classified according to various design and operational features. The three general classifications of pumps are reciprocating, centrifugal, and rotary.

purchased steam   Steam provided to a property from remotely located (off site) boilers owned by another entity such as a utility company or municipality, usually for heating purposes.

pyrometer   A thermometer that records high temperatures such as those occurring in a boiler furnace or a high-pressure steam line.

quick-closing valve   A valve whose automatic closure is fast acting.

> REAL ESTATE APPLICATION: Butterfly valves are generally used in quick-closing valve applications because the valve handle requires minimal movement (one quarter turn) for full opening and full closing of the valve.

radial load   A force that acts at right angles (perpendicular) to a component's axis (pump shaft, turbine rotor, etc.); also called *radial force*. Radial loads are generally the result of the weight of a piece of equipment (e.g., a pump impeller or turbine unit). Bearings are designed and installed on equipment for the specific purpose of handling this radial load.

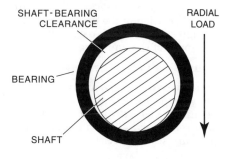

radiation   One of the three modes of heat transfer (see also *conduction; convection*). *Thermal radiation* does not involve physical contact between the heat source and the receiving object. Thermal radiation passes through transparent substances (air, glass) without warming them to any extent because transparent materials are poor absorbers of radiant energy. Examples of thermal radiation are the heat absorbed by a person sitting near a hot stove or the radiant heat absorbed by a building on a sunny day.

range   The pressure or temperature settings of a control system within the higher and lower limits.

> REAL ESTATE APPLICATION: In order to provide tighter control of the discharge temperature of hot water in a domestic hot water tank, one may consider adjusting the range of temperature control from 120°F (low limit) and 130°F (high limit) to 120°F (low limit) and 125°F (high limit). However, caution should be exercised when narrowing the range of a control device that starts and stops an electrically driven piece of equipment. Too narrow a range can result in short-cycling of the equipment as the pressures and temperatures of the system increase and decrease.

rating   The design operating parameters (e.g., speed, pressure, temperature) of a piece of equipment. Equipment is often rated at its maximum performance level.

reciprocating   Referring to a device in which a piston or plunger moves the fluid by means of a back and forth or up and down motion, as in a *reciprocating pump* or a *reciprocating compressor*. The two ends of a reciprocating pump are the liquid end where fluid enters and discharges from the cylinder and the power end where steam or an electric motor drives the piston.

> REAL ESTATE APPLICATION: A single-acting pump discharges once for each up and down cycle or stroke; a double-acting pump discharges twice for each cycle or stroke.

recirculating   A process in which the working fluid in a mechanical (e.g., pumping) system is diverted from its primary route either partially or wholly. Recirculating systems are typically employed in low-load and warm-up operations.

reduction gear   An arrangement of toothed wheels that allows transmission of rotary motion from one shaft to another. Reduction gears are sized and configured such that the speed of the driven equipment shaft is reduced from the speed of the prime mover. This concept allows the prime mover and the components being driven to operate within their most efficient speed ranges. Reduction gears can also be configured in a manner that reverses the direction of rotation of the driven equipment. Because turbines operate efficiently at high rates of speed (e.g., 11,000 rpm), reduction gears are needed to reduce the speed of the pump, generator, or other apparatus driven by the turbine.

regulating valve   See *automatic regulator.*

relief valve   A valve designed to open automatically to discharge fluid (liquid or vapor) when the pressure *(pressure relief valve)* or temperature *(temperature relief valve)* of a system reaches a predetermined limit. Most pressure relief valves have a coiled (compressed) spring-type arrangement as the pressure-setting device.

> REAL ESTATE APPLICATION: Caution should be exercised when adjusting the pressure or temperature setting of a relief valve. Adjustment of relief valves should be performed by authorized personnel only.

reset   The intentional setback of a system's operating temperature in response to a reduced or partial load condition.

> REAL ESTATE APPLICATION: Resetting of a building's chill water temperature from 42°F to 48°F under lighter load conditions that will extend over prolonged periods can result in substantial reduction in energy consumption

and subsequent cost savings. Reset can be performed manually by building operators or automatically via an *energy management system.*

resistance   That which opposes an acting force. Resistance of oil is the basis of the concept of viscosity (thickness, as of an oil). The friction encountered when water moves through a pipe increases the resistance of water to flow.

response time   In an automated control system, the time required for the controlled variable (e.g., temperature, pressure, valve position) to reach a specified value following activation of a command input or a system disturbance.

return   The piping, ductwork, or other means by which the working fluid (liquid or gas) from system terminal units is brought back to the central system components (chiller, boiler, air handlers, etc.). Return branch lines return fluid from the terminal units to the return main circuit (piping), and the return main lines return fluid to the central system components.

revolutions per minute (rpm)   The standard measure of the rotational speed of rotary machinery and equipment (e.g., pumps, motors, air handlers, blowers, turbines, electric generators). The rpm of equipment is normally stamped on the nameplate attached to the equipment and can be verified with a tachometer. The rpm of motor-driven equipment (pumps, air handlers) is a function of the frequency of the electric supply to the motor (cycles per second) and the number of poles (electrical contacts) in the motor.

riser   A vertical supply (or return) pipe that extends from one floor to another inside a plumbing shaft to conduct water, gas, or steam to (or from) the different levels of a building; also called *riser pipe* or *pipe riser.*

rotary pump   A general class of *positive-displacement pumps* (which see) typically used to pump oils. Gear pumps, screw pumps, and lobe pumps are examples of rotary pumps.

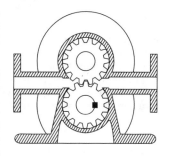

rotor   The rotating component of an electric motor or turbine; in a turbine, the cylindrical shaft to which the bladed wheels are attached. Steam discharged from fixed nozzles impinging on the turbine blades spins the rotor at high speeds. The turbine rotor connects to another shaft (e.g., electric generator or pump shaft) through a set of reduction gears.

rotary gear pump (cross section)

run   A horizontally positioned pipe as opposed to one that is positioned vertically; also called a *pipe run.*

safety factor   The ratio of extra strength or capacity to the calculated requirements of a system, component, or device necessary to ensure reliability, performance, and safety.

safety plug   A device that releases the contents of a container at a predetermined pressure above normal operating conditions and before rupture pressures are reached.

safety valve   See *relief valve.*

saturation point   For any liquid or vapor at a specified pressure, there is a corresponding temperature of vaporization known as the *saturation tempera-*

ture. Conversely, for any specified temperature, there is a corresponding *saturation pressure.* When a liquid reaches its saturation point, it begins to change to a vapor; when a vapor reaches its saturation point, it begins to change to a liquid.

REAL ESTATE APPLICATION: The saturation point (temperature) of water at atmospheric pressure (0 psig) is 212°F. The saturation point (temperature) of water at 120 psig is 341°F. When water reaches these temperatures at the given pressures, it changes into steam, referred to as *saturated steam.* The use of saturated steam is common in many buildings requiring steam for heating purposes where superheated steam is not required. Water at 212°F at atmospheric pressure (just prior to changing to steam) is referred to as a *saturated liquid.*

seal   See *gland seal; mechanical seal.*

sensible heat   See definition in Heating, Ventilating, Air Conditioning (HVAC) and Refrigeration Systems.

sensitivity   The ability of a control instrument to measure and act upon variations of the measured condition.

sensor   A device that undergoes a physical change or a change in electronic characteristics in response to a change in temperature, pressure, humidity, or other parameter.

REAL ESTATE APPLICATION: There are numerous types of sensors for a wide array of applications. Sensors typically send input signals (values) to control devices in order to control a system or a portion of a system. Some sensors are used to signal an alarm condition or initiate some other form of control.

series connection   In any mechanical or electrical system, an arrangement in which two or more components are physically situated one in front of the other as opposed to side by side—i.e., *parallel connection* (which see). A boiler system requiring very clean fuel may have two strainers arranged in series, the first strainer providing relatively standard filtration, the second providing fine filtration of very small particles.

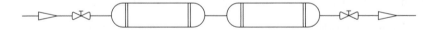

series connection (flow through two in-line fuel oil strainers)

set point   In an automated control system, the value of the controlled variable (temperature, pressure, valve position) that is to be maintained.

shaft seal   A device used to prevent leakage between a shaft (pump shaft) and its housing (pump casing).

sheave   A rotating, grooved, disk-shaped pulley device that has a belt wrapped around it and is used to transmit rotary motion from a prime mover (e.g., motor) to the driven equipment (e.g., air handler). The sheave (pronounced: shiv) is mounted on the end of the shaft of the prime mover and aligned with the opposing sheave, which is attached to the end of the driven equipment shaft.

shell-and-tube heat exchanger   A common type of heat exchanger consisting of a cylindrical shell, an inlet and outlet header and tube sheet, many copper tubes (having excellent heat transfer properties), and miscellaneous fittings, gaskets, gauges, and other components. A liquid (e.g., water) is typically pumped through the tubes, whereas a liquid or vapor (e.g., refrigerant or steam) flows around (over) the tubes.

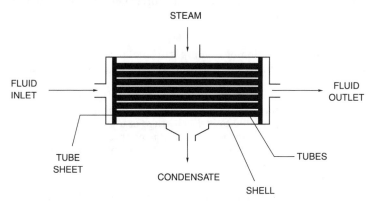

STEAM

FLUID
INLET

FLUID
OUTLET

TUBE
SHEET

CONDENSATE

TUBES

SHELL

shell-and-tube heat exchanger

short cycling   A situation in which a piece of machinery operating in an automatic mode (e.g., refrigeration compressor) starts and stops more frequently than is intended, often the result of faulty automatic controls or a control range being set too narrow.

sight glass   A glass tube used to indicate the liquid level in a tank, boiler, or other equipment.

silver braze   A high-melting, silver-containing solder or brazing alloy used for joining metallic objects (e.g., piping) when high-strength is required; also called *silver solder.*

sleeve   A cylindrical or tubular component that is slipped over a slightly smaller-diameter cylindrical-shaped component such as a pump shaft, conduit, or pipe.

soldering   Joining of two metals by adhesion using a metal with a low melting point (below 800°F). The joint is formed by heating the metals with a torch and filling the space between them (connection joint) with a lead- or tin-based alloy.

REAL ESTATE APPLICATION: Current federal and state laws and building codes specify that all solder on water pipes must be lead-free.

specific gravity   The ratio of the density (weight per unit volume) of a substance (gas, liquid, or solid) to the density of a known (standard) substance such as pure water, which has a specific gravity of 1 under standard conditions of temperature and pressure. Thus, when water and another liquid are poured into the same vessel, but not physically mixed, a liquid with a specific gravity of 0.9638 will tend to float on the surface of water while one with a specific gravity of 1.2362 will tend to sink below the water. A *hydrometer* is an instrument used to determine the specific gravity of a liquid.

specific heat   The ratio that represents the amount of heat required to raise the temperature of a unit mass of a substance 1°F compared to the amount of heat required to raise the temperature of an equivalent mass of water 1°F; water has a specific heat of 1.00.

specific volume   The total volume (cubic feet per pound) that a mass occupies under a given set of conditions; the reciprocal of density or the total volume of a substance divided by its total mass.

stack   See *vent stack*.

stage   Each distinct section of a pump, turbine, or other machine in which the working fluid (water, steam, etc.) undergoes a significant change in pressure or velocity.

REAL ESTATE APPLICATION: The number of stages of a pump or turbine will depend on such factors as its output capacity requirements and the water or steam pressure available to it. Each stage of a pump is characterized by its own impeller; each stage of a turbine is characterized by a set of fixed blades (nozzles) and a set of moving blades. In most real estate applications, pumps with multiple stages or turbines having more than two to three stages are uncommon.

standard international (SI) units   A universally recognized system of measurements based on the following seven base units.

Measure	Base SI Unit	Symbol
length	meter	m
mass	kilogram	kg
time	second	s
electric current	ampere	A
temperature	kelvin	K
amount of a substance	mole	mol
luminous intensity	candela	cd

The SI system utilizes factors of 10 with multiples (larger) or submultiples (smaller) of the base units.

The *metric system* also employs this decimal concept. The most commonly used prefixes in the SI unit system are:

centi   one-hundredth (divided by 100)
milli   one-thousandth (divided by 1,000)
kilo   a multiple of 1,000 (multiplied by 1,000)

A kilogram is equal to 1,000 grams. A millimeter is equal to one thousandth of a meter.

The following table lists some commonly encountered conversions from conventional units to SI units:

Multiply	By	To Obtain	Multiply	By	To Obtain
cubic feet	.0283	cubic meters	kilograms	2.205	pounds
cubic feet	28.32	liters	kilowatts	1.341	horsepower
cubic meters	35.31	cubic feet	liters	.0353	cubic feet
cubic meters	264.2	gallons (U.S.)	meters	3.281	feet
feet	.3048	meters	pounds	.4536	kilograms
gallons	.0038	cubic meters	square feet	.0929	square meters
horsepower	.7457	kilowatts	square meters	10.76	square feet

state   The physical condition of a substance—solid, liquid, or gas (vapor). *Change of state* refers to the process of transforming a substance from one state to another under specified conditions of temperature and/or pressure.

static head   Pressure due to the weight of a fluid in a vertical column; also, the resistance of a fluid in a vertical column due to lift.

steam   The vapor formed when water is heated to 212°F at atmospheric pressure. As it is generated in a boiler, steam is a vapor that nearly always contains a certain amount of water or moisture, even if it is heated above the boiling point (i.e., superheated).

steam trap   A device installed in steam pipes to allow drainage of condensate from the pipes without allowing the steam to escape. Steam traps are installed at the low points of a system, and there are different types of traps for high- and low-pressure steam systems.

> REAL ESTATE APPLICATION: To ensure proper operation of steam systems and equipment and components that operate on steam, automatic removal of condensate from the system is required. Leakage of steam from faulty steam traps can be very costly.

storm drain   A drain used to collect rainwater, subsurface water, condensate, and other nonsewage or industrial waste discharges and move them to a point of disposal.

strainer   A perforated metal basket or other device installed in most piping systems (e.g., condenser water or lube oil systems) to prevent the passage of scale, dirt, metal pieces, and other foreign matter that could obstruct other machinery parts (pumps, gears, valves) to which the piping is connected.

> REAL ESTATE APPLICATION: Strainer baskets need to be removed and cleaned periodically in order to maintain proper operating pressure within a system and ensure proper fluid flow. Strainers differ from filters in that their perforated openings are typically larger (coarser) while the openings of filters are smaller (finer).

subtraction meter   A meter installed in a branch pipe of a building water supply piping system, downstream of the building's main meter (i.e., on the discharge side). A subtraction meter measures the total water flow to a specific system (cooling tower, lawn irrigation system), usually in units of 1,000 cubic feet. Because the water flowing through this meter also flows through the main water meter, the subtraction meter's consumption reading is deducted from the main meter consumption reading during the reading and billing processes to accurately account for the water provided to each building system.

suction   In pumping systems, a term referring to the inlet side of a pump; also called *suction piping*. The outlet side of the pump is the discharge side.

suction lift   See *priming*.

sump   A pit or reservoir located below the grade of a gravity-type drain system, which is used to collect waste water, sewage, or other unwanted water and is emptied periodically by means of a pump (sump pump, waste water ejector pump). Also, a reservoir used for collecting and holding lubricating oil, as for a diesel engine.

superheated steam   Steam that has been raised to a temperature above its saturation temperature (saturation point); also called *superheated vapor*. Water heated to 212°F at atmospheric pressure (its boiling point) becomes saturated steam. If this steam were collected and heated again, thereby raising its temperature, it would become superheated steam. The temperature increase above the saturated temperature is referred to as the *degree of superheat*.

REAL ESTATE APPLICATION: Steam is superheated by capturing the saturated steam from the top of a boiler (steam drum) and redirecting the steam through the boiler's furnace. If saturated steam at a pressure of 600 psig with a corresponding saturation temperature of 489°F is superheated to 789°F, the degree of superheat is 300°F. Superheated steam is more common in high-pressure steam plants where dry (no moisture) superheated steam is required for the operation of steam turbines and other equipment. Higher-pressure steam has the capacity to perform more work than does lower-pressure steam.

supply piping   Terminology used to describe the piping that provides (distributes) the working fluid of a system from the central components (e.g., chiller, boiler) to the point of use. The *supply main* distributes the working fluid from the central components to the *supply branches* connected to the supply main, which then carry the working fluid to the terminal units.

surge tank   In a water supply system, a tank that supplies water to the system when there is a sudden drop in pressure in order to maintain a uniform flow.

sweating   The formation of liquid when relatively warm, moist air comes into contact with a cold surface such as a chill water pipe; *condensation*. Also used in referring to a method of soldering in which two pieces of metal (e.g., two copper pipes) are pressed together and heated with solder between them, forming a water-tight connection.

tachometer   An instrument that measures the speed (rpm) of a rotary piece of machinery (e.g., blower, turbine, diesel- or gas-fired emergency generator).

REAL ESTATE APPLICATION: There are various types of tachometers, both permanently mounted and portable. A *stroboscopic tachometer* matches the frequency of a strobe light in flashes per minute to the speed of a shaft in revolutions per minute or an engine in cycles per minute. The stroboscopic tachometer's frequency is adjusted by a hand dial. When the frequency of the strobe light matches the speed of the shaft, the shaft appears to be still (not rotating). A *chronometric tachometer* mechanically quantifies the revolutions per minute of a machine over a specified period (e.g., one minute) using a revolution counter.

tap   A tool used to cut internal threads. Also, the process of penetrating (cutting) a pipe to insert a pressure- or temperature-sensing device.

REAL ESTATE APPLICATION: A tap could be used to cut threads in an existing pump casing bolt hole so it would accept a new bolt of a slightly larger diameter.

tee   A pipe fitting shaped like the letter T, available in a variety of sizes. *Pipe tees* are designed to connect three sections of pipe together allowing fluid to flow in several directions. Two of the connections are "in line" while the third is at right angles (perpendicular) to the other two.

teeth   The hard metal grooved surfaces cut into the outer circumference of a gear allowing it to mesh with teeth of an opposing gear to transmit motion from one gear or pinion to another.

temperature   A measure of the vibration of molecules of a system or a measurement of the intensity of heat (not to be confused with heat or heat energy). A container of hot water at a given temperature and heat energy will maintain the same temperature but give up one half of the heat energy if it is 50% emptied.

temperature relief valve See *relief valve.*

thermal expansion The increase in size or volume of a solid, liquid, or gas resulting from an increase in its temperature. The incremental increase in expansion of a solid, liquid, or gas for a one degree temperature rise is referred to as the *coefficient of expansion.*

> REAL ESTATE APPLICATION: When filling a fuel oil tank, it is vital to account for the coefficient of expansion of the oil to allow for an increase in volume if there is an increase in the temperature during storage.

thermal insulation See *insulation.*

thermal radiation See *radiation.*

thermocouple A temperature measuring device that uses two dissimilar metal conductors (e.g., copper and iron wires) joined together at two points—a hot junction (measuring junction) and a cold junction (reference junction). Heat applied at the juncture generates an electromotive force (emf) because the two dissimilar metals have different temperatures; the amount of thermoelectric current as measured by an ammeter indicates the temperature at that point.

thermodynamics A science dealing with the study of energy, heat, work, the properties of the media employed, and the processes involved.

three-way valve See *diverter.*

thrust An axial force, usually in one direction along the axis (parallel) of a component such as a rotor or shaft; also called *thrust load.* The installation of a *thrust bearing* on the shaft of a turbine rotor or on the shaft of turbine-driven equipment is common due to the significant thrust forces generated during the operation of a turbine.

tolerance A permitted variation from a given dimension or quantity, often stated as a minimum and/or maximum with respect to pressure, weight, height, and other standards of measurement.

torque A turning or twisting force.

> REAL ESTATE APPLICATION: The starting of a motor and pump assembly results in significant torque of the motor and pump shaft.

trap A plumbing pipe drain fitting used to maintain a water seal against sewer gases, air, and odors.

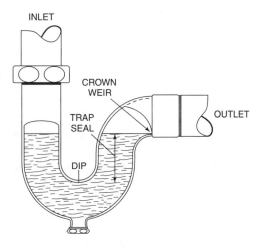

plumbing trap

trending   An automated pro-cess of gathering and recording historical information (values) about a system or component for the purpose of evaluating performance or other criteria.

> REAL ESTATE APPLICATION: Trending of HVAC systems and components, which can be accomplished with an *energy management system,* can prove invaluable in the evaluation of energy consumption or occupant comfort, troubleshooting, etc.

troubleshoot   The process of evaluating and resolving an operating deficiency of a system or equipment by means of testing, observation, trending historical performance, and the like.

tube   A thin-walled fluid-carrying pipe made of metal; specifically, *tubing* made of copper, which provides an excellent heat-transfer medium. Copper is easily heated, worked, and formed in a process called *annealing.* Copper tubes are produced in straight lengths for subsequent installation in heat exchangers.

tube sheet   A component affixed to the insides of both ends of a shell-and-tube-type heat exchanger shell (chiller or condenser) and through which numerous copper tubes are aligned and supported. In the production of the heat exchanger, the ends of the tubes are inserted through and secured into the holes in the tube sheet. Tubes inserted into the tube sheet at the inlet side of the heat exchanger are secured by having their ends rolled back into the face of the tube sheet. (See the diagram at *shell-and-tube heat exchanger.*)

turbine   A bladed wheel-and-rotor assembly (prime mover) that turns at a relatively high speed when a jet of high-pressure steam or gas emitted from a set of nozzles impinges on the blades. The basic components of a turbine are the rotor, blades, casing, and nozzles. Turbines operate with high-pressure steam or gas. Turbine operation is based on continuous alternating stages (sets) of stationary blades (nozzles) attached to the turbine casing and adjacent moving blades attached to the rotating rotor, which act together to allow the steam flow to do work on the rotor, the force of which work is then transmitted to the shaft to which the rotor assembly is connected.

> REAL ESTATE APPLICATION: Turbines are used to drive electric generators, pumps, chillers, compressors, and other equipment. When designed for variable-speed operation, a turbine may be operated over a wide range of speeds.

turbulent flow   Movement of a fluid characterized by eddies (small circular currents moving along the inside surface of a pipe) that cause thorough mixing of the layers of fluid. The mixing of the fluid caused by the turbulence yields a greater heat transfer rate than results from laminar (smooth) flow.

ultrasonic testing   A nondestructive method of testing metal materials (e.g., piping), using high-frequency sound waves to locate flaws.

ultraviolet (UV) radiation   Electromagnetic radiation occurring at wave lengths immediately below the visible spectrum of light.

union   A pipe fitting, consisting of two threaded-end connections and a center piece (nut), used to connect two threaded pipes, neither of which can be turned.

> REAL ESTATE APPLICATION: State or local codes may require the use of reverse-threaded pipe and fittings (instead of a union) for gas pipe connections.

up-feed system A hydronic (heating or cooling, water or steam) or similar pumping system in which the main piping is situated below (at a lower floor than) the branch lines and terminal units. Water or steam flows to the units in the up direction and returns in the down direction.

vacuum The absence of pressure. A perfect vacuum is –29.92 inches of mercury.

REAL ESTATE APPLICATION: The operation of chiller condensers is based on relatively cool water flowing through condenser tubes and refrigerant vapor flowing across these tubes, condensing the refrigerant vapor to a liquid. The result is a rapid reduction in volume of this vapor-liquid, establishing a natural vacuum (low-pressure area). Special pumps also serve to establish or maintain vacuums (low pressure areas) in various system equipment—e.g., chillers, steam turbine condensers. (See also *vacuum pump*.)

vacuum pump A pump (usually centrifugal-type) that removes air or steam to produce negative pressure in an enclosed space or system.

REAL ESTATE APPLICATION: Vacuum pumps are commonly used in large chiller operations to establish the operating pressure (vacuum) within the machines. The operating pressure of a chiller is critical to the efficient flow of refrigerant through the system.

valve A device usually made of steel, bronze, brass, or iron and installed in a piping system to isolate or control the amount and direction of flow of a contained fluid (water, steam, etc.) through the system. There are numerous types and sizes of valves for various system applications. In addition to controlling the amount and direction of fluid flow, some valves also control pressure or temperature.

valve manifold See *manifold*.

vapor A substance in the form of a gas, as opposed to a liquid or solid. Under other conditions of pressure and temperature, the substance could change in state to a solid or liquid.

vapor lock The formation of vapor (gas) in a tube (typically a vertical pipe) carrying liquids, thereby preventing normal flow or pumping of a fluid; also known as *air bound* or *air lock*.

velocity A standard measure of the rate of speed of an object, measured in feet per minute (fpm) or feet per second (fps).

REAL ESTATE APPLICATION: The movement of air through an HVAC duct and the speed of an elevator are both measured in feet per minute.

vent A pipe or other opening that allows for the escape of fluid (gas).

venting The process of removing air from the high point of a pump casing through a vent line and vent cock or valve. The presence and the pressure of air reduces the efficiency of a pump. The process of removing air or vapor from a pump that is under a vacuum is called *priming*.

vent stack A vertically positioned pipe to which individual plumbing vents are connected. A vent stack permits the flow of air from the various connected vents to the atmosphere.

vessel An enclosed tank or system for containing a liquid or vapor, usually under pressure.

REAL ESTATE APPLICATION: Pressure vessels and associated controls are normally inspected for physical integrity and proper operation on a periodic basis by an authorized entity (e.g., insurance carrier).

viscosity   A measure of a liquid's resistance to flow. A liquid with a high viscosity (heavy grade oil) flows sluggishly. A liquid with a low viscosity (gasoline) flows freely. The viscosity of liquids is affected by temperature—viscosity decreases with increasing temperature.

volumetric efficiency   A term used to express the ratio between the actual performance of a compressor, engine, vacuum pump, or the like and the calculated performance of the pump based on its displacement versus its actual pumping ability.

waste heat recovery   The use of waste heat in a building to preheat relatively cool domestic water before it is fed into a hot water heater.

water closet   A plumbing fixture used to receive human waste and discharge it through a waste pipe; a *toilet.*

water hammer   Loud noise occurring in a steam piping or hot water system, usually during warm up (start up), when condensation either expands quickly due to a rapid increase in temperature or is entrained with the steam and impinges on a pipe wall or fitting. A similar condition in water piping due to a sudden stoppage of water flow.

REAL ESTATE APPLICATION: In order to reduce water hammer in steam systems, moisture should be drained from the steam supply pipes before admitting steam to the system, and the steam inlet valves to the system should be opened slowly. There are also special fittings available for this purpose.

water main   In a municipal water system, a main supply pipe for conveying water for public use.

water meter   See *meter.*

welding   The process of joining two materials, usually metals, using heat produced by an electric arc (*arc welding*) or one or more gas flames (*gas welding*, often employing oxygen and acetylene). In some instances, a filler metal is used and pressure may or may not be applied to the materials being welded.

wiped bearing   A bearing surface that is damaged beyond repair. This condition could be due to a complete loss of lubricant or a clogged lubricating system, a very heavy overload on the bearing, misalignment of the bearings, or high concentrations of contaminants in the lubrication system, among other causes. A wiped bearing can result in a seized shaft and damage to the rotating machinery.

Life Safety and
Fire Protection Systems

addressable system A fire alarm system whose status and integrity can be monitored. An addressable system permits interaction by service and repair technicians, building operators, and others for purposes of testing and monitoring fire protection system components and enabling and disabling specific devices from a control panel.

> REAL ESTATE APPLICATION: Most modern fire alarm systems installed in buildings are computer-based addressable systems. This type of system allows operators to interface with the numerous system devices, each of which is identified by a specific address. (The address is also referred to as a *point* or a *software point*). The points and their corresponding devices or components are accessible from a central or remote fire system control panel or via a computer terminal and keyboard.

agent See *fire-fighting agent*.

all clear An announcement notifying building occupants that it is safe to re-enter the building or the specific floors that were evacuated. This announcement is made over the emergency public address system by an authorized member of the Building Emergency Response Team with permission from the on-scene fire department representative. (The fire department is the sole responsible party for authorizing the all clear announcement, even in the case of a false alarm.)

all-purpose fire extinguisher A portable device that can be used in effectively extinguishing class A, class B, and class C fires; also referred to as an *ABC fire extinguisher*. (See also *class of fire*.)

> REAL ESTATE APPLICATION: Most portable fire extinguishers installed in commercial and residential buildings for use by building occupants are the all-purpose or ABC type.

automatic elevator recall See *firemen's service* in Elevators and Escalators.

automatic sprinkler system See *sprinkler system*.

branch lines Piping that branches off from the cross main sprinkler piping and connects to the sprinkler heads. (See the diagram at *cross main*, which also shows branch lines.)

cabinet   See *interior cabinet.*

carbon dioxide (CO_2)   An agent used in extinguishing electrical or flammable liquid fires. CO_2 gas is clean, dry, noncorrosive, and nonpoisonous, and it will not support combustion. It extinguishes a fire by smothering it (displacing or diluting oxygen).

carbon dioxide (CO_2) fire-suppression system   An automatic system consisting of a number of large upright steel cylinders containing pressurized CO_2 gas along with associated manifolds, discharge piping and valves, and some means of detecting the presence of smoke or heat and thereby activating the system.

> REAL ESTATE APPLICATION: Automatic CO_2 fire-suppression systems are typically installed in confined spaces where discharged CO_2 gas can fill the entire space, thereby creating an inert atmosphere that will smother flammable liquid or electrical fires. Although carbon dioxide is considered nonpoisonous, it can incapacitate or be fatal to occupants trapped in a confined space when a CO_2 fire-suppression system is discharged.

carbon monoxide (CO) alarm   An automatic device installed in spaces where CO gas is likely to accumulate. Since CO is highly poisonous in low concentrations, the ability to detect its presence in certain areas is important.

carbon monoxide (CO) detector   A small instrument used for obtaining an air sample from a suspect space and testing for the presence of CO gas.

central station   A centrally located, privately operated facility that monitors fire alarm system activity at one or more buildings in a defined geographic area; also called *central command station.* The local fire department is dispatched to respond to priority alarms while the central station operator (fire alarm service company or other entity) responds to nonpriority alarms directly.

city box, city relay   See *master box.*

class of fire   Different types of fires behave differently and therefore require different fire-extinguishing techniques. There are four recognized general classes of fire:

1. Class A involves ordinary combustible materials (paper, wood, fabrics, etc.). The cooling effects of water as well as certain dry chemicals are the preferred methods of extinguishing a class A fire.
2. Class B involves flammable liquids (fuel oil, paints, paint thinner, greases, etc.). Smothering or blanketing flammable liquids and fire, particularly large fires, with foam fire-fighting agents is the preferred method of extinguishing a class B fire. However, dry chemical agents are preferable in some types of flammable liquid and hot oil fires.
3. Class C involves electrical systems and equipment. De-energizing the affected electrical circuit(s) is the only guaranteed way to isolate and extinguish a class C fire. Carbon dioxide (CO_2) gas is the preferred fire-fighting agent for assisting in extinguishing such fires.
4. Class D involves certain combustible metals such as magnesium or sodium. Class D fires require a heat-absorbing extinguishing agent which is not reactive with the burning metals.

Portable fire extinguishers will typically have a pictorial representation on the side of the device indicating the class of fire for which it is intended. (See also *all-purpose fire extinguisher.*)

class of service Fire protection standpipe systems are grouped into three general classes of service with respect to their intended use in fighting a fire.

Class 1 service consists of 2½-inch hose connections or hose stations capable of providing the heavy flow streams of water required in fighting the more-advanced stages of fires.

Class 2 service consists of 1½-inch hose for use in the initial response and control of fires in their incipient stage.

Class 3 service consists of 1½- and 2½-inch hose connections or hose stations for use in fighting small or large fires.

combustible Characterizing a material that is capable of burning in air (i.e., easily kindled) at temperatures and pressures that might occur during a fire in a building. (Compare *flammable.*)

compartmentation The division of large open spaces into relatively smaller, segregated spaces, often inherent in the construction of typical residential and office spaces. (See also *fire wall.*)

REAL ESTATE APPLICATION: A floor in an office building with larger numbers of discrete offices (i.e., more walls) will contain a fire more effectively than a floor of similar size with a wide open area of workstations. Because standard building construction walls, doors, and other components are fire rated, their mere presence helps to contain fire and smoke. Occupants closing the doors of rooms or offices while evacuating during a fire can help to contain the fire by compartmentation.

cross main The main sprinkler piping on a floor that ties into the fire standpipe riser. The cross main is connected to the branch lines which, in turn, supply water to the sprinkler heads.

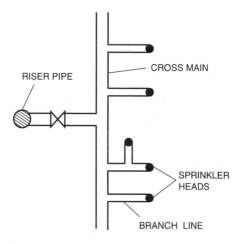

deluge system An arrangement of open sprinklers attached to piping and connected to a water supply through a valve that is opened by the activation of a system of detection devices installed in the same areas as the sprinklers. When this valve opens, water flows into the piping system and discharges from all of the sprinklers attached to it. The valve itself is referred to as a *deluge valve.*

REAL ESTATE APPLICATION: Deluge systems are used to extinguish high-hazard, rapid-spreading fires.

disable Disconnect or turn off; specifically, the process of intentionally rendering a software point (i.e., fire alarm system component) inoperable.

REAL ESTATE APPLICATION: Fire alarm points are disabled periodically to prevent false alarms. A smoke detector located in an electrical closet should be disabled prior to drilling a hole in the concrete floor of the closet because dust and smoke will be generated during the drilling process.

dry chemical fire extinguisher A portable fire extinguisher that discharges a fine dry powder via pressure from a gas stored in the extinguisher; sometimes also called *dry powder fire extinguisher.*

REAL ESTATE APPLICATION: A dry chemical fire extinguisher is generally suitable for class B (flammable liquid) and class C (electrical) fires. There is also a type of dry powder fire extinguisher that is specifically designed for use on class D (combustible metal) fires. Dry chemical agents can be very corrosive to equipment, particularly when the extinguishing chemical is exposed to moisture.

dry pipe sprinkler system A system employing automatic sprinklers attached to a piping system containing air or nitrogen (N_2 gas) under pressure; sometimes simply called *dry pipe system.* Release of the gas (as from the opening of a sprinkler) allows water pressure to open a valve known as a *dry pipe valve.* Water then flows into the piping system and out of any opened sprinklers. Under normal conditions, the sprinkler system piping and sprinkler heads are dry—i.e., they do not contain any water. This type of sprinkler system is sometimes referred to as a combination wet-dry system because there is water present on the wet (upstream) side of the dry pipe valve. A true dry sprinkler or dry standpipe system is completely dry. The piping system is charged with water by manual operation of a municipal water supply valve, fire hydrant, and fire engine truck equipment, using a standpipe connection typically located at street level and attached to the building structure.

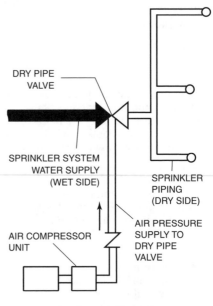

dry pipe sprinkler system

REAL ESTATE APPLICATION: Dry pipe sprinkler systems are employed in areas subject to freezing temperatures (e.g., unheated parking garages) in order to avoid the hazards of leaking or bursting pipes. Dry pipe sprinkler systems need to be inspected periodically for condensation (collection of moisture in the pipes). Condensation can collect at low points in the system due to fluctuations of outside air temperatures. This moisture needs to be drained periodically (e.g., prior to winter) in order to avoid freezing and bursting of the sprinkler piping. A moisture-collection chamber is typically located at the lowest point of the system to collect all of the moisture within the system at one spot. Caution should be exercised when opening drain valves to drain moisture from a dry pipe sprinkler system. Opening the valves in the wrong sequence could release the pressurized air or nitrogen from the system, opening the dry pipe valve and filling the entire system with water.

dry powder fire extinguisher   See *dry chemical fire extinguisher.*

duct smoke detector   A device mounted on the inside surface of an HVAC duct (usually a return air duct) for the specific purpose of sensing the presence of smoke within the duct; also called *return duct smoke detector.* The theory of operation of this type of device is that the presence of smoke in a given space will be detected by the duct smoke detector serving the space (i.e., in air returning from the space).

egress   An exit or way out. A continuous uninhibited path of travel from any point inside a building to the outside of the building at ground level is mandatory for designating an *emergency egress.*

   REAL ESTATE APPLICATION: The specific requirements for emergency egress are dictated by local fire and construction codes. These may include specified lighting levels, door opening characteristics, widths of corridors, etc. A second (alternate) means of egress may be required for a space if it exceeds a threshold of occupancy (e.g., more than 50 people) or if the linear distance of the natural path of egress from the farthest point in the space to the primary egress door exceeds a specified threshold (e.g., 75 feet).

emergency generator   A packaged unit consisting of a prime mover (diesel engine) plus an electrical generator and associated controls used to provide standby (backup) power to various electrical devices (e.g., emergency lighting, elevators, fire panels, fire pump, etc.) during a loss of normal electrical power; also called *emergency power generator.*

emergency lighting   A lighting system designed to provide necessary illumination in the event of a loss of normal electrical power in a building. Exit signs (red letters on frosted glass) are used to identify emergency egress routes (e.g., emergency stairwells).

   REAL ESTATE APPLICATION: Emergency lighting is typically installed in emergency stairwells and other components of the natural path of occupant egress from occupied spaces and other areas of the building. Emergency lights may be powered by an emergency generator or batteries or a combination of the two. The resulting illumination is typically less than that provided by normal lighting circuits but sufficient for occupants to exit from a space or building safely.

emergency stairwell   A vertical shaft enclosed by fire-rated walls and doors and containing a staircase for use by building occupants for egress, particularly during a fire or other building emergency. Since the use of elevators is prohibited during fires and certain other building emergencies, emergency stairwells provide a vital means of moving occupants to refuge floors or out of and away from the building.

   REAL ESTATE APPLICATION: Large buildings often require two separate means of egress from each floor and therefore have two emergency stairwells. Emergency stairwells typically have built-in life safety measures (e.g., fire-rated construction, emergency lights) in order to enhance occupant survivability.

emergency stairwell pressurization   See *stairwell pressurization.*

evacuation signal   The audible signal annunciated from a building's emergency public address system (speaker-strobe devices) during a fire or other emergency that directs occupants to evacuate their particular floor. The evacuation signal can vary slightly from building to building but often resembles a continuous "whoop, whoop, whoop" sound or a similar continuous alarm sound; also called *evacuation tone*.

> REAL ESTATE APPLICATION: Many high-rise building fire alarm systems are programmed to automatically sound the evacuation tone on the fire floor (floor of incident) and one or two floors directly above the fire floor in order to quickly evacuate the building occupants in immediate danger during a fire. Systems in smaller buildings are often programmed to automatically sound the evacuation tone throughout the entire building in the event of a fire alarm.

fire alarm box   A small square- or rectangular-shaped box, usually red in color and mounted on a wall, housing a lever which, when pulled, activates a fire alarm signal at the local fire department and/or at a central command station and within the building in which it is pulled; sometimes also called *pull station* or *fire alarm pull station* or referred to simply as a *fire alarm*. In some cases, the fire alarm box contains a thin piece of glass or plastic which, when broken, activates a fire alarm.

fire alarm system   An electrical system consisting of wiring, panels, and other devices installed in a building as a protective measure against fire. The fire alarm system sounds an alarm, both in the building and at the local fire department and/or central station, when actuated automatically by a smoke detector or other detection device or manually by a fire pull station.

firebreak   A system of fire-resistive floors, walls, doors, etc., employed to prevent the spread of fire within a building; also, a space between buildings to prevent the spread of fire from one building to another.

fire classification   See *class of fire*.

fire command center   A room or other specified area within a building where the main fire alarm panel(s), building emergency public address system, fire alarm system computer terminal, outside phone lines, etc., are centrally controlled. When responding to an alarm, the fire department typically reports to the fire command center to assess the building's situation.

fire damper   A device designed to close an HVAC air duct, isolating it in the event of a fire; also called *fire control damper*. A fire damper is attached to the inside upper portion of an HVAC duct where the duct passes through a fire-rated wall. The damper itself is weighted and attached to the upper portion of the duct by a fusible-linked hanger. A portion of the hanger melts when exposed to heat from a fire, thereby releasing the damper and slamming it in the closed position. Fire dampers limit the spread of fire through the duct and thus maintain the fire-rated integrity of the wall through which the duct passes.

fire department connection   A piping connection through which the fire department can pump water into a building's standpipe, sprinkler system, or other system for the purpose of extinguishing a fire. A *siamese* (double) connection is an example of a fire department connection.

> REAL ESTATE APPLICATION: In a dry-type sprinkler system, water pumped into the standpipe and sprinkler system via the fire department connection is the sole source of water. In a wet-type sprinkler system, the fire department connection would be used in the event of a failure of the building's primary water source (e.g., municipal water supply) or to supplement that source.

fire department standpipe   See *standpipe riser.*

fire detection system   An electrically based system of sensors (smoke detectors, heat detectors, etc.) and associated equipment such as fire alarm panels, which detects the presence of smoke or fire and provides an alarm signal to building occupants, building operators, and the fire department. The term fire detection system is often used synonymously with the term *fire alarm system.*

fire door   A door and door assembly made of fire-resistive materials, capable of providing a specified degree of fire protection when closed. Fire doors are usually provided with an automatic door-closing mechanism which ensures that the door returns to a (normally) closed position, thereby providing a *firebreak.* Otherwise, they are typically held in the open position by a wall-mounted electrically energized magnet that pulls on a metal contact attached to the door. Exceptions to this are hospitals and nursing homes, where staff are required to close the fire doors. (See also *fire-resistance rating.*)

REAL ESTATE APPLICATION: A smoke detector installed to operate in conjunction with a fire door would be mounted at the ceiling near the door and would release a device (e.g., de-energize an electromagnet) upon detecting the presence of smoke, causing the door to close.

fire extinguisher   A portable apparatus for putting out small fires by ejecting an extinguishing agent (water, CO_2, dry chemical, etc.). The agent is discharged manually by pulling a safety pin, pointing the discharge nozzle at the base of the fire, and squeezing the trigger or lever in short bursts.

REAL ESTATE APPLICATION: All portable fire extinguishers should be inspected periodically to ensure they are properly charged. A fire extinguisher used for any reason should be refilled immediately. Many of the portable fire extinguishers located within buildings today are all purpose (ABC-type), capable of extinguishing a range of classes of fires in their incipient stage.

fire-extinguishing system   An installation of automatic sprinklers, foam or gas discharge systems, fire hoses, etc., designed to provide fire-extinguishing capabilities to a space or building.

fire-fighting agent   A liquid, powder, or gas used to extinguish fires and/or retard combustion. Examples are water, carbon dioxide (CO_2) gas, foamwater, dry chemical.

fire hazard   The relative danger that a material, structure, space, or other thing will start and spread a fire or that smoke or gases will be generated by a fire in or on them. The *fire hazard rating* is typically represented by three designations—ordinary, high, or low—based on the contents (composition, materials) and the operations conducted within the building or space.

firemen's key box   A small wall-mounted container, usually consisting of a metal enclosure and a breakable glass front, which holds the keys to critical fire protection systems (e.g., firemen's elevator recall and elevator car operating panel switches) for use by fire department personnel during a building emergency. (See also *firemen's service* in Elevators and Escalators.)

REAL ESTATE APPLICATION: The firemen's key box should be placed in a readily accessible location on the ground floor of a building. Availability of a firemen's key box is an important consideration in properties that do not have 24-hour security.

fire panel   A rectangular-shaped panel, strategically located and mounted on a wall, for the purpose of monitoring and/or interfacing with a building fire alarm and detection system; also known as a *fire alarm panel.* Fire panels are used for enabling or disabling fire system component points in the system, determining the status and location of a specific alarm, acknowledging an alarm condition, etc.

> REAL ESTATE APPLICATION: A building's main fire panel is normally located in the fire command center. A large building may require subpanels in strategic areas, particularly when fire alarm systems monitor large numbers (hundreds) of detection devices and other fire alarm system components.

fireproofing   A material applied to a structural component (e.g., steel beams, decking) to provide increased fire resistance. Fireproofing material is usually applied by spraying it on the structural components after they are erected and before the electrical, HVAC, plumbing, or any other construction work is done.

> REAL ESTATE APPLICATION: Maintaining the integrity of fireproofing on all of the structural components in a building is very important. (Fireproofing material must be replaced if it is disrupted by any work done in the building.) A large fire on a floor with structural components or portions of structural components that are not fireproofed could place the entire building at risk with respect to structural integrity.

fire protection   Materials, systems, and procedures for preventing fire and/or minimizing the potential loss of life or damage to property resulting from a fire. Among other things, fire protection encompasses materials specified during a construction project, building operator and occupant training in fire prevention and emergency procedures, and design and installation of smoke detection and sprinkler systems.

fire pump   A pump that is an integral part of a building's water-based fire-suppression system, sometimes referred to as a *booster pump* since it is typically connected to the public water supply in order to increase the water pressure. Usually driven by an electric motor, fire pumps can be connected to private tanks or reservoirs. The electrical power to the motor is usually provided by either a normal (utility) or an emergency source (diesel generator).

> REAL ESTATE APPLICATION: Because a fire pump is used infrequently, it should be tested periodically to ensure it is operating properly. A building's fire pump should be automatically started and operated for 10 minutes (electric motor driven) or 30 minutes (engine driven) on a weekly basis in order to test the auto-start function and smooth operation of the pump. The auto-start function test helps to ensure the fire pump will operate as designed in the event of an actual fire (i.e., automatically). The test is performed by opening a petcock (test valve or release) on the discharge side of the pump. This simulates the opening of a sprinkler valve head by lowering the pressure of the system. A fire pump flow test should be performed annually in order to ensure that the pump performs according to its design specifications and the water supply and sprinkler system piping is not obstructed.

fire-resistance rating   A classification (A, B, C, etc.) based on the time (hours, minutes) that a material or component (e.g., wall, door) can withstand exposure to fire; also called *fire rating.* Fire-resistance ratings are determined by generally accepted standards or from the information derived from standard tests.

REAL ESTATE APPLICATION: Fire doors are rated in accordance with the time that they can endure and isolate a fire. A class A fire door is fire rated for three hours; a class B door is fire rated for 1 or 1½ hours. (The fire door rating is established by Underwriters Laboratories, Inc.) The highest fire rating for a wood door is 1½ hours. To meet a higher rating requirement, a metal door (which is rated up to 3 hours) would be needed. A fire-rated door cannot be machined (prepared for hanging) except by a firm or individual having a special license to do this work. Machining must be within close tolerances to retain the established fire rating.

firestopping   A material, often specified as noncombustible, which is strategically placed in concealed openings (usually between floors) to retard the spread of fire and smoke. Sheet rock, firestopping putty, or similar material must be used to seal openings in utility shafts, electrical and phone closets, plumbing and HVAC chases, etc.

REAL ESTATE APPLICATION: Because electrical and phone closets are often positioned one above the other in a high-rise building, smoke and fire are extremely likely to spread vertically through phone and/or electrical closets in the event a fire occurs in or near such a closet that does not have firestopping in place. Such vertical stacking sets up a unique situation where fire and smoke can travel upwards uncontrolled if the closets are not properly sealed. A commonly used firestopping is a moldable, formable clay-type material which is effective in sealing small openings around telephone and data cables that are pulled from one phone or data closet to another.

fire triangle   The three elements which must be present for a fire to exist and sustain itself—material (also referred to as fuel), a supply of oxygen, and heat (high temperature). If any of these is removed, the fire will be extinguished.

fire wall   An exterior or interior wall having a code-specified fire-resistance rating and the structural stability required to restrict the spread of fire to adjacent areas or buildings; also called *fire barrier*.

REAL ESTATE APPLICATION: Fire walls typically enclose the elevator shaft (core area) in a building. Corridor walls of common areas are also required to be fire rated (i.e., fire walls).

fire warden   A member of a Building Emergency Response Team (normally a designated tenant representative) who is responsible for directing the actions of the occupants on his or her respective floor during an emergency; also called *floor warden*. These individuals will normally receive their instructions via the building's emergency public address (PA) system. Fire wardens should be familiar with the general layout of a building's emergency egress routes as well as basic emergency response actions and emergency phone numbers.

flammable   Able to support combustion (burning); easily ignited and capable of burning very quickly. This term is preferred over the older *inflammable*. (Compare *combustible*.)

flow switch   See *water flow switch*.

flow test   See *water flow test.*

foam-water system   A fire-fighting agent that extinguishes fires by blanketing the fuel of the fire, thereby eliminating the supply of oxygen to the fire (i.e., smothering it). Foam systems are usually used in class B fires where they are effective in providing a blanket of foam over the flammable liquid.

fog   A fine mist of water applied to a fire; also called *fog application.* Fire hose spray nozzles typically have a position setting for the discharge of water in a fog pattern. The fog position can be used with a special applicator extension to provide a fog that serves as a cooling shield for the protection of fire fighters advancing into the intense heat of a fire.

fusible-link sprinkler head   A mechanical method of sprinkler actuation that involves the use of solders composed of different types of metals which are mixed together (alloyed) in such a way that they release at a predetermined temperature.

glass bulb sprinkler head   A type of sprinkler actuation that uses a glass ampule containing a temperature-sensitive liquid chemical which expands at a predetermined temperature to burst the glass; also called *frangible bulb sprinkler head.*

gravity water system   See *gravity feed* in Basic Engineering and Building Mechanical Systems.

Halon   The designated name for various halogenated fire-extinguishing agents. Halon 1301 (bromotrifluoromethane, $CBrF_3$), a gas, is a commonly used fire-suppression agent/system employed very effectively in computer rooms (total flooding systems) and other applications. Halon gas systems are similar to carbon dioxide (CO_2) systems with respect to gas storage, system installation, discharge, etc. Halon 1301 is expensive to produce and purchase (it is currently manufactured in limited quantities), but it is less toxic than CO_2, particularly in confined areas. Halon 1211 (bromochlorodifluoromethane [$CBrClF_2$]), is used for fire suppression in local applications rather than total flooding systems. These and many other members of the Halon family are halogenated hydrocarbons and, as such, are being phased out under the Clean Air Act and the Montreal Protocol. (See also *chlorofluorocarbons [CFCs]* in Environmental Management and Indoor Air Quality.)

REAL ESTATE APPLICATION: Given the potential damage water could cause in a computer or electrical environment, Halon 1301 was the preferred computer room fire-suppression agent because it is a gas. The discharge of Halon 1301 was at one time considered safe because it permitted the orderly evacuation of personnel from an area without mortal effects on human life. In the 1980s, however, questions were raised with respect to the temporary and long-term (permanent) health effects on personnel exposed to Halon gas, as well as its effect on the environment when discharged to the atmosphere. Because Halon has a combination of desirable fire-suppression characteristics that are hard to match, the introduction of effective, alternative computer room fire-suppression agents has been relatively slow and selective.

Water-based preaction sprinkler systems are becoming popular as an alternate fire-suppression system for computer rooms. Several other gas agents and gas agent-based systems are also becoming available for purchase. Selection of an appropriate fire-suppression system will depend on many factors, such as the safety of the occupants in the protected area, the ability of the agent to control and suppress fire, and the future availability of alternative agents. Information regarding Halon alternatives may be obtained by contacting such sources as the National Fire Protection Association (NFPA), local fire departments, fire protection engineers/consultants, or the building's property insurance carrier.

heat detector A fire detection device, usually ceiling mounted, which activates a fire alarm if the temperature in the monitored area exceeds a predetermined value *(thermostat-type)*, using a metallic element that expands or contracts (or melts) when the temperature changes. Devices that measure a sudden increase in temperature (15°F in 60 seconds) are referred to as *rate-of-rise (ROR) heat detectors.*

REAL ESTATE APPLICATION: Heat detectors are more common in areas where smoke detectors are difficult to monitor with respect to smoke sensitivity —e.g., a boiler room where fumes, dust, or dirt may be prevalent, making it difficult to avoid causing false alarms. The temporary installation and use of heat detectors during interior construction projects is one effective way to protect a property, particularly if existing smoke detectors are disabled or removed during the construction period.

hydraulically designed sprinkler system The sizing and layout of a sprinkler system in a building by using a computer to design a piping pattern in which pipe sizes are selected on a pressure-loss basis to provide a specified amount of water (gal/min/sq ft) applied relatively uniformly over the specified area; also called *hydraulically calculated sprinkler system.* The advantage of this type of design is that precise calculations can be made regarding the water pressures expected with the proposed layout and sizing. This usually results in a reduction in materials requirements and lower costs than when simpler methods (e.g., pipe schedule system sizing) are used.

impairment The unexpected or planned shutdown of a fire-protection system or a portion of the system.

REAL ESTATE APPLICATION: The impairment of a building fire-protection system, even for very short periods of time (e.g., 30 minutes), requires specific actions and precautions by the property manager, the management company, building engineers, and others. Some specific examples of actions which may be taken during a period of impairment are notification of the property's insurance carrier, notification of the fire department, and stationing a qualified fire watch. The specific actions required will vary depending on many factors (e.g., degree of impairment, areas affected by the impairment). An example of a planned impairment would be the intentional disabling of a sprinkler system's tamper switches and flow switches and closing of a sprinkler isolation valve on a construction floor in order to install additional sprinkler heads. An unexpected or emergency impairment could be caused by a frozen and ruptured sprinkler head or mechanical failure of a building fire pump.

interior cabinet A box, typically mounted on a wall or recessed into a wall inside a building, used to contain a hose rack assembly, fire department valve(s), fire extinguisher(s), and related items that must be kept accessible in case of a fire.

jockey pump A relatively small pump used to maintain adequate water pressure in a building's standpipe and sprinkler system during inactive periods. In essence, the jockey pump, rather than the fire pump, maintains the pressure in the system.

REAL ESTATE APPLICATION: Under normal conditions, a jockey pump should not operate too often. A jockey pump might start if a building operator opened a sprinkler drain valve on a particular floor to drain the sprinkler loop of a specific floor so that maintenance or repairs could be performed. Frequent operation of a jockey pump may indicate a leak somewhere in the system.

magnetic door holder   See *fire door*.

master box   A fire alarm box that connects the fire alarm system of a building to the local fire department; also called *master fire box* or *city relay*.

REAL ESTATE APPLICATION: The master box is typically located near a building's main fire panel, usually on the ground floor. It needs to be disconnected temporarily before testing a building's fire alarm system or performing maintenance on components that might cause an alarm. Some municipalities are shifting toward monitoring fire alarms at a central station operated by a qualified fire alarm service company instead of at the local fire station.

National Fire Protection Association (NFPA)   A nonprofit membership organization dedicated to making the home and workplace more fire safe. The NFPA conducts scientific research, develops and updates fire safety standards (through code-related publications), and educates and trains professionals and laypeople in fire protection and prevention practices (via seminars, handbooks, and other means).

The NFPA has no enforcement power. Governmental or institutional compliance with NFPA standards is entirely voluntary. However, the NFPA standards are internationally accepted and have been used for many years at all levels of government. Its National Electrical Code is the most widely accepted safety code in existence.

REAL ESTATE APPLICATION: The NFPA has an extensive list of fire and life safety related codes and standards publications available to the public. A few of the more popular ones are:

NFPA 1, Fire Prevention Code.

NFPA 13, Standard for Installation of Sprinkler Systems.

NFPA 70, National Electrical Code.

NFPA 72A-72H, National Fire Alarm Code(s) covering systems and components.

NFPA 101, Life Safety Code.

noncombustible   Incapable of catching fire and burning when exposed to a flame; used to characterize construction (and other) materials that will not ignite, burn, support combustion, or release flammable vapors when subjected to fire or excessive heat. Asbestos and CO_2 are examples of noncombustible materials.

post indicator valve (PIV)   A valve used as the connection between a municipal water supply and a building standpipe and sprinkler system. A PIV is located outside and adjacent to the property it serves. The valves have open and closed position indicators in order to identify the position (status) of the valve.

preaction system A system that employs automatic sprinklers attached to a piping system containing air that may or may not be under pressure and having a supplemental fire detection system installed in the same areas as the sprinklers. The supplemental detection system actuates (opens) a valve allowing water to flow into the sprinkler system piping to be discharged from any sprinklers that are open.

REAL ESTATE APPLICATION: Preaction systems are gaining acceptance in computer room fire-suppression applications, particularly given the environmental and human toxicity considerations of Halon and CO_2 systems. In the past, the mindset of the fire protection and computer industries was that water and electricity do not mix. The introduction of preaction sprinkler systems that employ added protection against inadvertent water discharge, combined with the change in computer technology from vacuum tubes to solid state and semiconductors, has influenced the direction of the fire protection industry. The use of water in a computer room in the vicinity of computer equipment is not as damaging as it was years ago, particularly given things like the use of on/off sprinkler heads, multiple-zone detection and activation techniques, the use of fine mist spray sprinkler heads, and strategic placement of sprinkler heads.

prealert tone The audible signal annunciated from a building's emergency public address system (speaker-strobe devices) alerting occupants of a report (detection) of a fire alarm emergency somewhere in the building. The prealert tone is followed by a prerecorded announcement instructing occupants to stand by for further instructions.

REAL ESTATE APPLICATION: The prealert tone concept is common in larger (e.g., high-rise) buildings where an incident detected on one floor does not necessitate the evacuation of the occupants of all floors.

priority alarm Referring to a fire-detection system and, more specifically, a fire panel alarm signal which is considered to be a high priority and typically results in evacuation of designated floors, fire department response, and Building Emergency Response Team action. A priority alarm may also indicate the initiation of other functions such as the automatic recall of building elevators, sprinkler system activation, etc. A priority alarm typically produces a loud buzzing or beeping sound and a red blinking light. The buzzing and blinking will continue until an operator acknowledges the priority alarm condition by depressing the acknowledge button on the fire panel.

pull station See *fire alarm box.*

refuge floor A concept practiced in high-rise properties during a building fire alarm in which the floors below the fire floor are used for occupant safe haven. The success of the refuge floor concept is based on two principles: (1) In most building fire incidents, it is prudent to evacuate occupants from selected floors (e.g., the fire incident floor and one or several floors adjacent to it), rather than from the entire building; and (2) in high-rise buildings, it is often safer to relocate the occupants from the evacuated floors to an area in the building below the fire floor (e.g., four floors below the fire floor) rather than evacuate the building. (This is particularly true for incidents occurring in very tall buildings.)

These two principles result in fewer people in the emergency stairwell for a shorter period of time. This, in turn, minimizes panic and fear and the potential for injury created during a building-wide evacuation. It also allows fire fighters and other Building Emergency Response Team members effective use of the emergency stairwells if required.

REAL ESTATE APPLICATION: In many high-rise buildings, emergency stairwell doors are normally locked from the stairwell side of the door for security purposes. Consequently, these doors must be unlocked during a building fire alarm to permit occupant access to refuge floors from the evacuated floors. Emergency stairwell door locks that are normally locked are connected to the building's fire alarm system (electrical relay) for automatic opening during a fire alarm.

riser   See *standpipe riser.*

searcher   A member of a Building Emergency Response Team whose responsibility is to search his or her floor or particular area of a floor in order to ensure the prompt, safe evacuation of personnel in the event of a fire alarm. Responsibilities of this person include assisting new employees and physically injured or impaired individuals to the emergency stairwell or other evacuation staging area, ensuring that all occupants evacuate his or her sector of responsibility, and informing the fire warden when the floor is clear of occupants. The searcher concept is more common at a large office or industrial building; it is also applicable to companies that have numerous employees in relatively large spaces.

siamese connection   See *fire department connection.*

smoke curtain   A barrier that is automatically lowered in the event of fire to restrict the spread of smoke.

REAL ESTATE APPLICATION: Some smoke curtains (e.g., those installed in front of an elevator) are required to be fire rated.

smoke damper   A damper designed to interrupt (halt) the airflow through a portion of a duct system in order to restrict the passage of smoke. This type of damper is installed in an HVAC duct and is operated automatically on detection of the presence of smoke.

smoke detector   A device for sensing the presence of smoke in a building or a portion of a building. Smoke detectors operate by means of a photoelectric detector, ionization detector, beam detector, flame detector, or heat detector. The type of detector selected will depend on the location and mounting, the area served, air movement, and the alarm function desired. Smoke detection systems, when combined with other methods of automatic fire protection (e.g., sprinkler systems), are an effective method of minimizing fire and smoke damage, property damage, personal injury, and loss of life.

REAL ESTATE APPLICATION: Smoke detectors usually provide early warning of a fire in a building. They can be individual, self-contained units or incorporated into a centrally located system designed for expansive annunciation and alarm functions. If incorporated into a central fire-protection and monitoring system, it is recommended that each smoke detector be zoned for quick and simple identification of the area in an alarm. The most common means of smoke detection in commercial properties is the ionization-type smoke detector.

Smoke detectors should be strategically positioned and zoned in order to provide effective monitoring and protection. Because smoke particles travel upward, smoke detectors are typically positioned on the underside of ceilings. In some cases, smoke detectors are positioned on the underside of a computer floor due to the added risk of electrical fire. Other examples of strategic areas for the placement of smoke detectors are electrical closets, telephone closets, elevator lobby areas, and HVAC return ducts. Smoke detectors need to be cleaned, maintained, and tested periodically in accordance with NFPA recommendations and local and federal code requirements.

speaker-strobe device   A component of a fire alarm system installed at various strategic locations in a building for the purpose of providing building occupants with audible (voice or alarm) messages or signals and visual (flashing light) signals during a fire alarm.

REAL ESTATE APPLICATION: Contemporary fire detection and fire alarm systems have both visual signals and prerecorded voice messages automatically emitted/annunciated through speaker-strobe devices during a fire alarm situation. Speaker-strobe devices also serve as part of an emergency public address (PA) system for other building emergencies.

spontaneous combustion   A fire that starts without the aid of a spark, open flame, steam pipe, electric heater, or other flame source. For a fire to start, an enclosed space and still air are necessary. These conditions prevent generated heat from being carried away from the oxidizing material. All materials absorb oxygen from the air and, as part of this chemical process, release energy in the form of heat.

REAL ESTATE APPLICATION: The addition of a flammable substance to a material that is in a confined space with still air increases the chances of spontaneous combustion. A rag that is only 3%–5% saturated with paint or oil is an example of a material that could ignite spontaneously under the right conditions.

sprinkler   In a fire protection sprinkler system, a device designed to discharge a stream of water and distribute it at a specified pressure and volume and in a specified pattern over a designated area. The *sprinkler head* discharges water when a fusible plug, holding a nozzle in the closed position, melts at a predetermined temperature due to a fire, thereby causing the nozzle to open. Sprinkler heads are typically mounted on the underside of a ceiling in a pattern and in sufficient numbers to provide the necessary coverage for fire protection. The layout or placement of sprinkler heads in a building or other space (minimum and maximum distances between them, the minimum and maximum distances from a wall, etc.) is regulated by federal and local codes.

REAL ESTATE APPLICATION: Some common types of sprinkler heads are:

1. Pendant—A very common type of sprinkler head in which the pipes are hidden (i.e., above the ceiling); the head hangs below the sprinkler branch line and sprays water downward onto the fire.

2. Quick response—A sprinkler that uses a more-sensitive thin metal melting piece for activation. This type will activate at lower temperatures (e.g., 105°F) than typical sprinkler heads.

3. Extended coverage—A type of sprinkler head that extends the usual maximum area of protection, having a water spray pattern with a larger diameter than that of a standard sprinkler head. This type of sprinkler may be installed in an area adjacent to another area which is not conducive to the installation of a sprinkler head.

4. Concealed—A sprinkler head that is flush mounted and has a cover piece that is usually factory or custom prepainted to match the ceiling color.

The cover plate drops away when its lower surface is exposed to heat as from a fire. This type of head blends in with the ceiling's finish and often is hardly noticed.

5. Upright—A sprinkler head that sits atop the sprinkler branch line and sprays water up into a shield, which deflects the water back down onto the fire. This type of head is used in sprinkler systems with exposed piping.

6. Early suppression fast response (ESFR)—A special type of sprinkler head that responds earlier (i.e., at a lower temperature) than a standard head and delivers a relatively high volume of water (e.g., 100 gallons/minute/head).

sprinklered   Used to refer to a building or an area of a building that has a properly functioning automatic sprinkler system.

REAL ESTATE APPLICATION: The phrase percentage sprinklered is often used in expressing the portion of a building that has automatic sprinkler systems. For example: "The building at 500 Main Street is currently 70% sprinklered."

sprinkler system   A piping system through which water flows when a device (sprinkler head) is activated by heat from a fire; also called *automatic sprinkler system*. Sprinkler systems consist of a network of systematically arranged pipes and strategically positioned sprinkler heads to protect a designated area. The piping system is normally concealed above a ceiling and supported by hangers that attach to an overhead deck. Automatic sprinklers are the most dependable and effective means of fire protection.

REAL ESTATE APPLICATION: There are four general categories of sprinkler systems—wet pipe, dry pipe, preaction, and deluge. Sprinkler systems need to be designed by a qualified engineer in order to ensure that sufficient water flow is achieved at all points in the system, particularly those areas farthest from the standpipe riser (remote areas) and higher floors. A building's sprinkler system piping sizing and layout is either specially sized or hydraulically designed (hydraulically calculated) prior to installation or modification.

stairwell monitor   A member of a Building Emergency Response Team whose responsibility it is to stand at the entrance to an emergency stairwell and direct occupants of a particular floor into the emergency stairwell and to an egress or an area of refuge during a fire alarm. The stairwell monitor should ensure that all the occupants on his or her floor have evacuated before he or she leaves the floor. As searchers enter the emergency stairwell, they should inform the stairwell monitor that their particular areas are evacuated of all occupants.

REAL ESTATE APPLICATION: Appointment of one or more stairwell monitors for each floor is typical in an office building, particularly a high-rise structure.

stairwell pressurization   A building system that employs fans (typically motor driven), ducts, duct openings, and other ventilation system components to supply air to a building emergency stairwell enclosure, thus creating a higher pressure in the stairwell than in the areas surrounding the stairwell and keeping any smoke generated by a building fire out of the stairwell areas; also called *emergency stairwell pressurization*. If properly pressurized, the stairwell will provide a smoke-free passage for building occupants during actual fire conditions.

REAL ESTATE APPLICATION: Stairwell pressurization is most often used in high-rise office buildings since the distance to the egress is often long and because use of building elevators is restricted to fire department personnel during a fire. The stairwell pressurization system is normally sized in such a way that several stairwell doors may be opened simultaneously on different floors (e.g., by occupants entering the stairwells) and a positive pressure will still be maintained relative to surrounding areas.

standpipe riser   A system of vertical piping, pumps, siamese (fire department hose) connections, sprinkler piping, valves, floor-by-floor hose connections, etc., filled with water for the purpose of fire fighting; also called *fire department standpipe*. The standpipe riser is normally located in the emergency stairwell of a building. The vertical pipe (riser) itself is typically referred to as the *standpipe*.

supervised signal   A means of monitoring the status of certain components and electrical circuits of a fire protection system.

REAL ESTATE APPLICATION: A fire protection system that is supervised would detect an abnormal condition of a sprinkler isolation valve (e.g., if the valve was closed by someone) and send a trouble alarm to the system's fire panel. The detection of the closing of this valve would be initiated through the movement of the valve's tamper switch.

tamper switch   A device that notifies building operators, engineers, security, and others when a valve in a fire suppression (e.g., sprinkler) system has been tampered with (partially or completely closed); also called *tamper device* or *valve tamper switch/device*. The notification signal is typically an audio and visual alarm at the main fire panel. The signal is created by a switch (relay) that is closed by the movement of a lever (indicator) attached to a portion of the valve itself.

REAL ESTATE APPLICATION: The purpose of tamper devices is to ensure that every isolation valve in a fire suppression system remains open at all times, except when maintenance or repair is being performed on a portion of the system. Tamper devices should be inspected and tested periodically by building engineers or fire alarm company service personnel.

valve tamper device   See *tamper switch*.

water flow alarm   An alarm that is actuated by a water flow switch in a fire sprinkler system. Water flow alarms create both an audible and visual signal at the fire alarm panel. A water flow alarm is a priority alarm and as a result typically sends an alarm directly to the fire department via the building's fire box (city relay) or to a central monitoring station. The water flow alarm, when initiated at the fire panel, will indicate the general location of the water flow (e.g., seventh floor sprinkler system).

water flow switch   A device permanently installed in a fire sprinkler system which is actuated when flow of water through the system exceeds a predetermined volume; also called *water flow device* or simply *flow switch*. Water flow switches are designed and initially installed such that the opening (operation) of any single sprinkler head or system drain valve on the downstream or discharge side of the device will actuate the water flow alarm.

REAL ESTATE APPLICATION: The purpose of water flow switches is to instantly notify building operators, engineers, security, and the local fire department of water flow in a fire sprinkler system due to an actual fire. Water

flow switches should be inspected and tested periodically by building operators or a fire alarm service company to ensure proper operation. The
building's city relay (master box) or central station relay should be disconnected before testing since actuation of the flow switch will transmit a fire
alarm. Also, these switches need to be disabled before portions of a sprinkler system are drained to avoid inadvertently causing a false alarm.

water flow test   A test conducted periodically on certain water-based fire
protection system components and equipment (sprinkler system water flow
switches, pumps, etc.) in order to ensure they are operating as designed with
regard to movement of water; also called *flow test.*

REAL ESTATE APPLICATION: Water flow switches are usually tested quarterly
to ensure that water flow through a sprinkler pipe would initiate an alarm
to the fire department, central alarm station, and building fire alarm system. The building's fire pump should also be tested periodically (annually)
to ensure that in an emergency it will function as designed.

water motor gong   An alarm device that is actuated by the movement of
water through a sprinkler system. Water motor gongs are located on the outside of a building and alert personnel that sprinklers are operating.

wet pipe sprinkler system   A fire protection sprinkler system consisting of
a standpipe riser interconnected with a network of systematically arranged
pipes containing water under pressure; also known as a *wet pipe system.*
Automatic sprinkler heads are connected to the network piping and riser so
that each one protects a designated area. Any single sprinkler head opened by
the heat from a fire will discharge water immediately.

REAL ESTATE APPLICATION: The wet pipe type of sprinkler system is used
almost exclusively in traditional commercial and residential property fire
protection applications. (Compare *dry pipe sprinkler system.*)

Heating, Ventilating, Air Conditioning (HVAC) and Refrigeration Systems

absolute humidity   See *humidity.*

absorbent   A liquid chemical that is sprayed into an air stream to remove moisture from (dehumidify) the air. (Compare *adsorbent.*)

absorber   See *absorption chiller.*

absorption chiller   A device containing liquid to absorb refrigerant vapor or other vapors. The low side in an absorption chiller machine, where the refrigerant-water vapors from the inside of the shell are absorbed by a lithium bromide (LiBr) solution, which is sprayed from a pump and nozzle arrangement into the chiller over absorber tubes carrying condenser water. The term *absorber* is typically used to describe the entire absorption chiller machine and associated components.

An absorber consists of four basic heat exchanger components which, when properly balanced, will cool a liquid to the desired temperature. The four main components are (1) evaporator, (2) absorber, (3) generator, and (4) condenser. In addition, a number of auxiliary components assist the four basic components in performing their functions: heat exchanger, two fluid pumps (refrigerant and solution), purge unit, vacuum pump, automatic decrystallization device, solution control valve, steam or hot-water valve, eductor, and a control center.

REAL ESTATE APPLICATION: The primary function of the absorption chiller is to lower the temperature of a liquid (chilled water) for use in an air-conditioning system or in process refrigeration. In air-conditioning applications at large properties, absorption chillers were very common prior to and during the mid-1970s, before the increase in use of conventional mechanical compression machines (electrically operated rotary centrifugal chillers or screw chillers).

accumulator   In a refrigeration system, a storage tank that receives liquid refrigerant from the evaporator and prevents it from flowing in the suction line to the compressor.

REAL ESTATE APPLICATION: If allowed to enter the suction side of the compressor, liquid refrigerant could cause significant damage. In some instances (e.g., abrupt load changes or light load conditions), the metering device may not reduce the amount of refrigerant flowing to the evaporator coil quickly enough, resulting in an excess of refrigerant for the given load. The accumulator is simply a trap that catches this liquid before it reaches the compressor. Surplus liquid is boiled and returned to the compressor as a gas.

acoustical duct lining   Soundproofing material that is applied to the inside of an HVAC duct to absorb and control sound and limit, reduce, or prevent transmission of sound from one room to another; material that is wrapped around the outside of the duct for the same purpose is called *insulation.*

adsorbent   A solid material placed in the path of an air stream to remove moisture from (dehumidify) the air. An adsorbent holds moisture without causing a chemical or physical change. (Compare *absorbent.*)

air balancing   A procedure of adjusting dampers, control devices, and other equipment in an HVAC system in order to provide the prescribed air flow to all areas served by the system in accordance with the intended design. (See also *constant volume system; variable air volume [VAV] system.*)

REAL ESTATE APPLICATION: Air balancing is normally required in specific areas of an HVAC system on completion of substantial tenant space modifications (construction projects). In addition, air balancing may be required throughout an entire central HVAC system periodically (e.g., after several years of minor system modifications or on completion of a system upgrade or conversion from a constant-volume to a variable-volume air system). Occupancy levels also need to be considered. As tenants occupy the building, air balancing is required to ensure that no floor or occupant uses more air than is allotted for that area of the building. (Firms that provide this service are qualified in Testing, Adjusting, and Balancing [TAB] air systems by the *National Environmental Balancing Bureau [NEBB],* described in Environmental Management and Indoor Air Quality.)

air blender   A stationary device permanently affixed to the inside of an air-handling unit or HVAC duct for the specific purpose of mixing the air that passes through it. The air blender consists of a series of fixed blades placed in opposing positions and at varied angles in order to redirect the various sections of the air stream. Minimizing stratification of the air ensures a fairly constant temperature throughout the air stream.

REAL ESTATE APPLICATION: Air blenders are sometimes positioned immediately in front of air-handling heating or cooling coils in order to increase the efficiency of the coil by ensuring consistent air temperatures throughout the entire cross-section of the air stream.

air changes   The number of times that a supply of air replaces the volume of air in a building, room, or other defined space in a given period of time, typically expressed in air changes per hour; also called *air exchange rate.*

REAL ESTATE APPLICATION: The frequency of air changes can be determined for a building by dividing the total volume of space into the total volume of air supplied to that same space. For example: If two air handlers each provide air to all five floors of an office building at the rate of 10,000 cubic feet per minute (cfm), the total volume of air being supplied to the building (the numerator) is 20,000 cfm (10,000 cfm × 2 air handlers). The volume of air changed is normally expressed in cubic feet per hour (cfh). Therefore: 20,000 cfm × 60 minutes = 1,200,000 cfh.

The denominator is simply the total volume of the area served by the air handlers. This is calculated by multiplying together the linear dimensions of a particular space—length, width, and height, measured in feet. If each floor is 150 feet wide and 100 feet deep, their respective areas are 15,000 square feet; multiplied by the height (10 ft), the volume of each floor is 150,000 cubic feet, and the five floors total 750,000 cubic feet (150 × 100 × 10 = 150,000; 150,000 × 5 = 175,000).

Thus, the number of air changes per hour is the volume of air supplied by the air handlers divided by the total volume of space served: 1,200,000 cfh ÷ 750,000 cu ft = 1.35 air changes per hour.

To calculate how frequently the air in a particular building is completely replaced, divide 1 by the number of air changes per hour. In this example, 1 ÷ 1.35 = 0.74 hrs; and the air changes completely once every 44 minutes (0.74 hr × 60 min = 44.4 min).

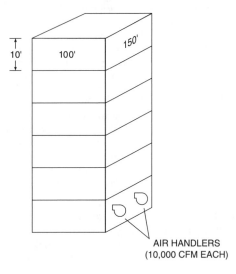

AIR HANDLERS
(10,000 CFM EACH)

air changes

air cleaner A device used to remove airborne particles and impurities from ventilation air supplied to a space. An air cleaner could be an air filter or an air washer. (See also *bag filter; carbon filter; electrostatic filter.*)

REAL ESTATE APPLICATION: HVAC air filters are positioned in the air supply stream and are typically rated in terms of efficiency, resistance to air flow, and dust-holding capacity. Efficiency is a factor of the smallest size particle—measured in microns (μ)—that can be trapped by the air cleaner. Air filters should be replaced periodically (e.g., semi-annually) as part of a scheduled preventive maintenance program.

air coil A tubing arrangement used with some types of heat pumps which may serve as either an evaporator or a condenser. (See also *coil.*)

air conditioner A system that removes heat and moisture (humidity) from the air entering a space and transfers this heat back to the outside air. The term air conditioner is usually accepted in the industry as referring to a small, local, stand-alone unit.

air conditioning The control of factors affecting the physical and chemical conditions of the atmosphere within a building or other structure. The factors, most of which affect human health and comfort, include air temperature, humidity, and distribution as well as air contents such as dust and particulates, bacteria, odors, and toxic gases.

REAL ESTATE APPLICATION: Air contents also affect building operation (e.g., dust in and on equipment).

air-cooled condenser A type of equipment in which heat is removed (rejected) directly to the air by sensible heat transfer. An air-cooled condenser consists of a coil, a casing, a fan, and a motor. The heat in the refrigerant gas is removed by transfer of sensible heat to air passing over the coil, which lowers the temperature of the refrigerant gas and changes (condenses) it from a vapor to a liquid. (See also *water-cooled HVAC unit*.)

> REAL ESTATE APPLICATION: Air-cooled condensers are very common in relatively small air-conditioning and refrigeration systems (roof-top units or split systems). They are used when there is sufficient space available for placement of the condenser (a roof or other outdoor area) and when it can be located in close proximity to the primary unit (i.e., within a few floors).

air exchange rate   See *air changes*.

air handler   A mechanical device whose primary function is to move air from one point to another, either locally or remotely, through an HVAC duct. The term air handler is generally accepted to encompass the fan that moves the air and the associated motor that drives the fan, as well as any ductwork, heating or cooling coils, humidification system, operating controls, or other components that comprise an *air-handling unit*.

air volume   The amount of air moved into, out of, or through a space, measured in cubic feet per minute (cfm).

> REAL ESTATE APPLICATION: The volume (cfm) of air provided through a duct can be estimated based on the design parameters of the air-handling unit serving the duct or by measuring the velocity of the air flow within the duct and multiplying by the cross-sectional area of the duct: air velocity in feet per minute × (duct width in feet × duct height in feet) = air volume in cfm.

air-water system   An HVAC system in which the heating and cooling water and ventilation air are supplied to individual terminal units from a centralized location.

> REAL ESTATE APPLICATION: Air-water systems are frequently used at the perimeter areas of a building. This type of system is practical for reducing the physical area required by the terminal units (induction units are used, as opposed to fan-coil units, which are used in an all-water system). The original air-water system is the high-velocity, high-pressure induction units, which were very common in commercial high-rise applications in the 1970s and early 1980s. (See also *all-water system; induction system*.)

all-water system   An HVAC system in which chilled water or hot water (in lieu of a refrigerant) is used as the cooling or heating medium, supplied from a remote source (central chiller plant or boiler), and circulated through the coils of the terminal (e.g., fan coil) unit, within the air-conditioned space. The water provided to the terminal unit is heated or chilled, depending on outside weather conditions, internal load, and other factors. Air flows across the water coil in order to temper the air supplied to the space. Air is provided from the outdoors to the fan-coil component of the through-the-wall air intakes in each individual occupancy unit. The fan-coil all-water system, with a central cooling and heating source, can be converted to an air-water system by centralizing the primary ventilation air supply. This would eliminate the through-the-wall intakes in individual units.

> REAL ESTATE APPLICATION: All-water systems are common in certain high-rise commercial property HVAC applications, particularly at the perimeter areas of a building. The heated (or chilled) water is effective in maintaining the required space temperatures, given the additional heating (or cooling) load conditions encountered at the skin of the building.

ambient temperature The temperature of the air surrounding an object.

American Society of Heating, Refrigerating and Air-Conditioning Engineers (ASHRAE) A trade organization that identifies and provides industry-accepted standards and requirements for addressing various heating, ventilation, and air-conditioning concerns, particularly those related to building occupants.

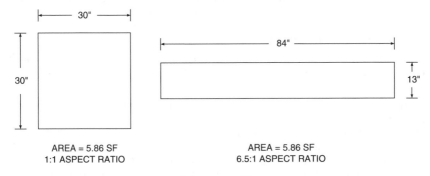

aspect ratio (duct cross section)

aspect ratio The ratio of the long side to the short side of a rectangular-shaped duct. This ratio is important to initial HVAC duct design, cost of materials, and installation. Ducts that have higher aspect ratios have greater duct surface areas compared with ducts of equivalent cross-sectional area (equivalent air volume) having lower aspect ratios.

> REAL ESTATE APPLICATION: In the accompanying diagram, the duct represented by the sketch on the left has an aspect ratio of 1:1 as compared to the sketch on the right which has an aspect ratio of 6.5:1. The duct on the right has a larger surface area and, therefore, increased insulation requirements compared to the duct on the left. The duct on the right is likely to require a higher construction class sheet metal gauge material, resulting in higher material and installation costs.

attenuator See *sound attenuator*.

bag filter A type of air filter that offers the advantages of greater HVAC air flow, a lesser drop in pressure (hence reduced energy use), and maximum dust-holding capacity. The bag filter achieves these benefits due to its pleated construction, which provides extended surface area. Bag filters are high-efficiency filters.

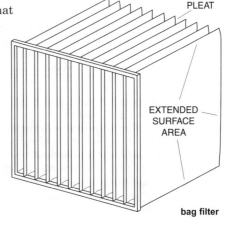

bag filter

baseboard heater A common type of space heater that employs a finned-tube electric heating element or a hot water coil or steam coil as a heating medium, sometimes in conjunction with a fan; also called *baseboard radiator unit.* When a fan is used, the heater is referred to as a *convection baseboard heater.* It is important that the inlet and discharge sides of a baseboard heater are unobstructed in order to prevent overheating. Most units have a built-in thermal protection device that prevents overheating.

REAL ESTATE APPLICATION: Baseboard heaters are used in single-family homes as well as commercial buildings and apartments. The primary advantages of baseboard heaters are low initial cost and ease of installation. They are often used for supplementary (rather than primary) heating because they can be costly to operate.

blow   The horizontal distance that an air stream travels upon discharge from an outlet such as a diffuser. Blow is a function of the velocity of the air in feet per minute (fpm).

brine   A liquid solution used as a heat-transfer medium in lower-temperature applications (i.e., below freezing). Ethylene glycol and propylene glycol are examples of brines; ethylene glycol is used in ice storage applications.

REAL ESTATE APPLICATION: Brines can also be used in freeze protection applications. Draining water from an outside air coil of an HVAC system and filling it with a brine solution during the winter season is an example. Caution should be exercised when using brine solutions in piping and other HVAC components because brines, sufficiently diluted with water, can be corrosive to metals. If not used properly, brines can also add to indoor air quality problems.

capacity   The ability of an air-conditioning or refrigeration system (or any part of it) to remove heat, typically expressed in Btu's per hour or tons per 24 hours.

capillary tube   A long copper tube with a small inside diameter that serves to control the amount of refrigerant flowing through the evaporator coil in a refrigeration system. It is essentially an inexpensive metering device installed between the condenser and the evaporator. Restricting the flow of refrigerant ensures that correct high-side and low-side pressures are maintained while the compressor is operating.

carbon filter   An air filter using activated (specially processed) carbon as an air-cleaning agent.

central chiller plant   A system of heating and cooling equipment (chillers, condenser water pumps, chill water pumps, secondary heating or cooling pumps, associated controls, and electric motor starters) that is centrally located and situated outside (remote from) the spaces being served. (See also *central fan system.*)

central fan system   A system of heating, ventilating, and air conditioning in which air is handled and treated by equipment and components situated outside (remote from) the spaces being served. The equipment is typically in a central location, and the air is delivered to the remote spaces by means of a fan and a system of distribution ducts. A central fan system is often employed in large buildings. (See also *central chiller plant.*)

REAL ESTATE APPLICATION: The central chiller plant and central fan system concepts are based on the theory that the numerous spaces within large buildings such as high-rises are more efficiently served by one large set of

HVAC and/or air-handling components than by many smaller sets of components situated at each of the terminal locations.

centrifugal chiller   A rotating machine that compresses gaseous refrigerants (e.g., Freon) by centrifugal force. The compressor portion is directly connected to a rotating machine (electric motor or steam turbine) that drives the compressor. Both motor and compressor are usually enclosed in a common casing (hermetically sealed). Both components are typically referred to in combination as a *centrifugal compressor.*

REAL ESTATE APPLICATION: Centrifugal chillers are frequently used in large commercial HVAC systems of substantial capacity. They are typically electric motor-driven, easy to operate, and reliable, but they consume significant amounts of electricity compared to nonelectric machines. Most centrifugal chiller units are water cooled (condenser water) although some smaller air-cooled units have been used in roof-mounted applications.

centrifugal compressor   See *centrifugal chiller.*

centrifugal fan   A rotating, multiblade device for moving air. Air is received along its axis and discharged radially.

REAL ESTATE APPLICATION: The forward-curved multiblade wheel is the most commonly used centrifugal blower for typical large-capacity heating and cooling applications. Centrifugal fans are very effective in moving air efficiently against pressure and are extensively used in HVAC systems involving ductwork.

charge   The amount of refrigerant in a system; the act of adding refrigerant to a system *(charging).*

chiller   A large piece of equipment that employs mechanical means and uses chemical refrigerants to chill water for building cooling. The refrigerant removes heat from the cooling medium which, in turn, is circulated through the air-handling system to cool the air supplied to various spaces in a building. The chiller is the main component of a building HVAC system.

REAL ESTATE APPLICATION: There are four types of chillers (methods of expanding liquid refrigerants)—centrifugal, screw, reciprocating, and steam absorption. The following drive mechanisms are examples of typical chiller prime movers:

• Electric motor (centrifugal or screw)
• Steam turbine (centrifugal)
• Diesel fuel- or natural gas-fired engine (reciprocating)

chill water   The primary cooling medium in large central HVAC systems. Water is chilled to a temperature of approximately 42–46°F (sometimes slightly warmer) for subsequent use in air conditioning or process refrigeration. (Relatively warm chill water, returning from central air-handling unit coils and various heat exchangers, is pumped into the evaporator section where its temperature is lowered.) The chill water circuit is a closed loop, recirculating the fluid through cooling coils, heat exchangers, or other devices, where it absorbs heat from other mediums (ventilation air, secondary cooling water for induction units, etc.).

chimney effect   See *stack effect.*

coil   An arrangement of pipes or tubing in layers or windings (spiral) or rows. An HVAC apparatus that air is drawn through or forced across in order to cool, heat, or dehumidify it. Heating and cooling coils are usually made of materials with excellent heat transfer properties (e.g., copper). Chilled water, a refrigerant, hot water, or steam flows inside the coils, thereby effecting the heat transfer. Fins are usually attached to increase the surface area and efficiency of the coil. Coils are capable of heating or cooling air at a constant moisture content or simultaneously cooling and dehumidifying the air.

REAL ESTATE APPLICATION: Coils are common in most building heating and cooling applications. They should be inspected and cleaned periodically in order to ensure unobstructed air flow and efficient heat transfer. They should also be inspected and tested for effective freeze protection prior to the winter season.

cold deck   One of two ventilation ducts in a dual duct HVAC system that supplies relatively cool air to various spaces. (Compare *hot deck*.)

cold wall   A type of refrigerator construction (e.g., walk-in cooler) in which the inner lining of the refrigerator serves as the cooling surface.

comfort zone   The area on a psychrometric chart that shows the conditions of temperature and humidity in which most people are comfortable. (See also *psychrometric chart*.)

REAL ESTATE APPLICATION: The comfort zone recommended by ASHRAE is a temperature range of 73–77°F with 30%–60% relative humidity. The recommended range of temperature and humidity can vary depending on the existing outside conditions. On a relatively cold day (20°F), it may be appropriate to maintain an inside temperature slightly lower than or on the lower end of the prescribed range (i.e., at or below 73°F). Conversely, on a hot, humid day (95°F and 50% relative humidity), it is acceptable and recommended to maintain an inside temperature on the upper end of the prescribed range (i.e., nearer 77°F). Humidity is part of the comfort zone parameters because it affects the ability to evaporate heat and thereby cool the human body. Higher relative humidity readings result in a higher perceived temperature and vice versa.

compression phase   One of the four stages of the basic *refrigeration cycle* (which see); the stage in which the refrigerant is compressed, increasing its pressure and raising its temperature. Refrigerant enters the compressor as a relatively low-temperature, low-pressure gas and leaves the compressor as a higher-pressure, higher-temperature gas. The compression of refrigerants as part of the refrigeration cycle utilizes two phenomena, evaporation and condensation: First the liquid refrigerant is evaporated, absorbing the temperature of its surroundings (e.g., air). When the vapor is subsequently condensed, it rejects heat to raise the temperature of its surroundings (e.g., water).

compressor   The primary component in a refrigeration or air- conditioning system. It draws a low-pressure refrigerant gas on the cooling side (low side) of the refrigeration cycle and compresses it in the high- pressure or condensing side (high side) of the refrigeration cycle. The compressor may be reciprocating (small refrigeration system) or rotary (large air-conditioning system).

condensation phase   One of the four stages of the basic *refrigeration cycle* (which see); the stage in which the heat of compression and the heat picked up in the evaporation (cooling) coil is transferred from the relatively high-pressure, high-temperature refrigerant gas (vapor) to condenser water or rel-

atively cool outside air. Because the refrigerant vapor is at a higher temperature than the air or water passing across or through the condenser, heat is
transferred from the warmer refrigerant vapor to the cooler air or water. As the
temperature of the refrigerant vapor decreases, it is returned to a liquid state
at a lower temperature and relatively high pressure. The condensation phase
of the refrigeration cycle is on the high side (high-pressure side) of the system.

condenser   One of the four primary components of an absorption chiller system; the heat-exchanger component in a refrigeration system. The condenser
receives hot, high-pressure refrigerant gas from the compressor and uses relatively cool water or air to cool the gas returning it to a liquid state. An *air-
cooled condenser* transfers heat to the surrounding air; a *water-cooled condenser* transfers heat from hot gaseous refrigerant to water. A water-cooled
condenser could be a part of a refrigeration system or an air-conditioning system. (See also *absorption chiller*.)

REAL ESTATE APPLICATION: The condenser in a chiller (shell-and-tube type) is
comprised of many copper tubes through which condenser water flows.
After absorbing the heat from the refrigerant, the condenser water flows to
a cooling tower where it gives up its heat to the surrounding air. The condenser water is then returned to the chiller to complete the cycle.

condenser fan   A motor-driven device used to move air though an air-cooled
condenser. Movement of the air increases its ability to remove heat from the
refrigerant or condenser water, thereby increasing the efficiency of the condenser.

condenser water   Water pumped through the condenser section of a chiller
(heat exchanger) for the specific purpose of removing heat from the hot
gaseous refrigerant. The condenser water is then pumped to another heat
exchanger, usually a cooling tower, in order to transfer the acquired heat to
the surrounding air; the lower-temperature condenser water is then circulated back to the chiller. (Condenser water in place is sometimes also referred to
as *working fluid*.)

REAL ESTATE APPLICATION: A *condenser water system* is an open system
because the condenser water gives up its heat through evaporation to the
surrounding air. Because evaporation results in a loss of condenser water,
makeup water must be added to the system during operation. The amount
of water added to the system depends on the load of the system over time.
    Makeup water from the municipal water supply is typically added to the
condenser water system automatically. This continuous addition of water
dilutes the chemicals in the system that protect the piping and other components from corrosion. Consequently, it is very important to add chemicals
to the system in order to maintain the appropriate chemical treatment levels. In some HVAC applications, condenser water removes heat from relatively warmer chill water in a heat exchanger (plate-and-frame type), and
the condenser water is then transferred to a cooling tower in order to reject
the heat to the surrounding air. The plate-and-frame application is effective during light load conditions when outside air is cool enough to lower
the temperature of condenser water for subsequent use as the primary
cooling medium in an air-conditioning system (in lieu of refrigerants).

condenser water pump   A rotating mechanical device used to move water
through a tube-type condenser and, in some cases, through a cooling tower.

condensing unit   The two components that comprise the high-pressure side (high side) of a refrigeration system or relatively small capacity air-conditioning system—the *compressor* reduces the volume of the vaporized refrigerant returning from the evaporator, and the *condenser* liquifies the refrigerant and returns it to the refrigerant control device.

conditioned space   A space within a building that is provided with heated and/or cooled (conditioned) air from a central system or a space in which another heating or cooling source is used (steam coils, electric radiant heat) in order to maintain a space temperature suitable for occupancy. *Conditioned air* is often referred to a *tempered air*.

> REAL ESTATE APPLICATION: A conference room in a law firm is an example of a conditioned space. Conversely, an emergency stairwell in a high-rise building probably would not be a conditioned space.

constant volume system   An HVAC system that delivers a constant airflow to all of the spaces it serves. Changes in space temperatures are made by increasing or decreasing the temperature of the air provided to the space. (In smaller, localized applications, space temperatures may be changed by switching the air-handling unit on and off.)

> REAL ESTATE APPLICATION: The airflow provided to spaces served by this type of system is constant because the motor that drives the air-handler fan that serves the spaces runs at a constant speed; it is driven by a single-speed motor and is incapable of operating at multiple speeds. Although the total air serving the various spaces is constant in volume, the percentage of fresh air serving the spaces can be varied (i.e., increased or decreased). This is accomplished through modulation of fresh air (outdoor air supply) dampers in coordination with the modulation of building air return dampers and exhaust dampers. These constant volume systems should and often do operate with a fixed minimum percentage of outdoor air in order to ensure adequate quantities of fresh air.

convector unit   See *induction system*.

cooling coil   A heat exchanger-type coil used for pre-cooling, cooling, or dehumidifying. Cooling coils typically consist of copper tubing (with attached fins) through which chilled water, refrigerant, or other liquid flows. (See also *coil*.)

cooling degree day   See *degree day*.

cooling tower   A major component of a central HVAC system that makes use of the ambient outdoor wet-bulb temperature, fans, and free surface areas to remove heat from condenser water by means of evaporation. The condenser water, with its temperature lowered, is returned to the building system where it removes the heat of vaporization from a refrigerant which, in turn, serves as the cooling medium for chill water (in large central HVAC systems) or air (in other supplementary cooling applications). The size of a cooling tower is measured in tons of capacity in relation to the heat (Btu's) removed from the condenser water delivered to the cooling tower (in gallons per minute).

Cooling towers are typically constructed of stainless steel although some are made (partially or wholly) of polyvinyl chloride (PVC polymer) and, less frequently, wood. The type of cooling tower construction will vary depending on various factors such as the physical location of the cooling tower and the specific application. There are two general classifications of cooling towers. In a *mechanical draft* tower, outside air is pushed up by fans located at the bottom of the tower (forced draft) or pulled up by fans located at the top of the cooling tower (induced draft). In a *natural draft* tower, air is drawn across the cooling tower's heat-transfer surface naturally due to the temperature difference between the condenser water and the outside air.

Condenser water can be cooled down to a temperature close to (approaching) the wet-bulb temperature of the surrounding air. Since the wet-bulb temperature is a function of both the dry-bulb temperature of the air and the relative humidity, the ability to remove heat from the condenser water is affected by the relative humidity of the surrounding air. The wet-bulb temperature and the size of the cooling tower are the primary indicators of the potential cooling capacity of a given cooling tower at any time.

REAL ESTATE APPLICATION: Cooling towers are typically associated with relatively large HVAC systems. They are always located adjacent to the building or on its roof. The operation of a cooling tower is relatively simple: Condenser water is sprayed through nozzles located at the top of the cooling tower, distributing the water evenly over a fill material (heat-transfer medium with a large surface area). Air transferred across or through the water removes heat from it, and the cooled water is collected in the cooling tower sump and returned to the central chiller plant.

cubic feet per minute (cfm)   The recognized standard unit of measurement of the volume of air flowing through a duct or into a defined space. The volume flow through a duct (cfm) depends on the size (dimensions) of the duct, restrictions and friction inside the duct, the speed of the fan supplying air to the duct, the number and size of discharge openings in the duct, the static pressure within the duct, and other factors.

cubic feet per minute (cfm) per person   The recognized standard unit of measurement of the volume of ventilation air delivered to occupants of a defined space (building, floor, etc.). ASHRAE standard 62-1989 adjusted the recommended office occupant ventilation rate from 15 cfm/person to 20 cfm/person. One fourth of the 20 cfm (i.e., 5 cfm) can be recirculated air returned from the occupants' spaces, provided it is filtered properly. The remainder (15 cfm) should be outside fresh air. (See also *air changes.*)

REAL ESTATE APPLICATION: The cfm per person can be estimated from the total number of occupants in the space, the total volume (cfm) of air provided to the space, and the percentage of fresh air and recirculated air provided to the space. The physical layout of ductwork and the location of diffusers is also important in determining the effective distribution of air to the occupants.

damper   A flat, rigid, rectangular galvanized steel device used for controlling the rate and direction of airflow in HVAC systems. Dampers are usually controlled automatically by small motors, actuators, linkage, or other means. (See diagram on next page.)

REAL ESTATE APPLICATION: Dampers increase the effectiveness and efficiency of HVAC systems serving buildings by varying the amount of outside air introduced into the building, depending on outdoor and indoor air conditions. (*Inlet dampers* control incoming air to an air handler; *exhaust dampers* control air that is discharged from the building to the outdoors, and *return dampers* control air returning from the various spaces in a building through the air handler.)

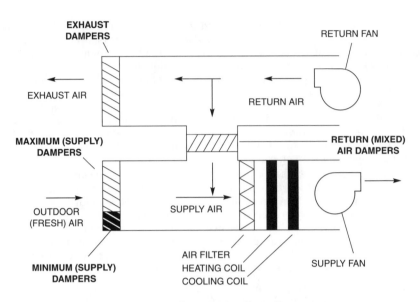

dampers (central air-handling unit)

defrosting   The process of removing frost and/or ice accumulation from an evaporator (coil). The *defrost cycle* is typically an automatic function of the operating cycle of a refrigeration (heat pump) unit. When a heat pump is operating in the heating cycle so that refrigerant is evaporating in the outdoor coil, frost will begin to form on the coil when the temperature at the outside surface of the coil falls below freezing (32°F). If the frost buildup continues, ice will form until the flow of air through the coil is restricted. This diminishes the coil's ability to transfer heat, and its efficiency will be decreased. Periodic defrosting removes frost to maintain a clear coil surface.

degree day   A unit that represents one degree of difference from a given stated average outdoor air temperature for one day; 65°F is the standard outdoor air temperature used as a baseline in determining degree days. Outdoor air temperatures greater than 65°F represent *cooling degree days*, because HVAC equipment would normally be in the cooling mode of operation in order to keep a building tempered. Outdoor air temperatures below 65°F represent *heating degree days* because HVAC equipment would normally be in a heating mode in order to keep a building tempered.

REAL ESTATE APPLICATION: If the average outdoor air temperature for a given day is 50°F, the number of degree-days is equal to 15 heating degree days (65 – 50 = 15). If the average outdoor air temperature is 86°F, the number of degree days is equal to 21 cooling degree days (86 – 65 = 21). Although other factors (humidity, solar conditions, wind, etc.) play an important part in establishing a building's heating or cooling load as it relates to weather, degree days are readily measured and, therefore, serve as the standard index.

dehumidification   A process of decreasing the percentage of moisture (water) in a given quantity of air.

REAL ESTATE APPLICATION: Humid air flowing across a cooling coil will naturally condense and dehumidify; depending on the temperature of the air as it is leaving the coil, it may have to be reheated to a specified temperature prior to delivery to a space. Similarly, cold air flowing across a heating coil will increase in temperature and therefore be dehumidified (i.e., its relative humidify will decrease). For this reason, air provided to building occupants in cold weather can be dry, particularly if no humidification systems are present in the building.

dehydrator   See *dryer.*

deodorizer   In an HVAC system, a device that removes various odors, usually by adsorption. Activated carbon filtration is commonly used for adsorption deodorization.

desiccant   A solid substance used to collect, absorb, and hold moisture; a *drying agent.* Commonly used desiccants are silica gel and activated alumina. Desiccant filters are used in refrigerant systems.

design conditions   The outdoor air conditions—dry-bulb temperature, wet-bulb temperature, moisture content—which can be expected to be exceeded just a few times a year for short periods. So-called *normal design conditions* vary by geographical location.

REAL ESTATE APPLICATION: An HVAC system is normally sized such that, when operating at less than 100% of capacity, it can satisfy the design conditions for its respective location. The term *design day* is often used when referring to those days when design conditions occur throughout the day. *Maximum outdoor design conditions* refers to the absolute maximum conditions of dry-bulb temperature, wet-bulb temperature, moisture content, etc., that may be reached, but not exceeded, throughout the year.

diffuser   An air distribution terminal outlet designed to direct airflow into a desired pattern; also called *air diffuser.* Diffusers are typically mounted flush with the underside of the ceiling surface but sometimes flush with a wall or floor. The term diffuser relates to the supply of air whereas the term grille relates to the return of air. (Compare *grille.*)

REAL ESTATE APPLICATION: Air diffusers are the most common means of distributing air to rooms or spaces in a building, particularly within interior (nonperimeter) areas. Internal loads due to concentrations of people, heat-generating equipment, outside walls and windows, interior configuration, etc., determine the number, size, and location of air diffusers.

direct-expansion (DX) unit   A self-contained, compact air-conditioning unit located within or adjacent to the air-conditioned space and consisting of the minimum elements necessary to produce cooling. The cooling medium in a direct-expansion unit is a chemical refrigerant, which precludes the requirement of a remote cooling source (e.g., chill water, brine). In this type of unit, the refrigerant expands as it flows through the thermal expansion valve into the evaporator (cooling) coil. Heating may be included with the unit but provided from a separate source.

REAL ESTATE APPLICATION: Commonly employed as a supplementary cooling source in restaurants, small computer rooms, etc., DX systems can be either water cooled or air cooled. Roof-top and split systems use an air-cooled condenser situated outdoors to reject the heat of vaporization; water-cooled systems use water from a municipal supply system for the same purpose.

distribution   The flow or movement of air through HVAC air handlers, ductwork, and other components such as dampers, filters, and diffusers, in order for the air to perform its function; also referred to as *air distribution*.

REAL ESTATE APPLICATION: The volume of air required for a space will vary, depending on the heating and/or cooling load in the space. The ability of the air to reach the space depends on the layout of the HVAC system duct-work and components, the sizing and length of the ductwork (hence, friction losses), the capacity of the fans or other air handlers, and the location and position of dampers, filters, diffusers, etc. The proper design of an HVAC system depends on the effective location of supply and return duct-work, diffusers, grilles, etc. Improper air distribution is often the cause of occupant complaints.

diversity   Differences in heating and cooling loads that cause variations in heating and cooling requirements. Factoring in diversity allows engineers to adjust the design capacity of piping, ducts, pumps, air handlers, etc., to yield a more cost-effective system. The diversity concept is applicable to HVAC systems serving multiple zones—for example, an induction-type water system that serves all four exposures of a building.

draft   The movement of air caused by a difference in air density; an *air current*. A draft or flow of air or gases in a chimney or flue is a result of heated air or warm gases rising because they are less dense than the surrounding, relatively cooler air.

REAL ESTATE APPLICATION: The downward movement of cold air along the perimeter window areas of buildings in the winter, due to the differences in density of the relatively cool air adjacent to the window and the warmer air within the space, is referred to as *cool downdraft*. High-pressure induction units are an effective means of eliminating the potential occupant discomforts caused by cool downdrafts.

drift   Loss of water from a cooling system due to cooling tower fans driving air out of the top of a cooling tower with entrained water. (Condenser water is sprayed across fill material to increase its free surface area so that more heat can be transferred from the water to the air. Sometimes water is taken up—i.e., entrained—by the air blowing across the water surface.) Also, carryover of water (e.g., condensate, spray water used for humidification purposes) from an air-handling coil into the air stream. This drift can be a direct result of excess humidity, improper design of air-handling components, excessive air-handler speed, or absence of *drift eliminators*—or a combination of two or more of these factors.

REAL ESTATE APPLICATION: The degree of cooling tower drift varies, depending on several factors.

1. The size, design, and type of cooling tower (forced draft, induced draft, natural draft).
2. Existing load and corresponding operation of the cooling tower (two or four forced-draft fans in use).
3. Outside air conditions (temperature, humidity, etc.).

Losses of condenser water due to drift need to be replaced (makeup water) in order to maintain proper water levels in the cooling tower and condenser water system. Addition of makeup water means chemicals will have to be added to the system in order to maintain effective water-treatment levels. Drift is a result of the mechanical effects of the cooling tower, whereas the loss of water as a result of air (wind) circulating around the cooling tower is called *windage* (which see).

drip pan   A pan-shaped panel or trough, permanently affixed to the underside of a heat exchanger (evaporator coil, air-handler cooling coil, etc.) to collect and carry away condensate dripping from the surfaces of the coil.

REAL ESTATE APPLICATION: Drip pans collect a significant amount of condensate when the air being drawn across a coil is warm and humid and the water inside of the coil is cool. They can be a breeding ground for algae and *Legionella* species. (See also *Legionnaires' disease* in Environmental Management and Indoor Air Quality.)

dry-bulb temperature   The actual temperature of the air, as opposed to the wet-bulb temperature which also accounts for the moisture content in the air.

REAL ESTATE APPLICATION: The dry-bulb temperature is always equal to or greater than the wet-bulb temperature at any given time. The dry-bulb temperature will match the wet-bulb temperature under conditions of 100% humidity (e.g., when it is raining). The difference between the dry-bulb temperature and the wet-bulb temperature will be the greatest on very dry days when there is little or no humidity.

dryer   A device to trap and absorb moisture. A component of a refrigeration system, usually installed permanently, for the purpose of trapping and absorbing moisture present in the refrigerant gas; also called *dehydrator*.

REAL ESTATE APPLICATION: *A refrigerant dryer* is recommended for most refrigerant systems and is essential for low-temperature systems. A full-flow dryer should be used in systems with hermetically sealed compressors, since exposure of the compressor motor windings to moisture will cause the insulation on the windings to deteriorate.

dual-duct system   An HVAC system that utilizes separate ducts to provide both cool air and warm air to the various terminal units within the spaces being served. Air is supplied to each duct from a common fan. The heating and cooling coils are located within the machinery room, downstream, but close to the fan unit in each respective duct. Advantages of a dual-duct system are (1) centralized air conditioning, service, and maintenance (the system's heating coils, drains, filters, etc., are all located within the machinery room, thus, saving on service time and material costs) and (2) individual temperature control (users are ensured maximum flexibility and instantaneous temperature response because of the simultaneous availability of cold and warm air at each terminal unit [mixing box] at all times).

duct   A channel, usually rectangular or square but sometimes circular in cross-section, through which air is moved. The *ductwork* is typically manufactured of sheet metal because of its ease of fabrication, air movement characteristics (laminar flow), light weight, and component attachment characteristics.

duct silencer   A device that absorbs sound by placing obstructions in the path of the supply air flow in a duct; also called *sound attenuator*. (The noise or sound level of a duct system is a function of the velocity of air movement through the duct.) Because a duct silencer significantly reduces the air pressure in the system, it increases sound absorption to a level that would normally be provided by an equivalent length of duct.

economy cycle   A form of reduced operation of HVAC or refrigeration equipment (air handler, condensing unit, chiller) using automatic controls and devices. Operation of equipment in the *economizer* mode provides a means of matching the output of the equipment to the required cooling load, resulting in increased operating efficiencies, reduced energy output, and a decrease in operating costs. The terms economy cycle and economizer are derived from the concept of economical operation of an HVAC plant.

REAL ESTATE APPLICATION: A building air handler operating in economizer mode introduces cool outside air as a cooling medium, as opposed to chilled water, which is more costly to provide since it involves the additional operation of a chiller machine. Operation of a building's central fan system in economy cycle is effective when outside dry-bulb air temperatures are between approximately 45°F and 65°F, depending on other factors such as building load, HVAC plant equipment and construction, outside air relative humidity, etc. The term *full economizer* is used when a central fan system with economizer capability is introducing the absolute maximum volume of outdoor air the system is capable of handling.

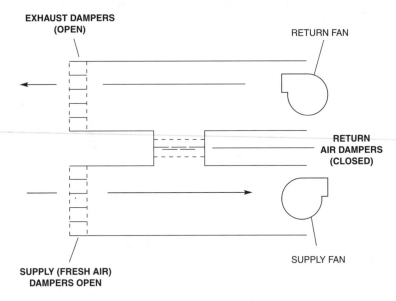

economizer

effective area   The actual or net flow area of an air inlet (damper or grille) or outlet device (diffuser). The effective area is equal to the gross surface area minus the area of any vanes or other obstructions.

effective temperature   The overall effect on the human body of the temperature, humidity, and movement of the air.

electric heater   A resistance coil that converts electrical energy to heat energy; also called *electric resistance heater*. All of the energy used is converted to heat. An electric heater may be permanently positioned inside a duct or convector unit through which air flows, or it may be mounted on a floor slab and radiate heat naturally with no convection effect.

REAL ESTATE APPLICATION: Some advantages of electric heaters are the relatively low initial purchase cost and ease of installation, particularly when alternate heat sources (e.g., steam, hot water) are not readily available. However, electric heaters are inefficient because they consume a considerable amount of electricity.

electric-pneumatic (EP) switch   An actuating device that receives a low-voltage electrical input signal and converts it to a pneumatic (air) output signal. EP switches are commonly used in HVAC control applications.

electrostatic filter   An HVAC filter that applies an electric charge to particles of dust, dirt, etc., so they will be attracted to an oppositely charged plate and removed from the airstream.

eliminator   A device installed at the discharge side of a spray coil humidifier to prevent entrained water from entering the duct system; also called *drift eliminator.*

entrainment   An abnormal condition whereby exhaust air being discharged from a duct, grille, or other HVAC component immediately re-enters the supply airstream (air intake) in an adjacent duct due to a difference in air pressure (vacuum effect); also called *re-entrainment.*

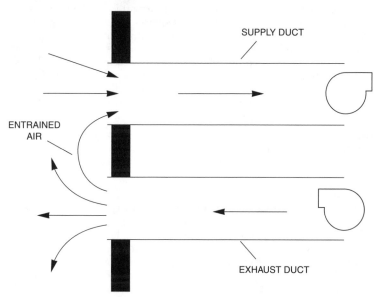

entrainment

evaporation loss   The loss of water in a condenser water system due to evaporation at the cooling tower.

REAL ESTATE APPLICATION: The rate of evaporation of condenser water varies, depending on outside air conditions, the temperature of the condenser water, the operational status of the cooling tower (two fans vs. four fans operating), etc. When considering the various causes of condenser water loss (e.g., evaporation, drift, windage, bleed), evaporation is the largest contributor in the open condenser water system. The amount of makeup water required to compensate for the loss of condenser water due to evaporation is fairly significant.

evaporation phase   One of the four stages of the basic *refrigeration cycle* (which see); the stage in which the low-pressure, low-temperature liquid refrigerant passes through an evaporator or cooling coil and extracts (absorbs) heat from a space. (The refrigerant passing through the cooling coil is converted to a gaseous state.) Heat will transfer from the relatively warmer air within the space to the coils that have been cooled by the evaporation of the refrigerant within the system. The evaporation phase is on the low side (low-pressure side) of the HVAC system.

evaporative condenser   A type of heat-rejection equipment in which sprayer coils or tubes are used to dissipate heat to the air by a combination of sensible heat transfer and latent heat transfer. Rejected heat is absorbed by water diffused over the coil surface and then transferred to the air passing over the coil. Vapor within the coil (e.g., refrigerant gas) condenses when cooled by the evaporation of water diffused over the coil surface. An evaporative condenser consists of a condensing coil, fan and motor, water distribution system, sump, recirculating pump, and casing. (See also *latent heat; sensible heat*.)

evaporator section   One of the four primary components of an absorption chiller system. In a refrigeration system, a coil containing refrigerant that vaporizes and absorbs heat, thereby cooling the surrounding space (e.g., walk-in cooler, refrigerator). The refrigerant (cooling medium) enters the evaporator as a liquid and is transformed into a vapor as it expands and absorbs heat from the surrounding air. In a chiller, the evaporator section cools the liquid medium for use in an air-conditioning system or process refrigeration. Liquid refrigerant (water) is sprayed over copper tubes that contain the chiller water, and evaporation of the sprayed refrigerant removes heat from the water inside the tubes. (See also *absorption chiller*.)

exfiltration   The unintentional outward flow of air from a building through a wall, joints, cracks, etc. Exfiltration reduces the efficiency and increases the costs of heating or cooling a building or other enclosed space. (See also *infiltration*.)

expansion phase   One of the four stages of the basic *refrigeration cycle* (which see); the stage in which the refrigerant liquid expands to a gaseous state when passing into the evaporator coil through the thermostatic expansion valve (TXV or TEV). As the relatively high-pressure, low-temperature liquid refrigerant passes through the thermal expansion valve, the pressure is reduced and the liquid begins to expand into a gas. The theoretical basis of the refrigeration cycle is the principle that a liquid (particularly a low-temperature liquid) expanding into a gas extracts (absorbs) heat from the surrounding area.

expansion valve   See *thermostatic expansion valve*.

exterior zone   The areas adjacent to the skin of a building (e.g., perimeter offices). Being affected primarily by outside (external) weather conditions, the heating and cooling loads encountered at the perimeter of a building are different from those encountered in the building's core or interior zone. (Compare *interior zone*; see also *perimeter HVAC system* and the diagram that accompanies *zoning*.)

fan   A device for producing an artificial current of air. Fans used to move air mechanically for the purpose of heating, cooling, and ventilation are radial or axial devices comprised of a wheel or blades, driving mechanisms (belts, rotor, and motor), and housing. (See also *centrifugal fan; propeller fan; vaneaxial fan*.)

fan-coil unit An integrated unit consisting of a fan that produces a flow of air and a coil containing chilled water or direct-expansion refrigerant used for cooling and dehumidifying the air. A heating coil, filters, and a humidifier are other components of the fan-coil unit.

REAL ESTATE APPLICATION: A common component of air-water HVAC systems, fan-coil units are usually used at the perimeter of a building for heating and cooling.

fan performance curve The graphic representation (chart) of the operating characteristics of a fan; also called *fan curve* or *performance curve.* The fan curve or chart will show how one operating characteristic, such as volume flow rate, varies as a function of another parameter (e.g., fan speed, damper position). Since any air-handling system is a combination of ductwork, filters, dampers, variable speed motors, etc., each system has an individual pressure-volume characteristic that is independent of the fan applied to the system.

REAL ESTATE APPLICATION: Fan performance curves are used to determine the relationship between the volume of air a fan can deliver and the pressure it can discharge at different air volumes. The graphic representations are based on the principle that the resistance to air flow (static pressure) in a duct system varies as the square of the volume of air flowing through the system. In practice, static pressure is calculated for a given system at the required air volume and established as a point on the fan performance curve. Remaining curve points are obtained by calculation based on the square principle.

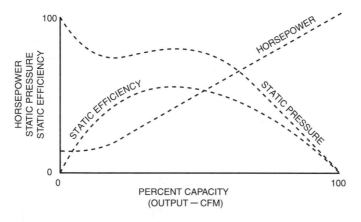

fan curve (centrifugal fan)

fan-powered box In a variable-air-volume (VAV) HVAC system, a variable-air valve and a small auxiliary motor-driven fan that mixes and moves induced air from the ceiling plenum, with the primary air supplied from the HVAC duct; also called *fan-powered terminal.*

REAL ESTATE APPLICATION: Common in variable-air-volume HVAC applications, fan-powered boxes are mounted near the terminal locations (e.g., diffuser within the ductwork) above the ceiling of the area being served. Compared to a straight variable-air-volume mixing box, a fan-powered box has the advantages of a constant supply of air to a space, hence, less fluctuation of noise levels and increased system capacity as a result of the motor-driven fan. The disadvantages are the additional cost to install motor-driven fans and increased maintenance in an area that is, to some degree, difficult to access, being above the ceiling and within an occupied space.

feet per minute (fpm)   The recognized standard unit of measurement of air velocity in an HVAC duct, diffuser, or other component.

fill The component of a cooling tower that provides a large surface area onto which condenser water is sprayed to increase its heat-transfer capacity. The fill area of the cooling tower breaks up the condenser water into fine droplets and provides a cooling surface for the water droplets. (The fill takes up the entire square footage of surface area of a cooling tower.)

fin-tube coil   A common type of heat exchanger (heating/cooling coil) in which metal fins are attached to the outer surface of a coil in order to provide a larger heat transfer surface area and increase the efficiency of the heat exchanger. (See also *coil*.)

flexible duct   An expandable, contractible, nonmetallic circular duct used to connect stationary HVAC ductwork to an HVAC terminal diffuser; also called *flex-duct* or *flexible hose*. The concept of the flexible duct is that it can be easily disconnected from a diffuser in one location and relocated and attached to a diffuser in another location.

REAL ESTATE APPLICATION: Flexible duct can restrict air flow, and there is a major cost consideration in that it is the only type of duct that can be used in some buildings.

flow hood   A device used to measure airflow at terminal locations such as diffusers. (Compare *pitot tube; velometer*.)

REAL ESTATE APPLICATION: A flow hood provides an enclosure around the duct opening in order to measure airflow. The opening is expandable so it will fit around various sized duct openings.

forced hot water heating system   A heating system in which a circulating pump is used to force hot water through various heat exchangers and terminal heating units (e.g., convectors).

free cooling   An HVAC cooling process that uses outside air to augment a building's mechanical cooling equipment or to ventilate a building when the heat content of the outside air (enthalpy) is less than that of the inside air.

freeze protection   One of several measures applied to a coil (air-handling unit) in order to prevent freeze-ups in cold weather conditions.

REAL ESTATE APPLICATION: The freezing of water in preheat, reheat, and chilled water coils can damage the coils and lead to costly repairs or replacement. Freezing can be caused by the introduction of cold air through an unprotected coil. In addition to design precautions (duct and coil layout, steam valve control, etc.), the following measures may be taken to protect a water coil from freeze-up:

1. Remove (drain) the water from the coil during the winter season.
2. Run the chilled-water pump when the outdoor air temperature drops below a specified parameter.
3. Lower the freezing point of the water in the coil by adding an antifreeze or glycol solution.

freeze stat A device that measures the temperature at a cooling or heating coil in an air handler and automatically shuts down (trips) a fan unit to protect the coil from freezing if a predetermined air temperature (low set point) is exceeded. Also, a device that measures the temperature of chilled water within a chiller and automatically shuts it down to prevent the chiller tube bundles from freezing solid if a predetermined water temperature (low set point) is exceeded.

Freon The trade name for the family of chlorofluorocarbon (CFC) refrigerants used in various refrigeration and air-conditioning systems. Freon was developed in 1930 and introduced as a commercial refrigerant in 1931. (See also *chlorofluorocarbons* in Environmental Management and Indoor Air Quality.)

frost control The switching of the operation of a refrigeration system to prevent or remove frost buildup on the evaporator coil. The frost control cycle is typically automated but could be manual or semiautomatic. Frost accumulation on the evaporator (cooling) coil is caused by moisture in the air coming in contact with the coil at a temperature below the freezing point of water (32°F). Frost buildup reduces the heat transfer (i.e., cooling) capabilities of the coil. (The frost control cycle of a refrigeration unit is commonly referred to as *defrost cycle;* see also *defrosting.*)

gas-fired chiller A reciprocating type of chiller that uses a natural gas-fired engine as the prime mover to drive the compressor; also called *gas engine-driven chiller.*

generator One of the four primary components of an absorption chiller, the generator section is located in the upper shell of the chiller. The term generator is derived from the generating medium, usually steam but sometimes hot water, that flows through tubes within this section of the chiller causing the refrigerant solution to vaporize and, thus, generating the refrigeration process. (See also *absorption chiller.*)

grille A louvered opening through which return air flows from a conditioned space back to the central heating/cooling system, for reconditioning, exhaust, re-supply, etc. (Compare *diffuser.*)

REAL ESTATE APPLICATION: The location of return air grilles is important but usually less critical than the location of supply diffusers. Return air grilles may be placed in the ceiling, wall, or floor; a wall, near the floor, is usually the best location. However, due to structural and architectural layout considerations, most return air grilles in large commercial buildings are located in the ceiling.

heat gain Heat added to a conditioned space or building from external or internal sources. Heat gain increases the cooling load of a space and, therefore, the degree of cooling required to maintain occupant comfort.

REAL ESTATE APPLICATION: Examples of internal heat gain sources are lighting equipment, people (body heat), motors, cooking equipment, and appliances. Examples of external heat gain sources are the sun and warm outside air infiltration.

heating degree day See *degree day.*

heat loss Heat that leaves a building through the walls, roof, basement floor, etc., particularly during cold weather conditions. The heat transfer from the inside to the outside of a building varies depending on the inside and outside temperatures, the construction materials used (thickness of window glass, insulation), and the quality of building construction.

REAL ESTATE APPLICATION: Heat loss is measured in Btu's per hour per square foot of material (concrete wall with 6-inch glass fiber insulation, for example).

heat pump   A self-contained heating and cooling unit, usually positioned within a window opening. A heat pump system employs a refrigeration cycle which, by design and control, moves heat either out of a space (cooling mode) or into a space (heating mode).

The theory of heat pump operation in a cooling mode is similar to the function of a through-the-wall residential air-conditioning unit and is a relatively simple concept to understand. Heat is removed from a space and pumped to the outdoors using a refrigerant and the basic refrigeration cycle (compression, condensation, expansion, evaporation). The operation of a heat pump in a heating mode is a more difficult concept to understand. Specific components within the heat pump (e.g., evaporator coil and condensing coil), operate in a reverse mode, thereby extracting heat from the outside air and pumping it indoors. The theory behind the heating mode of operation is that heat is available in outdoor air even if the air temperature is relatively low. However, the efficiency of a heat pump is significantly diminished when the air temperature drops below a certain level because less heat is available in the air. This decrease in efficiency requires the heat pump to operate for longer periods of time during cold weather in order to maintain the desired indoor space temperatures.

REAL ESTATE APPLICATION: Heat pumps provide a natural solution to year-round heating and air conditioning in buildings with a favorably balanced cooling-heating load. In other words, when the difference between the average maximum outdoor air temperature (cooling season) and average minimum outdoor air temperature (heating season) is not significant (e.g., 60 degrees or less), the heat pump is effective and economically competitive with alternate HVAC applications. Since a heat pump's single energy source is electricity, this type of system is economical whenever electrical utility rates are advantageous compared to the costs of alternate energy sources (e.g., steam, hot water, chilled water). Some of the advantages of a heat pump system are:

1. Initial cost savings—no central heating and cooling equipment (boilers, chillers, piping, etc.) required.
2. Simplified service procedures and account billing—use of a single energy source (electrical power).
3. Lower fire insurance rates—reduced premiums because of elimination of fire hazards associated with boiler and heating systems.

The use of heat pumps is very common in hotels, motels, and residential apartment units as well as commercial buildings (warehouses, research and development facilities, single-story structures) where installation of package units effects an initial cost savings.

heat recovery system   A system capable of extracting heat that would otherwise be wasted and transferring it to areas of the building that require heat.

REAL ESTATE APPLICATION: Potential secondary heating sources utilizing waste heat recovery include exhaust steam from a steam turbine-driven electrical generator, heat emitted from a large number of lights in a room or generated by equipment in a computer room, flue gas exhaust from a boiler, and waste heat from laundry water systems. Because waste heat recovery system design, equipment, and installation can be expensive, a cost-benefit analysis should be performed before such a strategy is implemented.

hermetic   Airtight; impervious to air. In HVAC applications, a refrigeration or air-conditioning compressor unit consisting of an electric motor and a compressor built into an integral (sealed) housing.

REAL ESTATE APPLICATION: Some of the advantages of a hermetic compressor (compared to an open compressor) are quieter operation, simpler lubrication (only two bearings required to support the motor and compressor), elimination of alignment problems between the motor and compressor, and no shaft seals—therefore no potential leakage of refrigerant.

high-pressure switch   A safety device in an air-conditioning or refrigeration system that stops the compressor when the discharge pressure rises above prescribed limits (due to inadequate condensing, excess air in the system, etc.); also called *high-pressure cutout*. The phrase "tripping out on high head pressure" is frequently used in the industry when describing the action of a high-pressure cutout switch.

REAL ESTATE APPLICATION: A high-pressure switch will often shut down air-conditioning units that provide supplementary cooling to tenant computer rooms and other areas when the flow of cooling water to the condensing unit is interrupted. Supplementary air-conditioning units that use municipal water for cooling should be secured (shut off) prior to planned city water shutdowns, plumbing repairs, etc., then restarted following restoration of the water supply. In such situations, if this type of water-cooled air-conditioning unit is not shut down and restarted manually, the unit usually will not restart automatically. This often results in overheating of the rooms or spaces being served by the unit.

high side   The high-pressure side of the basic refrigeration cycle or system. The condenser (condensation phase), located between the compressor and the thermal expansion valve, is on the high side of a refrigeration system. (Compare *low side*.)

high-velocity duct system   An HVAC duct system that uses higher air velocities and higher static pressure than a conventional system. The high-velocity conditions are the result of smaller duct opening dimensions and increased air-handler horsepower. The smaller duct size saves space during building construction. Special strength requirements apply during the fabrication and installation of high-velocity ducts.

hot deck   One of two ventilation ducts in a dual-duct HVAC system; the duct that supplies relatively warm air to various spaces. (Compare *cold deck*.)

hot gas bypass   A piping system in a refrigerating unit or air-conditioning chiller that diverts hot refrigerant gas from the condenser into the low-pressure side of the system. The hot gas bypass serves as a means of system capacity control by artificially loading the compressor. Under low load conditions, as the evaporator (cooling coil) pressure tends to drop, a constant-pressure valve on the discharge side of the compressor will admit hot gas from the compressor to the low side of the system (downstream of the thermal expansion valve and either before or after the evaporator coil, depending on the particular design).

This will help to maintain a constant suction pressure at the compressor, thereby maintaining a relatively constant compressor horsepower output.

hot gas discharge   The piping that connects the compressor to the condenser in a refrigeration or air-conditioning system. Refrigerant vapor discharged from the compressor is referred to as hot gas, hence the term hot gas discharge.

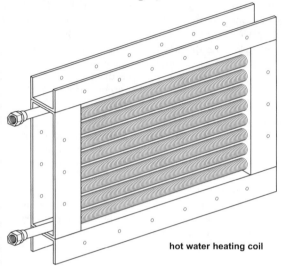

hot water heating coil

hot water coil   A coil, usually made of copper tubing with attached fins, used for heating the air supplied to a particular space. Hot water coils (also called *hot water heating coils*) are similar in construction, size, and appearance to single-tube steam coils. (See also *coil*.)

hot-water heating system   A system in which hot water flowing in pipes from a boiler to the heating terminal units serves as the heating medium.

humidification   The process of adding moisture (water) to the air. Humidification helps to control occupant thermal effects, dust and other airborne particulates, odors, static electricity, and other factors related to indoor air quality and health concerns. In a central HVAC system, humidification may be accomplished by means of a water-spray, steam-pan, steam-grid, or other type of *humidifier*. The water or steam is usually expelled as fine droplets and directed onto the surface of the heating or cooling coil. Water humidification systems typically utilize water from the local (municipal) supply system; steam humidification systems could utilize steam provided by a local steam utility company or generated by on-site steam boilers.

> REAL ESTATE APPLICATION: Humidification of air in an HVAC system is usually needed more in colder climates, where heating the cold outside air introduced into the building lowers its relative humidity to an uncomfortable level. Proper selection and maintenance of humidification systems for large HVAC systems for general building occupancy has received significant attention and concern. Water source humidification systems require frequent maintenance because of their mold growth potential and the likelihood of indoor air quality concerns arising. The concerns of steam source systems relate to the proper selection and use of water-treatment chemicals within the systems that generate the steam for humidification.

humidistat   A sensor or controller device that is operated by changes in humidity; also called *hygrostat*.

> REAL ESTATE APPLICATION: A humidistat may be located in an air-handling duct to measure the relative humidity of air moving through the duct. In a

steam humidification system, the humidistat would produce an output signal that would adjust a valve controlling steam flow in order to maintain a required level of relative humidity in supply air.

humidity The weight of water vapor per unit volume of air, expressed in grains of moisture per cubic foot of air. *Absolute humidity* represents the actual moisture (water vapor) content of air. Since warmer air has the ability to hold more water vapor than cooler air, 10 cubic feet of air at 90°F and 50% relative humidity would have a higher value of absolute humidity than 10 cubic feet of air at 50°F and 50% relative humidity

Relative humidity is the ratio of the amount (weight) of water vapor actually contained in a given amount (weight) of air as compared to the maximum possible weight of water vapor that the air could contain at that same (dry-bulb) temperature (usually expressed as a percentage). The warmer the air, the more moisture it can contain before becoming saturated. Therefore, 90°F air at 50% relative humidity contains significantly more water vapor (moisture) than 20°F air at 50% relative humidity.

REAL ESTATE APPLICATION: Cold outside air at 50% relative humidity introduced into a building via an HVAC air-handling system and heated to 70°F for occupant comfort may now have a relative humidity of approximately 10%. Because heat was added to the air, its ability to hold moisture increased, but the amount of moisture present in the air was unchanged. Therefore its relative humidity decreased. Steam or water could be added to this air (humidification) during the heating process to increase its relative humidity to a comfortable level. The American Society of Heating, Refrigerating and Air Conditioning Engineers (ASHRAE) states that relative humidity levels for typical office environments should be between 30% and 60%.

HVAC The universally recognized standard abbreviation for the science of providing an environment with the correct temperature, humidity, air movement, air cleanliness, ventilation, and acoustical level. HVAC is the acronym for heating, ventilating, and air conditioning.

hydronic system A heating or cooling system that involves the transfer of heat by a fluid such as water or steam circulating through a closed system of pipes. An induction-type heating/cooling system is an example.

hygrometer An instrument used to measure the amount of moisture in the air (i.e, relative humidity).

ice storage See *thermal storage.*

indoor air quality See definition and related terms in Environmental Management and Indoor Air Quality.

induction system A method of heating or cooling that moves air from a room across a heating or cooling coil by means of high velocity air being discharged through a set of nozzles; also called *induction units.* The air supply to the nozzles is referred to as primary air; the room air drawn across the coil and carried along (induced) by the primary air is referred to as secondary air; and the entire discharge air, composed of both primary and secondary air, is referred to as total air. (See also *primary air; secondary air.*)

REAL ESTATE APPLICATION: Induction systems are common in perimeter HVAC applications in various types of buildings; the induction unit type of HVAC system is particularly responsive to the quickly changing load characteristics encountered at the perimeter of a building. There are high-pressure as well as low-pressure induction systems. High-pressure systems are very common in high-rise buildings constructed in the 1970s and early 1980s.

infiltration   The unplanned (usually unwanted) introduction of air and moisture into a conditioned space through door openings, window openings, and other components of a building's shell. The degree of infiltration depends on several factors, such as the tightness of the building skin components (door seals, roof hatches, window gaskets, etc.), direction and velocity of the wind, the difference between outdoor and indoor air temperatures, and other factors. (Compare *exfiltration*.)

REAL ESTATE APPLICATION: Infiltration can be a source of sizable gains or losses of heat in a building. Installation and use of revolving doors in a high-rise building is one method of minimizing infiltration.

insulation   See *acoustical duct lining*.

interior zone   The areas of a building at its core, as opposed to those at its perimeter (exterior zone). Since many buildings are typically divided into two distinct zones (interior and exterior), the spaces comprising the interior zone are a significant percentage of the building's total space. The exterior zone comprises those areas such as perimeter offices, which are adjacent to the skin of the building. (Compare *exterior zone*; see also the diagram that accompanies *zoning*.)

REAL ESTATE APPLICATION: The heating and cooling loads and subsequent strategy for tempering the interior zone are very different when compared to the exterior zone. The interior zone load, particularly in large buildings, consists primarily of internal heat gain generated by equipment, people (body heat), lighting loads, etc. The perimeter zones are affected primarily by outside (external) weather conditions.

latent heat   Thermal energy absorbed or emitted in a process other than change of temperature; heat that is absorbed or released by a substance when it changes state—i.e., solid to liquid (ice to water), liquid to vapor (water to steam). More specifically, *latent heat of evaporation* is the amount of heat required to convert one pound of water into water vapor without raising its temperature; latent heat is removed from water vapor when it is condensed to a liquid. (Compare *sensible heat*.)

leakage   The loss (or gain) of air from an HVAC supply (or return) duct.

REAL ESTATE APPLICATION: Leakage of air out of or into a duct is usually caused by a combination of (1) the difference in pressure between the air within the duct and the air surrounding the duct and (2) openings at duct connections. It decreases the overall efficiency of the HVAC system.

leak detector   An instrument or piece of equipment (electronic sniffer, halide torch) used to detect refrigerant leaks in a refrigeration or air-conditioning system.

linear diffuser   An HVAC air-discharge outlet in which the ratio of the length to the width of the outlet exceeds approximately 10 to 1 (the

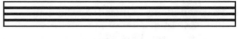

linear diffuser

width is typically less than 4 inches). Linear diffusers (also called *strip diffusers* or *slot diffusers*) are typically mounted flush with the ceiling.

REAL ESTATE APPLICATION: Because of the length and relatively large discharge area of a linear diffuser, it emits less noise than other types of diffusers handling an equivalent volume of air. In addition, when testing the airflow by placing one's hand in front of the diffuser, the airflow from a linear diffuser may seem inadequate.

liquid line   In a refrigeration or air-conditioning system, the tube or pipe that carries liquid refrigerant from the condenser or liquid receiver to the refrigerant control mechanism or thermal expansion valve.

liquid sight glass   A clear glass cylinder, encased in a metal body and installed in the liquid line of a refrigeration system to determine the amount of refrigerant charge in the system; also called *liquid line sight glass.*

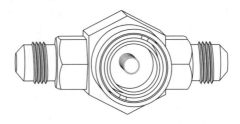

liquid sight glass

REAL ESTATE APPLICATION: Under normal conditions, a full glass indicates sufficient refrigerant in the system. If bubbles appear in the sight glass, the system is low on refrigerant and requires an additional charge.

load   The amount of temperature differential imposed on an HVAC or refrigeration system in a given amount of time; the required rate of heat removal (measured in Btu's or tons) per unit of time.

louvers   An assembly of overlapping metal blades or plates, either fixed or adjustable, designed to permit air to enter an air handler, room, or space. Louvers are installed in doors and windows and at the intake and discharge points of ventilation systems. Adjustable louvers can be repositioned to increase or decrease the opening, but they are not designed for precise adjustments.

low-pressure switch   A safety device in an air-conditioning or refrigeration system that stops the compressor when the suction pressure is reduced to a point that could produce a freeze-up in the evaporation section due to a loss of refrigerant charge or entry of air into the system; also called *low-pressure cutout.*

low side   The low-pressure side of the basic refrigeration cycle or system. The evaporator or cooling coil (evaporation phase), located between the thermal expansion valve and the compressor, is on the low side of the refrigeration system. (Compare *high side.*)

makeup air   Air from the outdoors that is introduced into a building through the ventilation system. Makeup air is, in effect, outside or fresh air; it is not ventilation air that has been previously circulated through a building.

makeup water   See definition in Water Treatment, Water Chemistry.

medium   A heat transfer surface material for a given heat exchanger, often seen as the plural media. The media in the fill sections of cooling towers are typically made of stainless steel or polyvinyl chloride (PVC). Also, material on which solids are deposited by filtration (*filter media*).

micron   A metric unit of measurement equal to one millionth of a meter or one thousandth of a millimeter; represented by Greek mu (μ).

REAL ESTATE APPLICATION: The efficiency of air filters for HVAC systems is classified according to the size of the openings through which the air passes, measured in microns. Airborne particles (also measured in microns) larger than the diameter of the filter's openings will be trapped in the filter.

minimum air   In a large central HVAC system, a mode of operation in which a minimum acceptable amount of outdoor (makeup) air is introduced into a building through the ventilation system. Minimum outdoor air quantities are achieved by using a separate set of *minimum air dampers* located in one (among several) of the air-handler units.

REAL ESTATE APPLICATION: Minimum air typically represents approximately 10%–15% of the total ventilation air provided to a building or portion of a building. Minimum air dampers and the minimum air operating concept should be reserved for extreme cold weather or warm weather (design) conditions, when recirculation and distribution of previously tempered air is significantly more cost-effective. The acceptable (ASHRAE) minimum cubic feet per minute per person fresh-air requirements should be considered during the design phase of minimum air damper sizing and selection. A separate set of dampers is typically used because of the ability to achieve a precise air volume using relatively smaller dampers compared with larger main air dampers. (See the diagram at *damper.*)

mixed air   In a large central HVAC system, ventilation air that is a mixture of air returned from various areas of a building and outdoor supply air introduced into the building. Air returned to the air-handling unit via the return air duct crosses over through the *mixed-air dampers* and combines with the fresh air in the supply air duct.

REAL ESTATE APPLICATION: Mixed-air dampers are controlled automatically; they modulate open and closed in conjunction with the supply and exhaust dampers in the same air-handling unit. The position of the mixed-air dampers is adjusted in order to maintain the discharge air temperature setting of the air handler, which will vary depending on outside air temperatures as well as inside space temperatures. (See the diagram at *damper.*)

mixing box   A device that controls the volume of airflow and mixes hot and cold air for distribution to a room. It consists of a sheet-metal box and a valve in which the hot and cold air provided by a dual-duct HVAC system is mixed and diffused.

moisture content   See *humidity.*

negative air   A condition that exists when the volume of air supplied to a space is less than the volume of air exhausted from a space, resulting in the air pressure within the space being lower than that in the surrounding areas; also called *negative pressure* or *negative air pressure.*

night setback   A reduced mode of HVAC operation during off hours when the building is unoccupied, usually at night.

REAL ESTATE APPLICATION: HVAC operators, particularly in buildings with large HVAC systems, either shut down the building's HVAC equipment or operate it in a *setback* mode—reduced fan speed, higher chill-water temperatures (in cooling season)—during unoccupied hours (night-time in an office building). Operating a central HVAC plant in a night setback mode will save considerable energy—and associated costs—over time.

occupied load   The number of occupants (density) in a given area. Specific numbers are usually not used when describing this load; reference is made, instead, to a building being heavily, lightly, or moderately occupied. Because the heat emitted by human bodies contributes significantly to the total heat gain within a space, the expected occupied load is an important consideration in the design and operation of HVAC systems. In addition, a heavily occupied area may develop higher concentrations of carbon dioxide (CO_2 gas) because of the larger number of individuals in the space.

oil safety switch   A safety control device in an air-conditioning or refrigeration system that stops the compressor if there is a lubrication failure (due to a leak, clogged strainer, refrigerant in the compressor crankcase, insufficient oil pressure, etc.)

oil separator   A device used to remove oil from gaseous refrigerant. Under normal operation of compressors in refrigeration and air-conditioning systems, oil is inherently pumped out along with the refrigerant gas. The oil separator is usually an integral part of the condensing unit; it separates the oil from the refrigerant and returns the oil to the compressor crankcase.

optimize start-stop   A function of an automated HVAC *energy management system* that starts and stops major components at the optimum time while achieving or maintaining appropriate temperature settings for the building occupants in order to achieve maximum energy cost savings. This option is typically encountered in large central HVAC systems.

> REAL ESTATE APPLICATION: Following a relatively cool summer night, a high-rise building with a 1,200-ton chiller and an energy management system using the optimize start-stop function may start the chiller at 7:00 A.M. based on average inside air temperature readings. The same building without the optimize start-stop option might automatically start the chiller one or more hours earlier (e.g., as normally scheduled for a day following a more typically expected warm summer night).

outdoor air   Air that is external to a building. Ambient surrounding air.

> REAL ESTATE APPLICATION: Outdoor air, also referred to as *fresh air* or *outside air*, is introduced into a building by air-handling units, heat pumps, etc. Outdoor air enters a building air-handling system through *outside air dampers;* also called *fresh air dampers*. (See diagram at *damper.*)

packaged AC unit   See *unitary system*.

perforated ceiling   A ceiling that contains narrow openings (perforations), which allow the introduction of conditioned air for purposes of heating and cooling. The principal feature of this method of air handling is that a greater volume of air per square foot can be introduced at a lower temperature, with minimal air movement in the occupied area and, therefore, less danger of draft. The perforated panels are typically numerous and well distributed. Because the discharge velocity is low, lower-temperature supply air can be used even with low ceiling heights. (Perforated ceiling HVAC applications are rarely used in modern-day HVAC systems.)

perimeter HVAC system   Broadly, a type of HVAC system that provides cooling and/or heating at the perimeter (skin, walls, facade) of a building. The design and capacity of perimeter HVAC systems are different from non-perimeter systems because of the quickly changing load characteristics encountered at the perimeters of buildings. An induction-type HVAC system (*perimeter induction system*) is an example. (See also *induction system.*)

pipe   The hot and cold water tubing of an induction-type heating and cooling system. The term is typically used when discussing the number of piping circuits in a particular system (e.g., two-pipe system or four-pipe system), which indicates the number of supply and return pipes providing water to and returning water from the terminal induction units. A two-pipe system can provide either hot or cold water to the terminal units at any given time; a four-pipe system can provide hot water and cold water to the terminal unit simultaneously.

piston effect   The air effect of the upward or downward movement of elevators in elevator shafts (i.e., air being pulled from a lobby or other space into the elevator shaft). The draft is a result of the negative air pressure (void) formed at the trailing end of the elevator car. Air from the lobby side of the elevator shaft will naturally fill this void, similar to air filling a cylinder of an automobile engine as the piston moves in it.

pitot tube   A device used to measure air velocity inside an HVAC duct.

> REAL ESTATE APPLICATION: The velocity of the airstream in feet per minute (fpm), multiplied by the cross-sectional area of the duct, determines the volume of air flowing through the duct in cubic feet per minute (cfm).

plenum   The confined space between a suspended ceiling and the structure above it—the underside of the deck or slab. The plenum is connected to a number of return air grilles, and air in the space is maintained at a slightly negative pressure.

> REAL ESTATE APPLICATION: The *return air plenum* concept is very common in high-rise building HVAC applications. It eliminates the requirement for installation of multiple ceiling return air grilles and associated return ducts throughout the space. Maintaining the entire ceiling plenum at a slightly negative pressure ensures circulation of air from the HVAC supply duct, into the conditioned spaces, and back to the return air duct. Because return air traveling through the plenum is redistributed throughout the building, the data and telecommunications cable lines and other materials used above the ceiling (within the plenum) must meet specific fire code and HVAC industry specifications. These materials are referred to as *plenum rated.*

plenum chamber   In an HVAC system, an enclosed space that is maintained at a slightly positive pressure and connected to one or more distributing ducts used for the movement of air.

pneumatic-electric (PE) switch   An actuating device that uses a control air (pneumatic) input signal and converts it to a low-voltage electric output signal. PE switches are commonly used in many HVAC control applications.

positive pressure   A condition that exists when more air is supplied to a space (room, building, etc.) than is exhausted from it, so that the air pressure inside the space is greater than the pressure of the air surrounding the space.

> REAL ESTATE APPLICATION: Maintaining a room at a slight positive pressure is one method of intentionally preventing pollutants from entering a room.

Emergency stairwells are sometimes maintained at a positive pressure in order to limit smoke infiltration from adjacent spaces during a building fire or smoke emergency.

precool   A concept whereby a space or building is cooled prior to occupancy, usually under relatively lighter load conditions. Precooling is usually used to (1) lessen the air-conditioning equipment cooling load encountered later in the day when the building is occupied and outside air temperatures are higher or (2) anticipate and stabilize the cooling load on a design cooling day.

preheat   The process in which steam or (less frequently) hot water flows through a coil in order to heat supply air to a specified temperature. The purpose of the *preheat coil* is to raise the temperature of the supply air to a minimum level for further conditioning (tempering). Because preheat coils are located closest to the fresh air intake dampers of an air-handling unit, this should be a nonfreeze type of coil, especially if the air encountered is below the freezing temperature.

pressure switch   A safety device (high-pressure or low-pressure switch) that shuts off (trips) HVAC or refrigeration system components such as compressors when the pressure of the operating fluid exceeds or falls below a predetermined limit.

primary air   In an induction-type heating (cooling) system, the air that is supplied from a duct and forced through high-pressure nozzles. The primary air induces the movement of room air (secondary air) across the secondary heating (cooling) coil within the induction unit. In most types of induction units, the primary air, although tempered, serves primarily as the motive force to pull secondary (room) air across the heating (cooling) coil. The majority of the heat transfer and subsequent heating (cooling) of the space takes place when the room air is pulled across the coils. (See also *induction system.*)

propeller fan   A type of axial-flow fan used in HVAC applications where there are no ducts or where there is little resistance to airflow. The name comes from the blades being in the shape of a propeller.

  REAL ESTATE APPLICATION: Propeller fans are used primarily in exhaust and circulation applications. They are also commonly used in air-cooled condenser fan systems.

psychrometer   An instrument used to measure the relative humidity of atmospheric air; also called *sling psychrometer*. A psychrometer consists of two thermometers, one with a wet bulb and the other with a dry bulb.

psychrometric chart   A tabulation of the relationship between the dewpoint temperature, dry-bulb temperature, wet-bulb temperature, humidity ratio, and relative humidity, used in HVAC load calculations and design.

purge pump   In a centrifugal-type chiller machine, a vacuum-type pump or small compressor that serves to evacuate air and moisture from the chiller and to recover and return refrigerant which is mixed with the air; also called *purge unit*. In an absorption chiller machine, the purge unit is required to remove all noncondensable vapors and to maintain a low pressure in order for the absorber to function properly.

  REAL ESTATE APPLICATION: In recent years, federal code requirements have mandated the use of high-efficiency purge units in order to minimize the release of refrigerant gas (containing chlorofluorocarbons or CFCs) to the atmosphere. High-efficiency purge units normally evacuate less than 0.1 pounds of refrigerant for every pound of air removed.

radiator   A heating unit usually fed by steam or hot water and typically located inside the room or space to be heated. A radiator transfers heat to objects by radiation within the visible range and to the surrounding air by conduction. The air, in turn, is circulated by natural convection (a difference in temperature creating a difference in density).

receiver   In a refrigeration or air-conditioning system, a storage tank located immediately after the condenser and before the metering device (thermal expansion valve). Liquid refrigerant is held in the receiver until it is needed for heat removal (cooling) in the evaporator coil.

reclaimed   Recycled, as reclaimed refrigerant.
> REAL ESTATE APPLICATION: Refrigerants containing chlorofluorocarbons (CFCs) are reclaimed in order to limit the need to produce new (virgin) CFC-containing refrigerants, which are required for the operation of existing refrigerant machines (e.g., chillers).

re-entrainment   See *entrainment*.

refrigerant   A gaseous chemical compound that is compressed into a vapor, cooled into a liquid, and then permitted to expand into a vapor as it is pumped through the refrigeration system or cycle. The chemical and physical properties of liquid refrigerants are such that they evaporate (vaporize or boil) at much lower temperatures than water so they are able to extract heat at a more rapid rate than water or other liquids. The refrigerant in a system is sometimes also called *working fluid.*
> REAL ESTATE APPLICATION: Some examples of commonly used refrigerants are R-11, R-22, R-123, and R-134a. The prefix R is interchangeable with the abbreviations for the various classes of chemical compounds: CFC (chlorofluorocarbon) or HCFC (hydrochlorofluorocarbon) or HFC (hydrofluorocarbon). Fully halogenated chlorofluorocarbons (CFC-11, CFC-12, CFC-500) are thought to pose the highest risk to the earth's ozone layer due to their high chlorine content. Hydrochlorofluorocarbons (HCFC-22, HCFC-123) also contain chlorine, but the presence of one or more atoms of hydrogen allows them to break down more quickly in the atmosphere, reducing their ozone depletion potential. Hydrofluorocarbons such as HFC-134a, which contain no chlorine, are considered environmentally safe—they have no ozone depletion potential. Under the Montreal Protocol, HCFC-123 (a low-pressure refrigerant) is targeted to replace the frequently used low-pressure refrigerant CFC-11, and HFC-134a (a medium-high pressure refrigerant) is targeted to replace medium-pressure refrigerants (CFC-12, CFC-500) as well as the widely used higher pressure refrigerant HCFC-22. (See also *chlorofluorocarbons* and *Montreal Protocol* in Environmental Management and Indoor Air Quality.)

refrigerant recovery unit   A storage device and associated fittings and connections that allows liquid refrigerant to be removed, temporarily stored, then returned to a refrigeration system or chiller during maintenance periods or a major overhaul.

refrigeration   The process of removing heat from a space or object and transferring it to another space or object or to the atmosphere, thus lowering the temperature of the space or object.

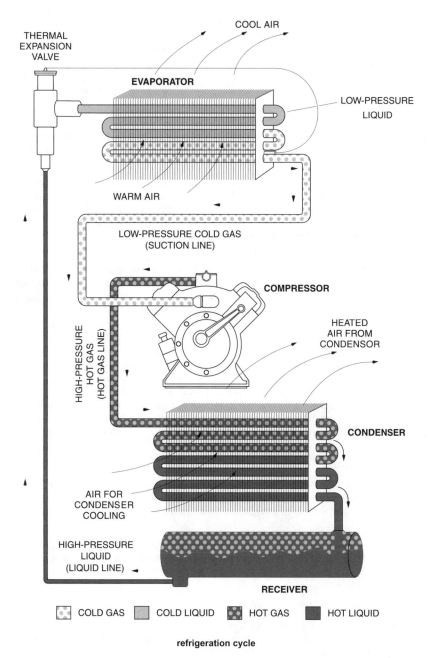

refrigeration cycle

refrigeration cycle   A closed cycle consisting of four phases in which a refrigerant is compressed, condensed, expanded, and evaporated, and the cycle is repeated continuously. The four phases of the *basic refrigeration cycle* occur in natural progression as follows—compression, condensation, expansion, evaporation (see diagram on the preceding page). The refrigeration cycle is based on the principle that a liquid expanding into a vapor (gaseous state) absorbs or extracts heat from a surrounding area. The term applies to both refrigeration (e.g., walk-in coolers) and air-conditioning (e.g., heat pumps, centrifugal chillers) systems. (See also *compression; condensation; expansion; evaporation.*)

refrigeration oils   Lubricating oils used in refrigeration systems that meet the specific requirements of such systems. Since some components of the refrigeration system (e.g., compressor) operate at relatively high temperatures, and others (e.g., condenser) operate at lower temperatures, the properties of refrigeration oils are diverse.

register   A device used to regulate the flow of air from an HVAC duct into a room. Registers may be located in the walls, floor, or ceiling of a room. The movable slats of a register are effective in shutting off the airflow but inefficient for fine tuning the flow of air into a room. Registers are used infrequently in modern HVAC applications.

reheat   The process of adding heat to air that has previously had heat added to it (e.g., in order to maintain the dry-bulb temperature within a particular space). *Reheat coils* are sometimes positioned downstream from a main air-handling unit. Optimum control of space conditions relative to both temperature and humidity can be accomplished using a reheat system.

> REAL ESTATE APPLICATION: The reheat concept was very common in large commercial building HVAC design applications in the 1970s. In a large constant-volume HVAC system operating in a heating mode, ventilation air could be supplied to twenty floors at a supply temperature just warm enough to satisfy fifteen of those floors that have a greater internal heat gain and consequently a lower heating load. Reheat coils located inside the HVAC supply duct on the respective floors could reheat the supply air to a higher discharge temperature to satisfy the greater heating load requirements of the five remaining floors. This approach offers efficiency of operation as well as control of comfort to each individual floor.

relative humidity   See *humidity.*

relief dampers   A set of flat rectangular devices and associated controls in an air-conditioning system or air-handling unit that opens automatically, relieving excess air pressure within a building or space. (See also *damper.*)

return air   Air in a given room, floor area, or other space that is being returned to the central air-handling HVAC system for re-conditioning, filtration, and re-distribution. The return air travels from the conditioned space through a return air grille, then into a return air shaft or return air duct. (Contrast *supply air.*)

return air plenum   See *plenum.*

return fan   A motor-driven fan that removes air from the various spaces in a building, returning it to the central air-handling system for re-conditioning, filtration, and re-distribution. The return-air fan is often located near the supply-air fan within a central air-handling system.

> REAL ESTATE APPLICATION: The return-air fan creates the low-pressure area that allows air to flow into and out of occupied spaces for effective circula-

tion and ventilation. Ventilation, and hence dilution of contaminants, would be inadequate without the pressure differential between the supply and return air.

rooftop unit   A direct-expansion (refrigerant) type of air-conditioning system in which all the components are situated on the roof of a building. A rooftop unit is similar to a *split system* application except that the evaporator section (cooling coil, air handler, filters) is located on the roof instead of inside the building. The rooftop unit consists of self-contained assemblies with:

1. A refrigeration section containing a refrigerant compressor, air-cooled condenser, and automatic controls.
2. An air-handling/evaporator section containing a supply fan, direct-expansion (refrigerant) cooling coil, filters, outside-air plenum, and return-air plenum.
3. An optional heating section with a self-contained gas- or oil-fired furnace, electric heating coil, or steam or hot-water coil fed by a remote heating plant (in the mechanical room of the building).

REAL ESTATE APPLICATION: Rooftop units are usually used in single-story buildings because the air-handling section is located on the roof of the building. Typically single zone, these units may also be ducted to serve multiple zones and possibly two floors. Rooftop units are often combined with through-the-wall units to provide cooling to large one- or two-story buildings. The primary advantage of this type of unit is low initial installation cost.

room temperature   The dry-bulb temperature in a given room or space; also called *space temperature.*

rupture disk   A pressure-relief mechanism similar to a relief valve that prevents over-pressurization and potential damage to a mechanical (centrifugal or screw-type) chiller due to abnormally high refrigerant pressure. Although serving the purpose of preventing damage within an air-conditioning chiller, the operation of a rupture disk could result in the uncontrolled release of refrigerant gas to the atmosphere. Such a release is costly with respect to replacement of the refrigerant and may be harmful to the environment. Recent design of certain rupture discs allows for partial rupture and recovery of the refrigerant gas, thereby minimizing the potential for releases to the atmosphere.

secondary air   In an induction unit-type HVAC system, air from the conditioned space that is drawn across the heating or cooling coil by the force of the primary air discharged from the induction unit nozzles. Heat is exchanged from the secondary air to the water in the coil in a cooling mode and from the water in the coil to the secondary air in a heating mode in order to lower or raise the temperature of the room. (See also *induction system; primary air.*)

secondary water system   A closed heating or cooling loop (circuit) through which water is pumped from a mechanical room to terminal (e.g., induction) units to provide heating or cooling at multiple locations or zones.

REAL ESTATE APPLICATION: The secondary chilled- or hot-water system provides flexibility in the heating and cooling of multiple zones. While primary heating and cooling systems temper air provided to multiple zones in a building to one temperature, the secondary water system can provide a different temperature to each zone. In some applications, it can also provide heating to one zone and cooling to another zone at the same time. Secondary water systems are common in large buildings, particularly in commercial high-rise HVAC applications where operator and system flexibility are required in different sections or exposures of the building.

self-contained air conditioning   See *unitary system*.

sensible heat   Thermal energy whose transfer from or to a substance results in a change of temperature; specifically, heat that changes the temperature of the air without changing the moisture content of the air. Changes in dry-bulb temperature readings indicate changes in sensible heat. (Compare *latent heat*.)

sequence of operation   An operating strategy, developed and programmed into a computer software system (*energy management system* program), which establishes and provides conditions and parameters (e.g., set points, start-stop times) to automate the operation of an HVAC system.

REAL ESTATE APPLICATION: Numerous sequence-of-operation strategies are typically programmed into the energy management system. Various subsystems often have their own specific sequence of operation. However, the overall effective operation of the entire HVAC system should be kept in mind when writing each sequence of operation. The various HVAC subsystems within an HVAC plant for which specific sequence-of-operation programs may be developed include the interior air-handling system, exterior or perimeter air-handling system, central chiller plant operation, and secondary heating/cooling system. Each sequence program would normally consider the following inputs:

- Day of the week
- Time of day
- Outside air temperature
- Average inside air temperature

setback   See *night setback*.

shading   The reduction of solar heat gain through glass by blocking the glass with a nearby object (overhang, adjacent building, trees, etc.). Shading objects reduces solar heat gain by keeping the direct rays of the sun off all or part of the glass. (Film can also be applied to the glass surface to reduce solar heat gain.)

sheet metal   A thin, flat, rolled metallic material commonly used in HVAC applications, particularly in forming ductwork that is rectangular in cross section.

short circuiting   A condition resulting from improper layout of ductwork (close proximity of a supply and a return or exhaust duct or removal of a ceiling tile near a supply duct) allowing the circulation of air from the supply duct immediately into the return-air pathway; also called *short cycling*.

REAL ESTATE APPLICATION: When a substantial amount of air is short circuited, building occupants may not receive adequate supplies of outdoor air, possibly leading to insufficient dilution of indoor air contaminants.

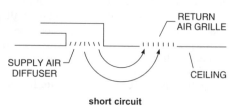

short circuit

sizing   A procedure for determining the size of heating and cooling equipment required for a space (building, home, room, etc.). Sizing will vary depending on the size of the area (square footage) to be heated or cooled, insulation and materials utilized in construction, window area, number of occupants, geographic location, lighting and equipment in the space, and other factors.

smoke test   A test in which nontoxic colored smoke is introduced into an HVAC system (air handlers, ductwork) or a specific space as a way to indicate the routes taken by air currents and/or to detect air leaks (infiltration, exfiltration).

REAL ESTATE APPLICATION: A smoke test does not always involve the introduction of smoke into an HVAC system. For example, smoke may be introduced into the main lobby of a high-rise building in order to attempt to determine the various air currents and leakage contributing to the building's *stack effect* (which also see).

solar collector   A device designed to absorb radiation from the sun and transfer this heat energy to a fluid passing through the collector (e.g., water).

solar effect, **solar heat gain**   See *solar load*.

solar heating and cooling system   An assembly of subsystems and components that converts solar energy into thermal energy for use in the heating and cooling of a building. Typically, a solar heating and cooling system will be used in combination with an auxiliary source of energy (boilers, chillers, etc.), particularly during long periods of cloudy or rainy weather.

solar load   Heat transmitted through materials (glass, roofs, etc.) by the sun's rays. Heat emitted from the sun can warm the air on the inside of a window even if the outside air is relatively cold. The *solar heat gain* associated with a building has a substantial impact on both the design sizing and strategy of operation of an HVAC system *(solar effect)*.

REAL ESTATE APPLICATION: Solar heat gain can have a significant impact on the effectiveness with which the thermal comfort of building occupants is maintained. The heat gain from the effect of the sun is measured in Btu per square foot of surface area of a particular material (glass, roofing membrane, etc.). Technology has played an important role in the design and manufacturing of efficient building products that provide effective insulation from the sun.

The solar heat gain in a building is dependent upon several factors (time of year, time of day, weather conditions, building construction materials, building orientation, etc.). Time of day, hence the altitude or azimuth of the sun, is a major factor challenging building operators and HVAC systems in keeping building occupants comfortable.

Contrary to popular belief, the solar effect, particularly on the southern exposure of a building, can be as problematic during the winter months as at any other time of year. The altitude of the sun in the winter is lower, therefore the radiant heat projects directly through the skin of a building (e.g., glass windows). To compound the problem, building HVAC systems are typically in a heating mode of operation in the winter, making it difficult to prevent the south side of a building from overheating.

sound attenuator   A device, usually prefabricated and installed inside a duct, to provide greater sound absorption than would normally occur in a similar duct of equal length. The air pressure loss through a sound attenuator is greater than that through an equal length of duct without an attenuator.

split system   A direct expansion (refrigerant) type of air-conditioning system, similar to a *rooftop unit* system except that the evaporator coil or air-handling section is remote (split) from the air-cooled condensing section. The evaporator or cooling coil section is almost always located indoors and the condensing section is located outdoors (e.g., on the roof of the building).

REAL ESTATE APPLICATION: The capacity of split-type air-conditioning systems typically ranges from 1½ to 100 tons. The refrigerant compressor may be furnished as part of the evaporator but is typically furnished as part of the condensing section (located outdoors) due to the relatively high noise level it generates. One condensing section can serve one or several remotely located evaporator sections. The evaporator section of a split system consists of a supply fan, direct-expansion (refrigerant) cooling coil, and filters. Electric, hot-water, or steam heating coils may be furnished with the air-handling section for heating purposes.

spray coil   In larger air-handling units, a heating or cooling coil onto which water is sprayed for the purpose of humidification and, under certain circumstances (e.g., in the summer cooling mode), to produce latent cooling. The device consists of a typical tube and fin coil and a pipe, containing nozzles, which is positioned at the top of the coil and close to the leading surface (first row of tubes). Atomized water is sprayed over the surface of the coil-and-fin assembly as air travels across the coil surface. (See also *coil.*)

spray cooling   A method of refrigerating by spraying refrigerant or cooled water inside an evaporator section of an absorption chiller or similar equipment; also, a method of humidifying and/or cooling by spraying water onto an air-handling coil.

stack effect   The tendency of air in a vertical passage (duct, elevator shaft, high-rise stairwell) to rise when heated due to the lower density of warmed air compared to surrounding cooler air of higher density; also referred to as *chimney effect.* Stack effect usually results from air infiltration and can impact heating and cooling costs adversely. (See also *infiltration.*)

REAL ESTATE APPLICATION: In buildings, particularly high-rise structures in colder climates, internal heated air is displaced by colder, denser, unheated outside air, resulting in an upward flow of air from the bottom to the top of the building. Penetrations or temporary opening of barriers in the building (loading dock doors, main lobby entrance swing doors, elevator machine room or roof hatches) allows for unobstructed passage of air of varying temperatures and densities, thereby increasing the stack effect. The effect can be reduced by creating and enforcing effective building ingress and egress—through installation of revolving doors, construction and installation of efficient entrance and exit enclosures and vestibules, and effective utilization of ventilation systems, etc.—in order to establish and maintain proper internal air pressures.

static pressure   The air pressure in an HVAC duct that results from a decrease in velocity (rate of airflow) within the duct.

REAL ESTATE APPLICATION: In a variable-air-volume (VAV) HVAC system, under light load conditions, VAV control boxes will modulate closed and decrease the amount of air emitted through the diffusers in various zones. The cumulative effect of the decrease in airflow through many VAV boxes will be an increase in the static pressure within the duct. A properly designed *energy management system* will sense this increase in static pressure and, in turn, decrease the speed of the motor-driven air handlers that provide air to the VAV boxes. As a result, static pressure will decrease to an appropriate level, and consumption of electricity by the variable-speed air-handling motors will be less than at full-load conditions.

static regain   The increase in air pressure inside a duct due to a reduction in velocity of air within the duct. The basic principle of the static regain method of HVAC duct sizing is to size a duct run so that the increase in static pressure (regain due to the reduction in velocity) at each branch or air terminal just offsets the friction loss of the succeeding section of duct. The static pressure is then the same before each terminal and at each branch.

steam humidification   See *humidification.*

stratification   Unmixed air in a duct that is present in thermal layers having temperature variations of more than 5°F.

> REAL ESTATE APPLICATION: Stratification can result from incomplete mixing of return air and outdoor air or an uneven temperature rise through the preheat coil due to a malfunctioning steam supply valve. Thorough mixing of air can be accomplished by the proper arrangement and design of the ductwork. Installation of an air blender in an air-handling unit can help to thoroughly mix supply air to a coil, thereby eliminating or minimizing stratification. In order to prevent freezing, proper freeze protection is essential in HVAC air-handling coils when the potential for stratification exists.

subcooling   Cooling of a liquid refrigerant below its condensing temperature. Subcooling enables the refrigerant to absorb additional heat in the evaporator coil of a refrigeration system, resulting in an increase in capacity and efficiency of the overall system.

summer-winter switch   A device common in central HVAC systems that switches components such as thermostats from a heating mode of operation (winter) to a cooling mode of operation (summer), and vice versa, when specified parameters are met—e.g., the outside air temperature is above or below 60°F. Summer-winter switching devices allow central HVAC systems and components to operate in either a heating or a cooling mode.

supply air   Air within an HVAC duct, plenum, etc., being delivered to a room, space, or area. (Contrast *return air.*)

switch   See *electric-pneumatic (EP) switch; high-pressure switch; low-pressure switch; oil safety switch; pneumatic-electric (PE) switch.*

takeoff   The connection point where subsections of HVAC ductwork branch off from the main HVAC supply duct.

> REAL ESTATE APPLICATION: An HVAC interior supply duct riser in a high-rise building will have a takeoff on each floor for the delivery of air to the floor.

temperature-humidity index   Actual temperature and humidity of a sample of air compared to air at standard conditions. Temperature-humidity index provides an

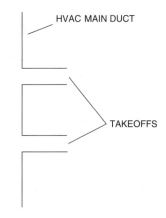

alternate means of evaluating the degree of existing relative humidity by comparing it to a standard and converting this ratio to a simple index value.

terminal unit   In HVAC systems, a heating and/or cooling unit at the end of a branch duct from which air is delivered to the conditioned space or at the end of a water or steam pipe where heat is exchanged to or from the air in the conditioned space. Examples of terminal units include convectors (induction units), radiators, baseboard heaters, and variable air volume boxes.

thermal storage   The preparation of cooling mediums during off-peak utility hours and storing them in tanks for use in HVAC cooling applications during peak utility hours. Chilled water is the most common form of thermal storage medium—it is a readily available fluid, is easy to store, and uses simple design applications. The making of ice for the same purpose is another common application called *thermal ice storage*.

>   REAL ESTATE APPLICATION: Electric utility providers have established the current market for thermal storage. Most have an excess capacity of electricity during off-peak hours (e.g., 6:00 P.M. to 8:00 A.M.), and therefore encourage the shifting of electrical energy usage from peak hours (8:00 A.M. to 6:00 P.M.) to off-peak hours. Thermal storage can accomplish this shift by producing ice or chilled water at night (using a refrigeration machine or electrically driven chiller) for HVAC cooling applications the next day. The thermal storage concept uses an amount of electricity in kilowatt hours (kwh) comparable to traditional cooling applications. However, the consumption of electricity is shifted to a time period when excess electricity is available. The transferring of this electrical load from daytime to nighttime hours decreases the electrical demand for the building and the utility provider. Some of the benefits achieved by the utility company as a result of thermal storage use by their customers include shifting of demand (flattening of the overall electrical consumption curve), lower cost of electricity production, and increased revenue.

thermostat   An instrument that measures and responds to changes in temperature and directly or indirectly regulates temperature by controlling HVAC equipment and other devices; also called *thermostatic control*.

thermostatic expansion valve (TEV or TXV)   A device that controls the flow of refrigerant into an evaporator (cooling coil) by sensing the temperature and pressure of refrigerant leaving the evaporator. A sensing bulb attached to the outlet of the evaporator coil provides the input to the thermal expansion valve. The thermal expansion valve is a small but vital component in a refrigeration system; it controls the output (space temperature set point) of the entire refrigeration or air-conditioning system.

through-the-wall unit   See *window unit*.

ton   A standard unit of measurement of cooling capacity equal to 12,000 Btu per hour. A ton of refrigeration is the amount of cooling provided by melting a ton of ice in 24 hours.

>   REAL ESTATE APPLICATION: The capacity of air-conditioning or refrigerating equipment is stated in tons or Btu's of heat removal capacity per hour. A residential window air-conditioner unit typically would be rated in Btu's (e.g., a 6,000-Btu/hour unit is equivalent to ½ ton), whereas a chiller for a large building would be rated in tonnage (e.g., 500 or 1,000 ton).

tube bundles   The groups of numerous copper tubes inside a chiller through which chilled water or condenser water flows.

unitary system   *Packaged HVAC equipment* consisting of one or more factory-fabricated assemblies designed to provide the functions of air moving, air cleaning, cooling, dehumidification and, sometimes, heating and humidification. Unitary equipment is classified as either self-contained or split-system. A *self-contained unit* houses all of the components in a single assembly. In a *split system* (which also see), equipment such as the evaporator coil and condensing unit are in separate locations. *Unitary air-conditioning equipment* is well suited to applications requiring supplemental summer cooling only and is often used in conjunction with existing or separate heating facilities of sufficient capacity.

vane   An assembly of fixed or adjustable blades or slats that controls airflow through a duct, diffuser, air handler, or other equipment. Also, an assembly of adjustable blades (usually referred to as variable-inlet guide vanes) that regulates the flow of refrigerant into the suction side of the compressor in a centrifugal or screw chiller; vane positioners control the angle (opening) of the vanes to control the flow of refrigerant.

vaneaxial fan   A direct- or belt-driven blower that consists of a disk-type wheel, with vanes on one side, installed in a cylinder.

variable air volume (VAV) system   An HVAC system that maintains thermal comfort by varying the amount of heated or cooled air delivered to each space (zone). During heavy (design) or low load conditions, the temperature of the air being delivered to the zones is reset (adjusted) for increased efficiency.

>   REAL ESTATE APPLICATION: Variable-air-volume systems are beneficial to building owners and occupants for two primary reasons: (1) They allow multiple zones with varied loads to be served from the same system (duct) without the use of additional terminally located water systems (heat exchangers), and (2) they permit the system to be operated more efficiently (i.e., at lower cost) than a *constant volume system* of similar capacity, particularly in high-rise applications. Moving air or water in a high-rise application is very costly because the majority of the air handlers and pumps used for this purpose are electrically driven. The cost of electricity on a Btu basis in most regions of the United States is significantly greater than the cost of steam, hot water, fuel, or other energy sources.

variable inlet vanes   A volume control device consisting of permanently placed dampers and controls used to vary the amount of incoming air at the inlet of an air handler depending on the capacity required. Given the increased use of variable-speed drive motors, variable inlet vanes are rarely used in HVAC fan applications.

velocity   The speed in feet per minute (fpm) of air traveling through a duct, diffuser, or other component. Velocity, along with the size and length of the duct, can be used to calculate the volume in cubic feet per minute (cfm) of air flowing through the duct.

>   REAL ESTATE APPLICATION: Air velocity is critical to maintaining occupant comfort in a space. Even if an HVAC system is delivering the required volume (cfm) of conditioned air to a space, discomfort may result if the air is not correctly distributed. Velocities lower than 10–20 fpm could cause a

sense of air stagnation while velocities higher than 50–60 fpm could result in drafts. Air velocities in the range of 25–35 fpm are considered most satisfactory in occupied zones.

velometer   An instrument used to measure the speed (velocity) of air moving through a duct.

ventilation   Introduction of a combination of outdoor air and recirculated air into an occupied space in order to temper the space and dilute the odors and contaminants emitted by the people and the objects in the space.

> REAL ESTATE APPLICATION: Proper ventilation is required to prevent indoor air quality problems. Ventilation can control air contaminants by dilution or by changing air pressure relationships.

ventilation efficiency   The ability of a ventilation (HVAC) system to distribute supply air and remove internally generated pollutants.

volume damper   An adjustable device installed in an HVAC system to control the volume of ventilation air to a particular area. Volume dampers are common in constant-volume systems where they serve to balance the airflow to several areas (e.g., different floors). In a constant-volume HVAC system, volume dampers are adjusted during balancing and remain in position until the system is rebalanced.

walk-in cooler   A refrigerated space maintained at a relatively cold temperature, often found in large supermarkets, restaurants, and similar commercial uses.

wastewater unit, water-cooled condenser   See *water-cooled HVAC unit.*

water-cooled HVAC unit   A type of heat rejection-method air-conditioning unit in which the heat of compression is transferred from the refrigerant gas to water in a heat exchanger coil. The water provided to the heat exchanger is often municipal (domestic-use) water.

> REAL ESTATE APPLICATION: City water-cooled HVAC units are very common in buildings where the structure and physical layout are not conducive to using air-cooled HVAC equipment. An engineer might specify a water-cooled supplemental HVAC unit in order to provide air conditioning to a small computer room on the 10th floor of a 30-story building if there is no practical alternate heat-rejection source available (e.g., a cooling tower). These city water-cooled condensing units are also referred to as once-through city water condensing units since the cooling water from the city domestic water supply enters the heat exchanger, passes through it, then flows out to the sewer system. For this reason, HVAC units that employ this type of heat rejection are also referred to as *wastewater units.* A *water-cooled condenser* or heat exchanger could use condenser water instead of city domestic water as the heat-rejection medium and pump this water to a cooling tower for subsequent heat rejection and recirculation to the water-cooled condenser of the HVAC unit.

windage   The loss of fine droplets of cooling tower condenser water that are entrained by air (wind, etc.) circulating around the cooling tower. (See also *drift.*)

window unit   A relatively small packaged (self-contained) air-conditioning unit containing refrigerant (e.g., Freon) and a compressor, an air-cooled condenser, a direct-expansion cooling coil, a fan, an air filter, and sometimes a heating coil. This type of cooling (or heating) unit is usually installed in a window or other wall opening *(through-the-wall unit)* and is designed to cool a single space.

REAL ESTATE APPLICATION: Window or through-the-wall air-conditioning units are common in apartment buildings, hotels and motels, and small office buildings. The cooling and heating coils are inside the unit. The heating coil can be supplied with hot water or steam or it could be a self-contained electric resistance coil. The primary advantage of window units is low initial installation cost. Some of the disadvantages are higher operating and maintenance costs per ton of refrigeration capacity, poor humidity control, high noise level, and shorter use life.

winter operation Operating a particular HVAC component during the winter season. The term usually refers to the winter operation of a cooling tower, which introduces the potential problem of water freeze-up in the basin, condenser water piping, nozzles, etc., or ice formation on fan blades, louvers, or other components, particularly when temperatures are below freezing.

REAL ESTATE APPLICATION: Winter operation of cooling towers involves specific additional operating procedures above and beyond those followed during the summer cooling season. Periodic draining of water from piping, circulation of water by means of a pump, and use of basin heaters are some examples of specific precautions that may be exercised during winter operation. Winter operation of a cooling tower may be required in a facility containing a large computer room with a cooling load significant enough to require year-round cooling.

zoning Establishment of independently controlled sections within an HVAC system, a zone being a space or group of spaces whose temperature, humidity, etc., is regulated by a single control.

REAL ESTATE APPLICATION: A single zone could represent one room or 20 floors, depending on the layout of the HVAC system. Multizone or multiple zones indicates more than one zone in a given area.

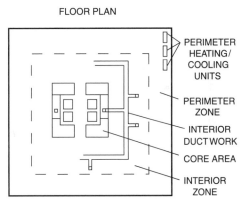

zoning

Boilers

air-fuel ratio   See *fuel-to-air ratio.*

air heater   A heat exchanger that removes heat from the combustion gases exhausting from the boiler and transfers it to the supply air entering the boiler. The air heater concept is very similar to the economizer concept utilized in boiler applications for pre-heating feedwater. (See also *economizer.*)

annual inspection   An inspection of a boiler or other pressure vessel conducted by a qualified entity (e.g., property insurance carrier or heating contractor) to ensure the system is safe for operation.

> REAL ESTATE APPLICATION: Boilers should be cleaned as part of the annual inspection process. The inside (fireside) tube surfaces in a firetube boiler should be mechanically cleaned (tubes punched) to remove any film or surface deposits from the products of combustion. Waterside surfaces should be inspected in order to ensure effective boiler water treatment.

atomizer   An integral component of a fuel oil burner which uses steam or air under pressure to break up oil into fine particles and project the oil spray in a pattern that is intercepted by and mixed with the combustion air provided by the burner. The atomized particles are very fine, forming a large surface area to be in contact with the combustion air.

black smoke   The color of smoke which, when emitted from a boiler stack (exhaust), indicates the lack of sufficient air for combustion. The cause could be too little air to properly burn the fuel or too much fuel for the volume of air admitted to the furnace.

blowdown   A process of removing water, sludge, and sediment from the bottom of a boiler in order to reduce the amounts of boiler water contaminants and dissolved solids.

boiler   An enclosed pressure vessel in which heat is transferred from fuel (steam generator type) or electric resistance heating elements (hot water type) to the water contained in the boiler in order to generate steam or hot water.

boiler efficiency   The effectiveness of a boiler in extracting the total heat value of fuel. Boiler efficiency is determined by dividing the heat absorbed per pound of fuel by the heat value per pound of fuel. This efficiency formula accounts for the ability of a boiler to effectively mix and ignite all of the fuel provided to the boiler. It also accounts for the effectiveness of the boiler heat transfer surfaces in the transfer of heat from combustion gases to the boiler water.

boiler flame   The flames of combustion present in operating boilers. For oil fired-boilers, a yellowish, orange, or golden flame indicates an optimum mixture of fuel and air at the fuel oil burner. A white flame indicates the presence of a considerable amount of excess air in the combustion process. A dark orange or orange-red flame indicates insufficient air or excess fuel in the combustion process. In properly functioning gas-fired boilers, the flame is light blue.

boiler horsepower   A recognized standard capacity rating for a boiler equal to the evaporation of 34.5 lbs of water per hour at 212° F. This is equivalent to 34,475 Btu and is basically a measure of a boiler's steam generating capacity.

boiler tubes   Long, hollow, cylindrical-shaped metal tubes made of iron, steel, etc., through which the heat of combustion (firetube boiler) or water/-steam (watertube boiler) flows. Heat is transferred from one side of the tube to the other in the generation of steam for heating, power generation, and other uses.

breeching   The uptake portion of the boiler (furnace) that connects the boiler furnace to the exhaust stack. Also referred to as *uptake.*

burner   A device utilized for the final conveyance of a fuel (gas) or a mixture of fuel and air to the combustion area of a boiler. (See also *fuel oil burner.*)

carryover   A situation in which water or moisture escapes (carries over) from a boiler into the steam supply lines. The results of carryover can be serious (e.g., potential for pipe rupture), particularly in larger, high-pressure boiler applications.

combustion   A chemical reaction that results in the development of heat. In order for combustion to take place, oxygen must be present. Fuel oil combustion in a boiler consists of the following:

1. Sufficient air for rapid oxidation.
2. Thorough mixing of the air and fuel particles.
3. Temperatures high enough to ignite the oxygen component of the air and the combustible elements of the fuel.

combustion air   Air that is provided to a boiler or furnace by means of a blower-type arrangement (typically electrically driven) in order to burn the fuel. The volume of air supplied to a boiler needs to be regulated in order to provide a proper fuel-to-air ratio for efficient combustion. (See also *fuel-to-air ratio.*)

draft   The difference in pressure between the stack gases of a boiler and the atmosphere that is responsible for producing a flow of gases through the boiler and boiler stack.

REAL ESTATE APPLICATION: Heated air, as from combustion, is less dense than air in the atmosphere and will rise up the stack naturally (natural draft). However, most boilers utilize electrically driven blowers to create a draft (forced draft).

economizer   A heat exchanger, located between the boiler furnace and boiler stack, that transfers the heat of combustion exhaust gases to incoming boiler feedwater flowing through finned tubes. (Compare *air heater*; see also *econ-*

omy cycle in Heating, Ventilating, Air Conditioning [HVAC], and Refrigeration Systems.)

REAL ESTATE APPLICATION: Economizers are more common on larger capacity boilers.

excess air Air that passes through a boiler (furnace) and boiler flue in excess of what is required for the complete combustion of the fuel. Excess air decreases the efficiency of a boiler by reducing the temperature of combustion and causing incomplete combustion of fuel oil particles.

REAL ESTATE APPLICATION: Excess air in a boiler is indicated by white-colored smoke being emitted from the boiler flue stack or by low flue-gas temperatures.

feedwater Water provided to a boiler for subsequent heating and conversion to steam.

fireside Pertaining to the area and surfaces in a boiler in which combustion takes place. The fireside of a watertube boiler is between the outside surfaces of the tubes and the boiler (furnace) casing, whereas the fireside in a firetube boiler consists of the inside surfaces of the tubes. (Compare *waterside*.)

REAL ESTATE APPLICATION: The terms fireside and waterside are commonly used when referring to these specific areas and surfaces of a boiler: "Is the corrosion occurring on the waterside or fireside?"

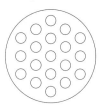

firetube boiler A large steel cylinder vessel in which hot gases of combustion pass through tubes that are surrounded by water that fills the space between the tubes and the boiler shell. One of the two general classifications of larger size steam generating boilers, the other being *watertube boiler* (which see).

fireside
(firetube boiler, section view)

fitting Any valve, gauge, etc., attached to a boiler vessel; also called *boiler fitting.*

flame-monitoring equipment A sensing device and system that monitors the presence of fire in a boiler and shuts down the boiler (closes the fuel oil or gas supply valve) during a flame-out (loss of fire). Flame-monitoring equipment consists of some type of photoelectric cell (fire eye) and associated safety controls to prevent unwanted spraying of fuel into a boiler furnace immediately following a flame-out condition.

flareback A minor explosion of a boiler (furnace) caused by the ignition of an accumulation of furnace gases or unburned fuel or fuel vapor.

flue A heat-resistant passage for the removal of combustion products from a furnace or boiler to the atmosphere.

flue gas analysis Quantitative measurement of a boiler's stack gases in order to determine its efficiency of combustion. Since it is impractical to measure the combustion gases within the boiler itself, the products of combustion are measured and compared to the volume of air required for a given fuel.

forced draft The means of providing combustion air to a boiler (furnace) using an electrically operated fan or blower; sometimes called *forced draft blower.*

foundation The structure that supports the weight of a boiler and allows for expansion and contraction and other miscellaneous movement; called more specifically *boiler foundation.*

fuel-to-air ratio The ratio of fuel (gas) to combustion air supply flowing to a boiler measured by weight or by volume. The fuel-to-air ratio is an important factor in the combustion efficiency of a boiler.

fuel oil burner A principal component of a boiler's combustion control system. The two basic components of a fuel oil burner are the fuel oil atomizer and the air register. (See also *burner*.)

fuel oil manifold An arrangement of piping and piping connections in close proximity to the boiler(s) and connected to the fuel oil supply and return piping. (See also *manifold* and the accompanying diagram in Basic Engineering and Building Mechanical Systems.)

> REAL ESTATE APPLICATION: An operator switching the source of fuel from one boiler to another may do so at the fuel oil manifold serving the boilers.

furnace The part of a boiler in which combustion takes place. Furnaces are capable of withstanding very high temperatures. In large-capacity boilers (not commonly found in real estate and facility applications), the furnace is a separate section within the boiler system. In firetube boilers, there is no furnace as such; the furnace area of this type of boiler is the boiler itself (one large drum).

gas-fired Pertaining to a boiler that uses natural gas as its fuel source.

handholes Small openings located in the shell or skin of a boiler, tank, or other pressure vessel that allow access for purposes of inspection, cleaning, and repair. Handholes are typically located at the bottom sections of firetube boilers, and they are secured with matching size plates and gaskets that are clamped to the inside seating surface of the handhole.

hydrostatic test A pressure test of a boiler system (shell, drum, tubes, etc.) by completely filling the boiler with water, closing all outlet valves to gauges, piping, etc., and applying hydrostatic pressure to the boiler by means of a small pump. Sometimes specifically called *boiler hydrostatic test.*

incomplete combustion A condition in a boiler in which the fuel is only partially burned. An indication of poor efficiency of the boiler, incomplete combustion is usually the result of an inadequate air supply, insufficient mixing of fuel and air, or too low a temperature to produce and sustain combustion. It can produce hazardous carbon monoxide (CO).

interlock An electronic control device that actuates electric switches to close the fuel valve and prevent ignition of the fuel (i.e., shut down boiler operations) in the event of an unsafe condition (e.g., excess temperature or pressure in the system).

low-pressure boiler In accordance with the American Society of Mechanical Engineers (ASME) Boiler Code, a boiler in which the maximum safe working pressure for steam service is 15 pounds per square inch (psi) or less.

low-water cutout A safety device required on automatically fired steam boilers. The cutout prevents the continued firing of a boiler that contains insufficient water by immediately shutting it down when the water level decreases to a predetermined level. This type of device is also found on domestic hot water boilers.

natural gas A low-pressure, highly combustible, unrefined hydrocarbon fuel gas used in boilers. Natural gas is typically brought to a facility through underground piping controlled by a utility company.

oil-fired Pertaining to a boiler that uses fuel oil as its fuel source.

packaged boiler A boiler unit containing all of the required components, including boiler, burner, controls, and auxiliary equipment, assembled as a unit. Only connections to water, fuel, electricity, flue stack, and heating distribution piping are needed.

pilot A small, constantly burning flame that is used to ignite the gas at the main burner of a gas-fired boiler.

primary air Combustion air provided to a burner that mixes with the fuel. (Compare *secondary air*.)

purge cycle A process of removing the air from a boiler (furnace) immediately prior to ignition (light off).

REAL ESTATE APPLICATION: The purge cycle is very important, particularly following a flame-out condition, to ensure the removal of any excess fuel vapors from the furnace. The combination of excess fuel vapors in a furnace and the failure to purge could result in a boiler explosion or flareback during the light-off sequence.

rich mixture An excess supply of combustion air or fuel to a boiler furnace. A high air-fuel ratio (excess air) is referred to as air-rich, while a low air-fuel ratio (excess fuel) is referred to as fuel-rich.

secondary air Combustion air provided to a burner flame at the point of combustion. (Compare *primary air*.)

soot A black, powdery substance consisting primarily of small particles of carbon; a result of incomplete combustion.

REAL ESTATE APPLICATION: Soot deposits on boiler tubes can lead to a significant decrease in the efficiency of a boiler.

stack A vertically positioned, cylindrical or rectangular-shaped metal enclosure (usually tin or steel) that permits and directs the passage of boiler flue gases to the atmosphere. (See also *flue*.)

sulfuric acid corrosion A form of corrosion that can occur on the fireside surfaces of a boiler, particularly in areas closer to the combustion gas uptakes. The corrosion occurs when sulfur products (oxides) in the combustion flue gases mix with moisture, forming sulfuric acid. Moisture is present only when the temperatures in the uptake (stack) area fall below the dew point. For this reason it is important to maintain sufficiently high stack temperatures and exercise caution regarding the method, frequency, and duration of securing idle boilers.

therm An amount of heat equal to 100,000 Btu.

REAL ESTATE APPLICATION: Therms are sometimes used by natural gas providers as units of consumption in calculating customer billing rates.

total air The total of primary air plus secondary air and any excess air provided to a burner of a boiler.

uptake See *breeching*.

waterside Pertaining to the area and surfaces of a boiler where the circulation of water occurs. The waterside of a watertube boiler is at the inside surfaces of the tubes, while the waterside in a firetube boiler is between the outside surfaces of the tubes and the inside surfaces of the boiler shell. (Compare *fireside*; see also the accompanying diagram.)

REAL ESTATE APPLICATION: The terms waterside and fireside are commonly used when referring to these specific areas within a boiler.

water softening   See *ion exchange* in Water Treatment, Water Chemistry.

watertube boiler   A type of boiler characterized by water circulating through the tubes and the hot gases of combustion circulating around the tubes and inside of the boiler shell. One of two general classifications of larger size boilers; the other being *firetube boiler* (which see). Watertube boilers are generally very large and are not common in typical real estate and facilities boiler and heating system applications.

white smoke   The color of smoke which, when emitted from a boiler stack (exhaust), indicates a significant amount of excess air being admitted to a boiler (furnace) for combustion.

Water Treatment, Water Chemistry

acidic   Characteristic of a solution with a relatively low pH (between 0 and 7 on a pH scale of 0 to 14); the opposite of alkaline. (See also *alkaline; pH.*)

> REAL ESTATE APPLICATION: *Acidity* is the most important characteristic of water in determining its corrosion-forming tendency. Untreated water with a low pH dissolves the various oxides and exposes metallic surfaces to corrosion.

activated carbon filtration   A type of water filtration and purification system that removes contaminants from drinking water by surface adsorption; also called *granular activated carbon filtration.* In relation to the net volume of carbon granules used, activated carbon presents a large surface area onto which contaminants can adhere (be adsorbed).

aerobic bacteria   Slime-forming bacteria that thrive in the presence of oxygen.

algae   One of the three most common types of microbes (micro-organisms) that can naturally occur in HVAC cooling systems (see also *bacteria* and *fungi*). Algae are simple plants that require sunlight in order to survive. As a result, algal growth is common on exposed outside surfaces such as cooling tower decks. Algae can grow and multiply rapidly, resulting in fouling and clogging of cooling water systems. Algae also provide a food source for bacteria and a surface to which other contaminants can become attached.

algicide   A type of chemical used to kill algae in cooling systems. Chlorine is widely available and commonly used for this purpose.

alkaline   Characteristic of a solution with a relatively high pH (between 7 and 14 on a pH scale of 0 to 14); the opposite of acidic. *Alkalinity* is a measure of the acid-neutralizing power of a solution. Calcium and magnesium carbonates are the primary sources of alkalinity in water. (See also *acidic; pH.*)

> REAL ESTATE APPLICATION: Alkalinity is the most important characteristic of a water in determining its scale-forming tendency. The amount and type of alkalinity in a water system (e.g., water supply to a condenser water system) are important determinants of the type of water treatment program required.

anaerobic bacteria   Bacteria that can thrive in the absence of oxygen. Anaerobic bacteria can create corrosive acids.

anode   A positive electrode that releases electrons into metal during corrosion; the surface where corrosion occurs. The area along the surface of a metal that attracts free electrons is the *cathode* (negative electrode). On a metallic surface, the cathode area controls the rate at which corrosion occurs at the anode.

REAL ESTATE APPLICATION: In contact with water, pure iron and (to a lesser extent) other metals begin to break down at the anode, releasing negatively charged particles (electrons) into the metal. The electrons are pulled through the metal to the cathode, where a chemical reaction combines them with oxygen and water to form metallic hydroxides—e.g., ferrous hydroxide, $Fe(OH)_2$. The dissolved minerals in the water provide the link back to the anode. This process is similar to a standard battery corrosion cell. Chemical reactions at the anode start corroding the iron back to its natural state—i.e., iron oxide, FeO.

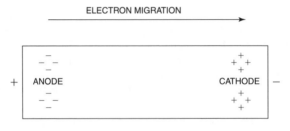

anode (cathode)

Representation of the theory underlying
electrolytic corrosion.

automatic feed control   A method of providing chemicals to a heating or cooling system other than manually (e.g., a small pump, meter and associated piping, fittings and controls).

REAL ESTATE APPLICATION: Advantages of automatic feed control include a relatively constant distribution of chemicals to the system, which minimizes significant fluctuations in the water chemical levels, and time savings when compared with manual addition of chemicals.

bacteria   One of the three most common types of microbes (micro-organisms) that can occur naturally in HVAC cooling systems (see also *algae* and *fungi*). The presence and subsequent buildup of bacteria in a cooling system can result in a thick slime, which can eventually foul or clog heat transfer surfaces and tubes, causing significant damage as well as operating inefficiency. Bacteria can also cause corrosion of the metal surfaces of a cooling system.

basic   Synonymous with *alkaline*, which see.

biocide   A class of chemicals used to destroy or prevent buildup of microorganisms (e.g., bacteria, algae, fungi) in a cooling (condenser water) system. The compounds may be further classified as oxidizing or nonoxidizing. Chlorine is the most widely used and cost-effective oxidizing biocide. (See also *chlorination*.)

biodispersant   A chemical that inhibits the attachment of microbes and microbial deposits to cooling water system surfaces.

REAL ESTATE APPLICATION: Biodispersants loosen existing deposits so they can be flushed away and increase the effectiveness of chemical treatments by exposing new layers of microbial slime or algae to the attack of biocides. Use of biodispersant chemicals as a supplement to a chlorine chemical treatment program can be very effective.

biological fouling The coating and clogging of pipes, heat exchangers, and other heat-transfer surfaces due to uncontrolled growth of algae, fungi, and bacteria. The fouling of heat transfer surfaces can significantly reduce the efficiency (heat transfer capacity) of heat exchangers, thereby increasing energy costs, maintenance (clean up) costs, and down time.

bleed The continuous removal of water from a heating or cooling system, specifically open recirculating systems such as cooling towers, in order to limit the concentration of solids. Most condenser water systems have automatic bleed. *Bleed-off* is normally expressed in gallons per minute (gpm).

REAL ESTATE APPLICATION: As water evaporates, solids remain in the cooling tower, and their concentration (percentage of solids) in the water increases naturally. The percentage of solids in the system (cycles of concentration) also increases as makeup water and its associated solids are added to the cooling tower. When the concentration of solids in the system exceeds a predetermined level compared to their concentration in the makeup water, water must be purged (bled) from the system in order to decrease the concentration of solids.

blowdown The process of removing (purging) water (e.g., from a condenser water system or a boiler) in order to avoid an excessive concentration of dissolved solids. Sometimes also called *bleed.*

REAL ESTATE APPLICATION: Most cooling towers in a condenser water system have automatic blowdown (bleed). When the cycles of concentration (percentage of solids in the system) reach a predetermined level in a cooling tower, the bleed line valve will remove water and associated solids from the system. The same concept is used for removing solids and sludge from the system in boilers. (Compare *blowdown* in Boilers.)

calcium carbonate ($CaCO_3$) One of the two most common dissolved solids present in municipal water supplies, the other being magnesium carbonate ($MgCO_3$).

REAL ESTATE APPLICATION: Since water dissolves almost anything it contacts, it is difficult to control the percentage of solids in any water system. Calcium and magnesium carbonates enter a building's heating and cooling system through the municipal makeup water supply. These compounds can precipitate (come out of solution) to form rock-hard deposits on metal surfaces, particularly in heat exchangers.

cathode See *anode.*

chemical treatment program A water-treatment program that uses a variety of chemicals in order to control corrosion, scale, fouling, and microbial growth.

chlorides A class of very soluble compounds which, when present in water in high concentrations, can increase the corrosive potential. Chlorides are seldom part of the scale-deposit problems; however, they play an important part in the control of water contaminants. Since chlorides are soluble, chloride tests provide a means of indirectly measuring the level of total dissolved solids in a water system.

chlorination   The most widely used and cost-effective biocidal treatment program for use in cooling water systems. *Chlorine* is toxic to and kills all types of microbes; however, its effectiveness depends on the pH of the water. Also, chlorine is only effective against what it contacts directly. This can pose a potential problem in the treatment of thick mats of algae. Microbes can sometimes develop a resistance to chlorine. For these reasons, chlorination should be supplemented with other forms of chemical treatment.

closed recirculating system   A heating or cooling system in which water flows in a continuous circuit; also called *closed circuit; closed cycle; closed loop.* There is no evaporation and, therefore, no makeup water is required except to compensate for miscellaneous leakage.

> REAL ESTATE APPLICATION: An HVAC chilled water system is a closed recirculating system. Because makeup water is rarely added to it, the water in a closed system retains its chemical levels over longer periods of time and requires less-frequent addition of chemicals.

conductivity   The measure of the ability of an aqueous solution to conduct electricity, expressed in *total dissolved solids (TDS)* or *micromhos (μmhos).* The higher the percentage of solids in a solution, the higher the conductivity, and the greater the potential for corrosion.

> REAL ESTATE APPLICATION: Measuring conductivity of boiler water and cooling water systems is necessary in order to control the amount of dissolved solids in the system. An increase in dissolved solids beyond the saturation point will result in the formation of deposits, which can lead to corrosion.

corrosion   The return of a metal to its original, natural form; the deterioration of metal in the presence of water, air, and other metals. Iron returns to iron oxide as a result of corrosion. One indicator of the corrosive tendencies of water is pH—water that is more acidic (below pH 7.0) is more corrosive. Warmer water temperature and increased water flow over metallic surfaces can also increase corrosion rates. Corrosion can occur over a large general area (general corrosion) or in a localized area (corrosion pitting or oxygen pitting).

> REAL ESTATE APPLICATION: Steel is often used in HVAC system components (e.g., condenser water systems, cooling towers). Steel is processed from iron ore by removing oxygen from iron oxide (FeO). The resulting pure iron has a tendency to return to its original state through oxidation (oxygen corrosion): iron + oxygen = rust; $2Fe + O_2 = 2FeO$.

corrosion control   The process of minimizing the corrosion of metallic surfaces in heating and cooling systems. The method of corrosion control will depend on the type of system (e.g., heating vs. cooling system, open vs. closed system) as well as makeup water characteristics, system material (heat transfer surface) characteristics, and other factors.

> REAL ESTATE APPLICATION: Some examples of corrosion control methods include chemical corrosion inhibitors (e.g., chromates, nitrites), control of pH in the range of 7.0–8.5, formation of a thin film of calcium carbonate on metal surfaces, and mechanical *deaeration* of water. The use of corrosion inhibiting chemicals in conjunction with effective pH control is the most common approach to corrosion control in building HVAC cooling systems.

coupon A test material (e.g., a strip of mild steel) installed in a heating or cooling system for the purpose of monitoring corrosion. Test coupons are installed at a strategic location in the system and periodically evaluated to measure the amount of corrosion.

cycles of concentration The ratio of the concentration of a chemical or mineral (chlorides or total dissolved solids) within a system (e.g., condenser water system or cooling tower) compared to the concentration in the makeup water (water supply).

REAL ESTATE APPLICATION: In a cooling tower, the concentration of total dissolved solids (cycles of concentration) naturally increases as condenser water evaporates from the system because the solids do not evaporate with the water; they remain in solution with the condenser water. As makeup water containing additional minerals is fed to the system, the total dissolved solids increases. When the cycles of concentration reach a prescribed limit, they should be removed from the system through a bleed line. (See also *bleed; blowdown.*)

deaeration A process of removing oxygen and other noncondensable gases such as carbon dioxide from a solution (e.g., boiler feed water). Deaeration is not required in cooling systems. (See also *dissolved gases.*)

dissolved gases Oxygen (O_2) and carbon dioxide (CO_2) gases are soluble in water. In solution, they can cause localized or pitting corrosion on heat transfer surfaces.

REAL ESTATE APPLICATION: Dissolved oxygen can be troublesome in both heating and cooling systems where it combines with metals (acting as cathodes) to start the corrosion process. Dissolved carbon dioxide can be troublesome in heating systems only; if present in boiler water, CO_2 can combine with steam condensate (H_2O) to form carbonic acid (H_2CO_3).

distillation A purification process in which water is separated from contaminants by boiling it to form a vapor (steam), then cooling (condensing) the vapor to form (purified) water.

fungi One of the three most common types of microbes (micro-organisms) that can occur naturally in cooling systems (see also *algae* and *bacteria*). Fungi are particularly destructive to wood, which is often used in constructing cooling towers.

galvanic action Corrosion occurring between two metals having different electrical charges. Galvanic action is substantially increased in the presence of moisture (water).

hardness The concentrations of calcium (Ca^{++}) and magnesium (Mg^{++}) ions in water, measured in parts per million (ppm) of calcium carbonate ($CaCO_3$). The hardness of water (dissolved calcium and magnesium) is representative of its alkalinity (15–50 ppm of $CaCO_3$ is classified as soft water, 100–200 ppm as hard water, and greater than 200 ppm as very hard water).

REAL ESTATE APPLICATION: Calcium and magnesium are the two most common troublesome dissolved solids present in water. If not effectively controlled, calcium and magnesium carbonates will precipitate out of solution and form hard scale-like deposits on heat exchanger surfaces, decreasing their efficiency. Other impurities that contribute to water hardness include iron (Fe), manganese (Mn), and zinc (Zn).

inhibitor   A treatment chemical added to condenser water or other aqueous systems to reduce scale and/or corrosion formation.

ion   An electrically charged (positive or negative) atom or group of atoms. When mixed together, positive and negative ions neutralize each other's respective charges, forming a chemical compound.

> REAL ESTATE APPLICATION: The transfer of positive and negative charged ions within a heating or cooling water system can result in unwanted scaling and/or corrosion of heat transfer surfaces. Most dissolved mineral impurities found in water are present in the form of ions. The theory behind chemical treatment of heating and cooling system water is to stabilize the ions.

ion exchange   A treatment system that conditions water prior to its entry into the heating or cooling water system; also called *water softening.* Normally, a polystyrene resin carrying excess sodium (Na^+) ions is used in removing and/or exchanging dissolved solids that contribute to the scaling and corrosion processes—sodium ions are exchanged for calcium (Ca^{++}) and magnesium (Mg^{++}) ions.

lay-up   The chemical treatment and securing of a heating or cooling system for a prolonged period (e.g., a week, a month, the winter season).

> REAL ESTATE APPLICATION: There are two general methods of lay-up—wet and dry. The choice depends on the type of system, the expected duration of lay-up, anticipated maintenance downtime requirements, and other considerations. In a *wet lay-up,* the water in the system is treated chemically (usually to upper limits) and recirculated for several hours. The treated water then remains in the system throughout the lay-up period. In a *dry lay-up,* the water in the system is treated with a chemical specifically designed for dry lay-ups. The water is recirculated for several hours and then completely drained from the system. (The chemical leaves a coating on the piping and heat exchanger surfaces, which should remain dry throughout the lay-up period.)

Legionnaires' disease   See definition in Environmental Management and Indoor Air Quality.

limits   The maximum (upper) or minimum (lower) levels of chemicals in a water system. Since many heating and cooling systems are not treated with chemicals continuously (automatic feed), it is common practice to allow the chemical levels within the system to float within a defined range (from a prescribed upper limit to an acceptable lower limit) prior to adding chemicals to the system.

litmus   An organic chemical indicator of acidity or alkalinity (pH values). *Litmus paper* will turn red for pH values below 4.5 (acidic) and blue for pH values above 8.3 (alkaline).

makeup water   Fresh water from a municipal water supply (or other external source) added to a heating or cooling system to compensate for water losses due to evaporation, bleed-off, system leaks, or other factors.

> REAL ESTATE APPLICATION: Compared to a closed recirculating (chill water) system, makeup water consumption for an open recirculating (condenser water) system is substantial due to evaporation losses through the cooling tower.

manual feed A water treatment process in which chemicals are manually introduced (fed) into a heating or cooling system by an operator (building engineer, service technician) rather than automatically controlled; also called *slug feed*.

microbes Microscopic organisms that are often present in HVAC cooling (condenser) water systems and can cause fouling, clogging, and corrosion. The three most common types of microbes are *bacteria, algae* and *fungi* (which also see). They can enter the cooling water system through the cooling tower (from wind, as airborne debris) and via makeup feed water from an external (municipal) supply. Microbes (also called *micro-organisms*) are the most common cause of cooling system chemical treatment failure.

micromho (μmho) A unit of measurement of total dissolved solids (TDS) in a solution (water system). The total dissolved solids is determined by measuring the *conductivity* of the solution (i.e., its ability to conduct electricity). The greater the conductivity, the higher the micromho value. The *mho* is the reverse of the ohm, which is the unit of measure of resistance or resistivity. (See also *ohm* in Electrical, Lighting, Data, and Telecommunications Systems.)

neutralization The consumption of an acid by a base (alkali) and vice versa. The basic concept underlying chemical water treatment, the goal of which is to stabilize the many impurities and minerals present in heating and cooling water systems by the addition of certain specified chemicals.

noncondensable gases See *dissolved gases*.

open recirculating system A heating or cooling (e.g., condenser water) system, in which water flows in a repetitive circuit through heat exchangers and reservoirs, at least one of which is open to the atmosphere; also called *open loop*. Cooling towers, evaporators (condensing units), and air washers are examples of system components open to the atmosphere. Because of the evaporation of water from these components and the additional loss of water resulting from system bleed-off, makeup water is required to ensure proper fluid levels within the system. Additional chemicals will also be required in order to maintain proper concentrations.

osmosis See *reverse osmosis*.

ozone A gas whose molecules contain three atoms of oxygen (O_3); regular atmospheric oxygen is diatomic (O_2). Ozone, which occurs naturally as a result of lightning discharges, is a powerful oxidizing agent and an effective antiseptic and bleaching agent.

REAL ESTATE APPLICATION: Ozone can be generated artificially by the controlled discharge of electricity in oxygen or air. Such methodology has been used to effectively control mildew, algae, and bacteria in HVAC cooling water systems (cooling towers).

parts per million (ppm) The number of units (by weight) of a dissolved substance in a million units (by weight) of solution, commonly used for expressing concentrations of various water impurities such as calcium, magnesium, iron, lead, and oxygen.

pH A measure of the relative acidity or alkalinity of a solution (e.g., boiler water or condenser water). The pH scale is logarithmic and ranges from 0 to

14. A solution with a pH value of 0–7 is acidic; one with a pH value 7–14 is alkaline, and solutions with a pH of 7.0 are considered neutral. Since the pH scale is logarithmic, the pH values of solutions vary by a factor of 10—pH 5 is ten times as acidic as pH 6; pH 4 is 100 times as acidic as pH 6, and so on. pH can be measured precisely using an electrometric pH-meter; alternatively, a color indicator can be added to the solution and the resulting colored liquid compared with standard shades of colors. (See also *acidic; alkaline; litmus.*)

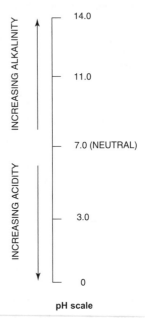

pH scale

phosphate   A type of chemical compound used in the treatment of boiler water.

> REAL ESTATE APPLICATION: Phosphate treatment is very effective in reducing scale although it tends to increase the dissolved solids in boiler water. Addition of phosphate transforms scale-forming salts (primarily sulfates) into a soft sludge. The accumulated sludge is periodically removed from the boiler through a blowdown procedure.

pit   A recessed cavity in a metal surface, such as a condenser water pipe, resulting from localized corrosion, which is usually due to high levels of dissolved oxygen. *Pitting* eventually leads to leaks in the system.

reverse osmosis   A common method of water filtration and purification; the opposite of *osmosis.* In osmosis, a semipermeable membrane allows the passage of water (under pressure) but does not allow the passage of dissolved substances. In principle, a semipermeable membrane separating solutions of different concentrations allows the free flow of solvent or water from the solution of lesser concentration to that of higher concentration until equilibrium (equal concentration) is achieved. In reverse osmosis, a semipermeable membrane is used to remove salts (ions) from natural (impure) water. A *reverse osmosis system* combines four water treatment methods—mechanical filtration, ultrafiltration, reverse osmosis, and activated carbon adsorption.

sacrificial anode   Any of several strategically placed pieces of metal having a higher corrosion potential than the metal of the heating or cooling system components. In this form of corrosion control, the sacrificial anodes (e.g., strips of magnesium or zinc) corrode instead of the equipment.

> REAL ESTATE APPLICATION: Sacrificial anodes should not be the only means of corrosion control. This method should be used as a supplement to other forms of water treatment and monitoring.

scale   An accumulation of dense crystals, primarily comprising inorganic mineral compounds such as calcium carbonate, magnesium silicate, calcium phosphate, and iron oxide, which adhere to the surfaces of heating and cooling system components. These minerals typically dissolve in water, but under certain conditions, they precipitate out of a solution as particles that will not dissolve, eventually forming a crust (scale) on interior surfaces.

> REAL ESTATE APPLICATION: Scale deposits are one of the major problems that develop from water impurities. Scale can form in both heating (boiler) and

cooling systems. The formation of scale will reduce heat transfer efficiency, thus increasing energy consumption; it also promotes corrosion. Scale can be controlled by chemically treating the water to limit the concentration of minerals that can cause scaling.

The ability of scale to form increases with increasing pH (alkalinity) and higher water temperatures as well as other factors such as time, mineral concentration, and system surface areas and configurations. The basic principle of chemical treatment for scale is to condition the water in a way that keeps the mineral compounds in a soft sludge state and prevents them from adhering to metal surfaces. When a specified level or percentage of sludge is accumulated, the water in the system needs to be purged (e.g., via blowdown or bleed). In addition, the pH of the system may have to be lowered to decrease the alkalinity, but not so low as to become acidic and lead to corrosion.

shock   A treatment method in which a significant quantity of chemicals is introduced into a heating or cooling system in a single dose as opposed to smaller quantities being fed into the system continuously.

side stream filtration   A common type of mechanical filtration process in which solids are removed from a liquid (water) through diversion into a filtration device off to the side of the primary liquid flow route.

sludge   A sedimentary deposit of the solid matter present in water, not always found at the place where it was formed. It is typically removed from a system by mechanical means, such as blowdown.

slug feed   See *manual feed.*

suspended solids   Solids present in the water supply or atmospheric air that remain dispersed in the liquid or gas rather than dissolving. Examples of suspended solids are bacteria, silt, dirt particles, and decomposed organic matter such as leaves.

REAL ESTATE APPLICATION: Suspended solids must be considered with respect to their contribution to water problems. The most potentially damaging source of suspended solids, particularly in cooling or potable water systems, is bacteria. Suspended solids can typically be removed from a system by filtration.

titration   The incremental (e.g., drop-wise) addition of a measured volume of a liquid of known concentration to a known volume of another liquid of unknown concentration until a point is reached at which a definite effect is observed, usually a change in color of an indicator.

REAL ESTATE APPLICATION: Titration is a common chemical testing procedure used in the analysis of water solutions, as in an HVAC system, to measure the concentration of chemicals in a water treatment program.

total dissolved solids (TDS)   The total amount of solid impurities (e.g., calcium and magnesium carbonates) in solution in a water-containing (e.g., cooling or heating) system. TDS can be determined by measuring the conductivity of the water. (See also *conductivity; dissolved solids; scale*).

REAL ESTATE APPLICATION: Because water partially dissolves almost anything it contacts, the TDS in a heating or cooling system, particularly one that requires addition of makeup feed water, will always increase until the solids are removed. Makeup water also contains dissolved solids, which are added to the system. When calcium and magnesium carbonates precipitate out of solution, they can form scale that deposits on heat transfer surfaces. Precipitation occurs when the water in a heating or cooling system is over-saturated with dissolved solids (high TDS). It can also occur if the water temperature of the system is too high or if the chemical treatment program is not effectively applied or controlled. As the temperature of water increases, its ability to hold dissolved solids in solution diminishes, and the solids precipitate out of solution. For this reason, heating systems (e.g., boilers) are more subject to deposit formation than are cooling systems.

water softening   See *ion exchange.*

water treatment program   A comprehensive approach to monitoring and controlling corrosion, scale, fouling, and microbial growth in heating and cooling water systems using a variety of methods and procedures. Water treatment programs can include traditional chemical treatment, use of sacrificial anodes or ozone generators, analysis and monitoring of chemical levels, preventive maintenance, and other specific strategies.

Electrical, Lighting, Data, and Telecommunications Systems

access line The connection between a subscriber's facility (e.g., corporate offices) and a public network (e.g., public switched network or public telephone network).

across-the-line starter A device that allows a motor to be started at full line voltage. Across-the-line starters are normally equipped with thermal overload relays.

adapter A device that enables different sizes or types of plugs to mate with one another. Also, a low-voltage, step-down transformer used to convert voltages or to allow electronic devices (e.g., laptop computers) to use an external power source (usually line voltage) in lieu of batteries.

> REAL ESTATE APPLICATION: Devices that permit two or more electric cords to be connected to a single wall or floor outlet are also referred to as *adapters*. Fire department and building inspectors may express concern about a potential fire hazard if these types of adapters (or extension cords) are used extensively for providing power to electrical devices instead of connecting them directly to wall outlets.

adjustable frequency drive (AFD) A solid-state electronic device that varies the frequency of the voltage supplied to a motor, thus, changing its speed. Also, referred to as *adjustable speed drive (ASD), variable speed drive (VSD),* or *variable frequency drive (VFD)*.

> REAL ESTATE APPLICATION: Adjustable frequency drives are very common in HVAC applications where they are used to reduce the voltage and speed of heating and cooling equipment (circulating pumps and ventilation fans) during light load conditions. The cost savings associated with the reduction in voltage applied to the motors driving this HVAC equipment can be significant.

alternating current (AC) An electric current that reverses the direction of electron flow at regular intervals. The frequency of the current is the number of cycles in a given period, generally a second. (See also *frequency* and accompanying diagram.)

> REAL ESTATE APPLICATION: Alternating current is used almost exclusively in commercial and residential electrical systems today.

alternator   An electric generator that produces alternating current by the rotation of its rotor; also referred to as an *alternating current (AC) generator.*

ambient light controls   An automated lighting control system that uses a sensor to measure the level of light within a given space—provided by the natural surrounding conditions (e.g., sunlight)—and a dimmer switch to vary the output of the lamps (light fixtures) within the space to maintain overall optimum lighting levels at the highest efficiency. The level of background illumination that results from existing outside light being admitted to an inside space, measured in *footcandles* (which see). Obviously, the ambient light level is dependent upon the time of day and year (sun elevation and orientation), weather (sunny, cloudy), and other conditions. (Compare *dimmer.*)

REAL ESTATE APPLICATION: Ambient light controls installed in spaces at the perimeter of a building with windows can effect cost savings through lower electricity usage. All sides of a building, even the north side, have significant levels of ambient light available during daylight hours. Use of ambient light allows dimming of the lights (by regulating the current to the fluorescent ballasts), thus reducing the electricity consumed while providing constant, adequate lighting for people working in the space.

American wire gauge (AWG)   A standard designation for the physical size (diameter) of an electrical conductor (wire). The gauge varies inversely with the actual wire diameter determined by the circular mil area—i.e., the higher the gauge number, the smaller (finer) the wire. (See also *circular mil.*)

ammeter   An instrument that measures the electric current in a circuit in units called amperes (amps). An ammeter is always connected into an electric circuit in series (end to end) rather than across two points of a circuit (parallel).

ampere (amp)   The standard unit of measurement of the rate of flow of current in an electric circuit or conductor; also referred to as *amperage* and sometimes abbreviated *a*. The rate (1 ampere) at which electrons flow in an electric circuit having a potential difference of 1 volt and a resistance of 1 ohm.

REAL ESTATE APPLICATION: The amperage of an electrical component multiplied by the voltage of the circuit is the electrical load (wattage) of the equipment. The amperage of a given component is normally listed on a nameplate attached to the equipment. This information, when combined with the known voltage of the circuit, the local utility rates, and the estimated or actual hours of use of the electrical component, can be helpful in calculating the annual cost to operate the equipment.

analog   The representation of data (or method of automated control) by continuously variable physical quantities (like a pen moving over a chart); also spelled *analogue.* (Compare *digital.*)

annunciator   A device that emits an audible signal (alarm) when specific parameters are met, alerting the building operator and/or occupants to the changed status of a particular system (e.g., fire alarm system).

anode   The positive terminal (side) of a battery.

arc   A glow, sometimes appearing as a curved line, that can form when an electric circuit is broken; a result of the sudden, unexpected movement of electrons across a conductor and ground or between two conductors.

armature   The heavy current winding of an electric motor or generator that is moved by magnetism. Also the winding in a solenoid or relay.

armored cable   Two or more individually insulated electrical conductors (wires) enclosed in an outer protective metal covering, usually a helical winding (the ground wire, if present, is bare), commonly referred to as *BX* or *BX cable;* sometimes also called *armorflex.*

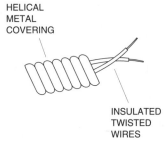

armored (BX) cable

REAL ESTATE APPLICATION: Grounded armored cable is often used for electricalwiring in commercial applications. Its flexibility allows for a more efficient method of installation than rigid metal conduit, particularly when many bends are required.

arrester   A device installed in an electric circuit that transfers overvoltage or overcurrent to a ground in order to protect the electric circuit and the components or equipment it serves. The arrester can be likened to a normally open valve or circuit breaker that closes when a high-voltage surge occurs, discharging the excess current. The overvoltage or overcurrent can result from lightning or a sudden, abnormal rise (surge) in the current, thus the specific names *lightning arrester* and *surge arrester.*

attenuation   The decrease in magnitude of a wave (loss of signal strength) as it travels through a transmitting medium (material) such as a cable. The received signal is weaker than the transmitted signal due to losses in the transmission medium.

automatic transfer switch (ATS)   A device that automatically switches an electrical conductor from one circuit to another during a loss of power (or, subse-

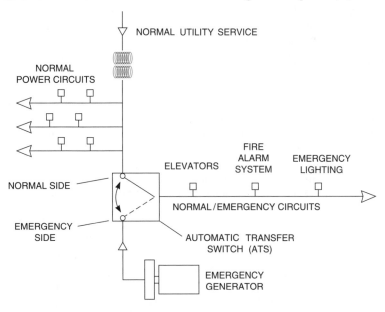

automatic transfer switch

quently, during a restoration of power) without interrupting the flow of current.

REAL ESTATE APPLICATION: An automatic transfer switch could be used to change the electrical conductors providing power to an elevator from a normal power supply to an emergency power supply.

ballast   A device designed to stabilize current flow. A resistance device used to provide the required starting voltage and operating current for fluorescent, mercury-vapor, and other electric discharge lamps. Ballasts used in lighting applications are typically electronic although those in some older installations may not be. (Use of *ballast* in roofing applications is covered in Architecture, Construction, and Project Management.)

battery   An electrochemical cell used to store chemical energy for conversion later to electric energy (direct current).

REAL ESTATE APPLICATION: Battery systems are frequently used in emergency power applications, but they are limited in the amount of energy they can provide and how long a time they can function. Therefore, battery systems are used in lower power applications, such as emergency lighting, or as a temporary power source in an emergency (e.g., starting an emergency generator) or to continue operation of a computer system during the transition to emergency power (i.e., the time between the loss of normal power and when emergency power is available from a generator).

battery backup   A battery that provides temporary power to a machine or system (e.g., telephone system) when its main source of power fails.

baud   A unit of data transmission speed, sometimes variable but usually simply meaning bits per second—i.e., 600 baud = 600 bits per second; also referred to as *baud rate*.

bit   Fundamental unit of information expressed in digital form.

bonding   The connecting together of all building and equipment electrical grounds to eliminate differences in electrical ground potential.

brush   An electrical conductor (usually a strip or block of carbon) that provides electrical contact between a rotating and a stationary element in a motor or generator.

bug   An unexpected, usually reparable, defect or fault in any type of equipment. In the realm of computers, a program (software) or hardware malfunction. Problems in a system are literally called bugs; to resolve or eliminate the problem, one would *debug* the system.

bus bar   A heavy rigid electrical conductor, usually comprised of uninsulated copper or aluminum, that carries a large current and serves as a common connection between a source of electric power and the main electrical feeders or circuits; sometimes called simply *bus*.

REAL ESTATE APPLICATION: Bus bars are typically located within the main switchboard of a building, usually in the basement or sub-basement area.

bus duct   A pre-fabricated conduit used to enclose a bus bar (of copper or aluminum material) running through it; also referred to as a *bus duct riser*.

REAL ESTATE APPLICATION: A bus duct riser is used in high-rise buildings where relatively large amounts of electricity are used throughout the structure. The conduit traverses from one floor to the next through small closet-like rooms constructed one above the other.

BX cable   See *armored cable.*

byte   The standard unit of computer information storage. A collection of bits that operate as a unit, most are 8 bits long. The capacity of storage devices (e.g., computer memory) is typically stated in bytes.

cabinet   An enclosure for rack-mounted equipment. A cupboard or compartment, usually of steel, for housing electric panels.

cable   A group of small-diameter conductor strands twisted together or a group of electrical conductors (wires) which are insulated from each other and twisted together around a central core.

cable loss   The amount of radio frequency (RF) signal attenuated (diluted) by coaxial cable transmission. Cable attenuation is a function of frequency, media type (cable material), and distance (cable length). (See also *attenuation.*)

cable tray   A permanent wire management assembly consisting of a ladder-type metal framework used to support insulated electrical conductors for routing purposes. Cable trays are more common in areas where there are few or no walls, suspended ceilings, or underfloor ducts through which conductor cable can be routed, and they are typically located overhead (ceiling height). Cable trays have framework on the bottom and sides only; the tops are open to facilitate laying and management of extended lengths of cable.

candlepower   The illumination intensity of a light source measured at a specific angle and expressed in *candelas.*

capacitance   The property of an electric current that permits the storage of electric energy in an electrostatic field (area of potential difference) for release at a later time.

capacitive reactance   The opposition to alternating current due to the capacitance of a capacitor, cable, or circuit.

capacitor   A storage device used in electric circuits in order to ensure the current of the circuit remains fairly constant (smooth) during abrupt changes in voltage.

REAL ESTATE APPLICATION: Capacitors are used extensively in telephone and radio circuits. They are also sometimes installed near large motors with high inductance in order to maintain a high power factor and, thereby, decrease the current consumed by those motors.

cathode   The negative terminal (side) of a battery.

cathode ray tube (CRT)   An electronic tube that has a screen upon which a beam of electrons from the cathode can be directed to create images; a computer display terminal or television screen.

cellular floor   A type of raceway (electrical cable distribution system) consisting of longitudinal cells under the floor, which are interconnected by means of header ducts placed at intervals chosen for maximum coverage. A cellular floor system is similar to an underfloor duct (raceway) system but more complex. (See also *raceway* and accompanying diagram.)

central processing unit (CPU)   The heart of a computer, but often used as a synonym for computer. The CPU contains arithmetic and logic functions that process programmed instructions.

charge   A condition of capacity (electric potential) of a battery. Also, to increase the capacity (electric potential) of a battery by introducing an electric current (charge) into the battery over a prolonged period.

chase   See definition in Architecture, Construction, and Project Management.

circuit   See *electric circuit.*

circuit breaker   A device that automatically trips (disconnects an electric circuit) upon reaching a predetermined level of abnormally high current flow (i.e., overload). A circuit breaker can be used repeatedly as a protection device without replacing any parts, unlike a *fuse* which, once blown, must be replaced. The proper nomenclature for the three positions of a circuit breaker are as follows: Closed (provides electric circuit continuity, allowing current to flow); open (effected manually to interrupt or open the electric circuit so current does not flow); and tripped (occurs automatically due to an overcurrent condition [power surge], thereby interrupting the flow of current).

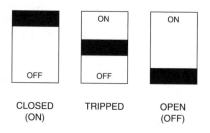

circuit breaker positions

   REAL ESTATE APPLICATION: Circuit breakers provide a means of separating or grouping electrical loads by physical location, type of equipment, etc. A circuit breaker may be opened (tripped intentionally) to isolate (disconnect) a circuit or electrical load. A breaker that has been tripped automatically needs to be reset (turned full off; open position) before it is turned on again (closed position) to restore the circuit.

circular mil   A unit of area commonly used in determining the cross-sectional size of a conductor (wire), equal to the area of a circle having a diameter of 1 mil or 0.001 inches. (See also *mil.*)

clean power   Electric power that is relatively free from electrical noise and harmonics, thus providing a consistent frequency.

coaxial cable   A transmission line comprised of a conductor centered inside a metallic tube or shield, held in place by a dielectric material (insulator), and usually covered by an insulating jacket.

   REAL ESTATE APPLICATION: Coaxial cable was once considered typical in low-voltage data and telecommunications transmission applications but is now nearly obsolete in these uses. It is still used in some residential applications for transmitting radio and television signals.

coil   An insulated (usually copper) wire wound in a circular pattern (spiral) along the length of an iron conductor or similar device. Current passed through such a coil creates an electromagnetic effect (referred to as *flux*), which results in movement of the conductor. Likewise, a conductor moved past a coil induces a magnetic flux that results in a flow of current.

color rendition   The measure of how well a fluorescent source (lamp) renders colors as compared to an incandescent source (lamp) of the same color temperature. The comparison is stated as the lamp's color rendering index (CRI)—the higher the CRI, the better the color rendition.

common return   A conductor (wire) that serves as the electrical return for more than one circuit, also called *common neutral.*

commutator   A cylindrical device composed of copper bars alternated with mica insulation and connected to the armature in a generator such that rotation of the armature, in conjunction with fixed (hard carbon) brushes, converts alternating current (AC) input to direct current (DC) output.

REAL ESTATE APPLICATION: A commutator may be found in some elevator equipment to convert AC voltage to DC voltage to power the elevator controls.

conductance   The ability of a material to allow electrons (electricity) to flow freely in a conductor or circuit; also called *conductivity.* The opposite of *resistance* (which also see) or resistivity.

conductor   A material suitable for carrying an electric current. A material that allows the free passage of current when connected to a battery or other source of electrical energy. Copper wire is typically used as a conductor in electrical systems. Aluminum wire is also used, generally in larger-sized cables.

REAL ESTATE APPLICATION: Almost any material can become a conductor of electric current, sometimes with a negative impact (i.e., electric shock).

conduit   A pipe in which cables are enclosed for protection. Conduit is usually made of metal and can be run vertically floor to floor or horizontally along a floor or ceiling. Conduit is also used to provide the means of pulling cable from floor to floor—i.e., in a *chase*—or between buildings. Because of its safety, flexibility, and relatively low cost, conduit and cable is the most commonly used system for providing electrical feed to panels, motors, lighting fixtures, control circuits, etc.

REAL ESTATE APPLICATION: Conduit is manufactured from a variety of materials for different uses. Rigid steel conduit is used where maximum protection of enclosed conductors (wires) is required (e.g., high-voltage applications); it may be embedded in concrete. Aluminum conduit may be used where corrosion or weight is a consideration, but it is not suitable for embedment in concrete. *Electrical metallic tubing* (which see) may not be used where it would be subject to severe physical damage or exposure to corrosive materials. Polyvinyl chloride (PVC) rigid nonmetallic conduit, which lacks the strength and durability of metallic piping, may be used in wet or corrosive environments. PVC is also used to coat the exterior of steel conduit to protect it from exposure to oils, excess moisture, or corrosive materials (acid, alkali).

connected load   The combined (total) load in kilovolt-amperes (kva) on an electric system if all of the individual loads connected to the system (copy machines, computers, lighting fixtures, etc.) are energized simultaneously.

REAL ESTATE APPLICATION: The connected load is sometimes provided on the electrical engineering drawings for company or tenant construction projects. This information can be useful to the manager in helping to ensure that the connected load does not exceed the capacity of the transformers providing electric power to the area or floor.

contactor   A device that opens and closes to interrupt (break) and connect (make) an electric circuit providing power to an electrical load (equipment).

REAL ESTATE APPLICATION: Contactors are often magnetically energized as an integral part of a magnetic controller. The function of the controller is to quickly open or close a circuit to prevent arcing of current between the contact and the load side of the electric circuit (equipment), particularly in higher voltage applications.

continuity   The uninterrupted flow of an electric circuit. An electric circuit that contains no open contacts (tripped circuit breakers, cut wires). The continuity of an electric circuit can be determined with a megohmmeter. (See also *megger.*)

continuous rating   The maximum constant load that can be carried by a piece of electrical equipment without exceeding a designated temperature rise.

contrast ratio   The relationship between the lighting levels at work surfaces (task levels) and the lighting levels in the surrounding areas.

REAL ESTATE APPLICATION: Lighting contrast ratio is an important consideration in the design of lighting systems. Contrast ratios typically do not exceed 3:1—i.e., if the work surface area light level is 60 footcandles, the surrounding area should be at least 20 footcandles.

control center   See *motor control center.*

controller   A device for regulating the operation of electrical apparatus to which it is connected. A motor starter is a controller whose main function is to start and accelerate an electric motor.

current   See *alternating current; direct current; electric current.*

current limit starter   A motor starter that limits the amount of current supplied to a motor during startup in order to protect the motor and its windings and insulation from excessive voltage. Since the starting current for a motor can be as much as nine times its normal operating current, use of a current limit starter is vital to the safe operation of motors.

current transformer   A device that provides a means of reducing the line current of an electric circuit to a value that may be used to operate lower-current measuring and control devices. These transformers are completely isolated from the main circuit.

REAL ESTATE APPLICATION: Current transformers are used in connecting consumption meters to electric circuits to measure electricity usage.

cutout   A device (switch) that interrupts (opens) an electrical connection.

cycle   In an electric circuit, one complete repetition of an alternating current that varies periodically in value and direction, first flowing in one direction and then in the opposite direction. The frequency of the current is the number of cycles occurring during a given time period, usually stated in *cycles per second,* abbreviated *cps.* (See also *frequency* and the accompanying diagram.)

debug   See *bug.*

dedicated circuit   An electric circuit that is connected to one specific electrical load—i.e., provides power to a single piece of equipment or system.

REAL ESTATE APPLICATION: A dedicated circuit may be used to provide power to a corporation's vital computer system. One advantage of a dedicated circuit is that power supplied to the vital equipment is unaffected by the power requirements of other electrical components within the same area.

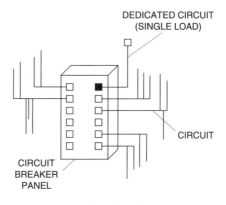

dedicated circuit

delta connection   One of two methods of joining (configuring) the three wires of an alternating current (AC) generator or transformer, named for its shape which resembles a triangle. (See also *Y connection*.)

demand   The electrical load on a system over a specified time interval, usually expressed in kilowatts (kw) or kilovolt-amperes (kva). The electrical demand of a system can be thought of as the instantaneous electrical load rather than the total usage over an extended period.

REAL ESTATE APPLICATION: Electric utility companies often include a separate demand charge for customers who use larger amounts of electricity. The demand charge can often represent a significant portion of the total bill— as much as 25%–50%). The demand charge is often thought of as a penalty for the highest, short-term, consecutive (e.g., 15-minute) period of electrical consumption during a given billing period. The charge in dollars per kilowatt usage for a customer's electrical demand is significantly higher than the utility company's charges for general electricity consumption.

demand side management   The concept of controlling the electrical demand of a facility (i.e., the total combined instantaneous load) through use of controlling devices *(energy management system)* or, from a long-term perspective, local utility incentive programs.

diagnostics   Programs or procedures used to test a piece of equipment, a communications link or network, or any similar system.

dielectric material   See *insulation*.

diffuser   A device, normally an integral component of a lighting fixture, that scatters (uniform distribution) or softens the light emitted from a concentrated source. An acrylic prism lens and a parabolic lens are examples of common light diffusers.

digital   The representation of data using numerical digits or discrete units. (Compare *analog*.)

dimmer   A device that varies the current flowing through a light fixture or lamp, used to reduce (or increase) light output.

REAL ESTATE APPLICATION: Dimmers are typically used with incandescent lights. Fluorescent lights may be dimmed via *ambient light controls* (which see).

direct current (DC)   Electric current (movement of electrons) that flows in one direction only.

REAL ESTATE APPLICATION: Once the primary means of transmitting electricity, direct current is seldom used in today's electrical systems.

direct digital control (DDC)   A method in which HVAC and other control devices are operated (sequenced) by electrical or electronic means in lieu of alternate methods (manual, pneumatic). The power supply for direct digital control is typically low voltage (e.g., 12 volt input signal, 4–20 milliamp output signal).

REAL ESTATE APPLICATION: The engineering and installation of new HVAC systems (and the conversion of existing HVAC system controls) employ direct digital controls almost exclusively. Some benefits of direct digital control are enhanced remote operation, precision control, quick response, full automation, and computer integration resulting in more efficient and effective control overall. Direct digital control is often associated with HVAC operation but can be used effectively in many other electrically compatible control applications such as door locks and lighting systems.

direct lighting   Illumination predominantly from a preferred direction or to a specific work area, work surface, or object.

disconnecting switch   A device that isolates an electric circuit or one or more pieces of equipment (e.g., HVAC equipment mounted on a roof) from the source of electric current, usually a circuit breaker, a fuse switch, or a fuse-circuit breaker assembly; also called *disconnector.*

REAL ESTATE APPLICATION: The term *main disconnect* is used in referring to the first circuit breaker within a facility, which is located at the source of electric power entry into the building. If opened or tripped, the main disconnect interrupts the flow of electricity to the entire electrical distribution system of the building.

distribution circuit   The means of transmission of electric power within a facility. (Most large properties use a *three-wire distribution circuit,* which see.)

distribution system   The means of distributing electricity from the power-generating station to a facility. Electricity is distributed by means of feeders that are divided and subdivided, from larger capacity initially to increasingly smaller capacity. At each change in circuit capacity of the system, there is a distribution center where circuit protective and switching equipment is grouped.

REAL ESTATE APPLICATION: Some of the typical nominal voltages in electrical distribution systems and circuits are as follows:

13,777 volts	Distribution voltage prior to a facilities substation
480 volts	Larger mechanical equipment in large facilities
277 volts	Some lighting circuits in large facilities
240 volts	Larger residential and office equipment (e.g., large copy machines)
208 volts	Same as 240 volts
120 volts	Typical office and residential equipment power

Within the context of electrical distribution systems, low-voltage equipment is for circuits operating at 600 volts and below; high-voltage equipment is for circuits operating above 600 volts.

double-pole switch   In electric wiring, a switching device that has two blades and associated contacts for opening and closing both sides of a circuit simultaneously.

REAL ESTATE APPLICATION: A double-pole switch may be used in a lighting application where a single switch is required to simultaneously turn two groups of light fixtures on and off.

downlight A relatively small diameter (4–7 in) ceiling fixture, which may be recessed, surface-mounted, or suspended, used to project light in a downward direction. A downlight may use an incandescent or a fluorescent bulb.

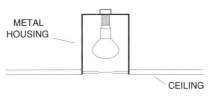

downlight

duplex receptacle Two electrical outlets combined into a single unit for installation into an outlet box. A double-duplex receptacle consists of four receptacles combined into a single unit. (See also *receptacle.*)

effective value A term referring to the actual value (rating) of the voltage or current in an alternating current (AC) circuit. Since the voltage of an AC circuit modulates from a minimum value to a maximum value (60 times per second in a typical AC circuit), the actual value is an average of the maximum and minimum values. (Mathematically, the effective value is the square root of the arithmetic mean of the squares of all the voltage values measured during a complete cycle. The electrical average is equal to 0.707 times the maximum value, also referred to as root mean square [rms].)

electrical degree See *phase.*

electrically supervised An electric wiring system that uses the flow of a small current in the circuit (too small to actuate the device being supplied) to energize an alarm signal upon failure of any device or equipment in the circuit.

REAL ESTATE APPLICATION: Fire detection systems in buildings are typically supervised systems. Usually referred to as fully supervised, a main fire panel in such a fire detection system monitors or supervises many of the detection devices within the system. If the circuitry containing a smoke detector has been disrupted for some reason, thus impeding the ability of the device to detect smoke, the main fire panel would signal an alarm, alerting an operator or the building management about this condition.

electrical metallic conduit (EMC) Threaded tubing, usually fabricated of steel, in which electric wiring is enclosed to support and protect it from damage.

electrical metallic tubing (EMT) Unthreaded conduit, fabricated of thin-walled steel, in which electric wiring is enclosed to support and protect it from damage.

electrical non-metallic tubing (ENT) A round corrugated plastic tube in which electric wiring is enclosed and protected. ENT is normally concealed in concrete or in ceiling construction having a fire rating of at least 15 minutes, provided the ceiling is not used as a return air plenum. ENT is used in corrosive environments where metallic tubing or conduit would deteriorate.

electric circuit A closed loop formed by a conductor (wire) and a power source (battery, generator, etc.) such that electrons flow due to a difference in electric potential (voltage). The minimum requirements for an electric circuit are a power supply, a load, and a path for current flow. Free electrons are always present in a conductor. In an electric circuit, electrons are repelled by the negative terminal of the power source and attracted to the positive terminal. The power source does not provide the electrons, it drives them. As long as the circuit is closed, electrons will flow around the loop producing electricity.

REAL ESTATE APPLICATION: The many electrical loads in a building (systems, equipment) are grouped together and served by individual electric circuits.

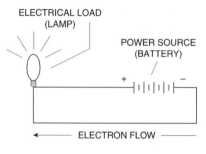

electric circuit

electric current   The flow of electrons in an electric circuit, expressed in amperes (amps). The current flowing through a circuit varies depending on the voltage (potential difference) and resistance of the circuit. The standard symbol for electric current is I.

electric heating element   That part of an electric heating device (stove coil, space heater), consisting of an electrical resistive material, insulated supports, and terminals for connection to a source of electric power, that converts electrical energy to heat; sometimes also called *electric heat lamp.*

electricity   The flow of free electrons in a circuit due to a potential difference (voltage) in the circuit—free electrons meaning electrons that are always present in a conductive material and move when a potential difference exists. (See also *generator.*)

electric lock   A type of lock in which the movement of a bolt or latch is actuated by the application of a voltage to the terminals of the device.

electric space heater   A device consisting of electrical resistive material to which electricity is supplied, resulting in heat energy.

REAL ESTATE APPLICATION: Electric space heaters are popularly used for emergency heating or as a temporary measure, typically in smaller space-heating applications. Most managers of real estate discourage the permanent use of electric space heaters due to their inefficiency and fire hazard potential.

electric strike   An electrical device that secures the lock on a door such that it can only be released by completing an electric circuit, the process being controlled from a remote location; also called *electric-release strike.*

electric water heater   A water heater (usually fully automatic, with operating and safety controls) consisting of a storage tank with one or more electric heating elements.

electrolyte   The liquid solution (e.g., sulfuric acid) contained in a battery in which electrodes (conductive plates) are placed. The potential of the battery is dependent on the materials used for the electrodes and the electrolyte.

electromagnetic interference   See *interference.*

electromotive force (emf)   The force required to maintain a potential difference between two points when a current flows between them. The amount of energy derived from an electrical source (e.g., generator) per unit quantity of electricity passing through the source. A device that has the ability to maintain such a potential difference is also referred to as being electromotive. (See also *potential difference.*)

electron   An elementary charged particle containing the smallest mass and carrying a negative electric charge. The movement of electrons through a conductor is what constitutes an *electric current.*

Electronic Industries Alliance (EIA)   A national trade organization of electronic manufacturers responsible for the development and maintenance of industry standards for the interface between data-processing machines and data communications equipment.

emergency egress lighting   See *egress* and *emergency lighting* in Life Safety and Fire Protection Systems.

emergency power generator   See *emergency generator* in Life Safety and Fire Protection Systems.

end bell   The end structure of an electric motor which positions and holds the bearings.

ethernet   A baseband local area network (LAN) specification developed jointly by Xerox Corporation, Intel Corporation, and Digital Equipment Corporation to interconnect computer equipment using coaxial cable and transceivers.

facsimile (fax)   An exact detailed copy; the process of transmitting and reproducing printed matter and photographs, originally by telegraph but now by telephone lines; also the equipment for transmitting and reproducing facsimiles.

fault   An unintentional, low-resistance connection between two or more conductors or an open or broken conductor. In other words, a defect in the insulation or conductive capacity at any point in a circuit or of any device in the circuit resulting in either an interruption of current flow or an unintended path of current flow.

feeder   In power distribution, a group of electrical conductors that originate at a main distribution center and supply one or more secondary distribution centers.

fiberoptic   Transmission of light energy through glass fibers. A technology that uses light as an information carrier. Fiberoptic cables are a direct replacement for conventional coaxial cable and wire pairs. The glass-based transmission cable occupies far less physical area for an equivalent transmission capacity. A thousand signals can be transmitted simultaneously in a single fiber. The fibers are also immune to electrical interference.

file server   A computer station dedicated to providing file and mass data storage to the other stations on the local network.

filter   An arrangement of electronic components designed to pass signals in one or more frequency bands while simultaneously reducing (attenuating) signals in other frequency bands.

flat cable   An arrangement of three or more flat copper conductors embedded in a plastic (usually polyester) film, used in *undercarpet power systems.* Also, an assembly of three or four conductors in a plastic housing designed for insertion into a matching U-shaped channel raceway for branch distribution of power to ceiling-mounted light fixtures.

REAL ESTATE APPLICATION: Undercarpet installation of flat cable offers an alternate method of distributing electric power within offices without the need for underfloor ducts or channels in walls or ceilings. The wiring is run from a wall box, installed directly on concrete slab, wood, or other flooring (taped in place), and covered with carpet squares. Outlets may be floor mounted or enclosed in workstation paneling. Separate types of flat cabling are similarly used for undercarpet installations of telephone and data transmission systems.

flexible metal conduit   The preferred method of providing final wire connections to motors and similar equipment where vibration or movement may be present.

floodlight   A projector-type lamp used to illuminate a specific object or area to a level of brightness considerably higher than the surrounding illumination.

fluorescent lamp   A low-pressure electric discharge lamp. Ultraviolet light is generated by the passage of an electric arc through mercury vapor; the inner surface of the lamp tube is coated with a phosphor that absorbs the ultraviolet radiation and converts some of it to visible light.

REAL ESTATE APPLICATION: Fluorescent lamps are the most practical source of general illumination for interior commercial office space because of their low brightness, high efficiency, long life, and overall cost savings. The 40-watt rapid-start type is the most popular fluorescent lamp and is available as either a 4-foot straight tube or a 2-foot U-shaped lamp. (See diagram at *parabolic light fixture.*)

footcandle   A unit of illuminance equal to the amount of light on a surface one foot away from a candle. The metric conversion of footcandles is lumens per square meter. Illumination in offices (expressed in footcandles) is typically measured at the work surface (e.g., desk or workstation).

frequency   The number of complete cycles of the voltage and current of an electric circuit during a given time period. In generating electricity, since the magnetic field is strongest at the center, as the conductor enters the field, current begins to flow and builds to a maximum at the center of the field and then diminishes to zero, reverses and repeats to the end of the cycle. The standard unit of measure for frequency is *hertz* (cycles per second), abbreviated *Hz;* 60 Hz (60 cycles per second) is the standard frequency of alternating current in the United States.

REAL ESTATE APPLICATION: Most modern day electrical systems and equipment in the United States operate on 60 Hz alternating voltage (60 Hz AC). In other words, the voltage and current changes from

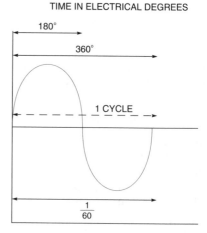

TIME IN ELECTRICAL DEGREES

frequency
(60 Hz or 60 cycles per second)

a positive value to a negative value and back (a complete cycle) 60 times in one second. This curve is called a *sine wave* or *cycle*.

The 60-cycle frequency is evident in the rpm classification of AC motors. For example, a two-pole motor is designed to operate at 3,600 rpm (revolutions per minute). If one divides 3,600 rpm by 60 to determine revolutions per second, the result is 60 cycles per second (cps). This happens to match the frequency of the applied alternating voltage and current. In other words, for a motor having two poles (one pair), the applied voltage frequency (60 Hz) will result in an equal motor speed (60 cps or 3,600 rpm). For a motor having four poles (two pairs), the resulting rpm is (60 cps × 60 sec/min) ÷ 2 pair = 1,800 rpm.

fuse A device used to protect against excessive current (voltage). It consists of a short length of fusible metal wire that melts when current through it exceeds the rated amount for a definite time.

gaseous lamp A lamp that contains a gaseous substance which enhances its light output. (See also *mercury vapor lamp; sodium vapor lamp.*)

REAL ESTATE APPLICATION: Gaseous lamps are popular in outdoor lighting applications or in large spaces with high ceilings when high output is required. Gaseous lamps have the disadvantage of requiring a period of time to light when they are cold or after a power interruption.

general lighting Lighting designed to provide a uniform level of illumination throughout an area.

generator A machine that converts mechanical energy (from a steam turbine or diesel engine) into electric power; also called *generator set*.

REAL ESTATE APPLICATION: Power plants contain large equipment (e.g., turbines) that converts mechanical energy to electrical energy for use in towns, cities, large buildings, etc. Electricity is generated by passing many conductors (attached as an integral part of a rotating element, such as a turbine rotor) through a magnetic field of wound conductors (coiled wires). Conductors at the stationary portion of the generator (stator) carry the electricity away from the generator.

glare Excessive lighting contrast; uncomfortable brightness.

REAL ESTATE APPLICATION: Light fixtures that are not designed properly can create glare by bouncing light off of luminaire reflectors at high angles from the vertical.

globe light A light fixture, often spherical in shape, that consists of a lamp within an enclosure (usually of glass). The enclosure protects the lamp, diffuses and redirects the light, and enhances the aesthetics of the light fixture.

grid A plan or layout of relatively large-sized multiple, sometimes redundant, electrical conductors; also called *electrical grid*. In larger towns or cities, the utility's electrical infrastructure (distribution network) is often referred to as a grid, as it serves multiple sites and has some redundancy factored into its operation.

ground The connection of the framework of electrical equipment to a common point, usually the earth, using low-resistance metallic conductors; also called *grounded system*. Such connections, called *ground connections,* eliminate the buildup of static electricity and reduce the potential for operating personnel to receive electric shocks from normal leakage of current or a breakdown of insulation.

ground fault   An unintentional electrical short-circuit or insulation fault between one or more conductors (wires) and ground (e.g., the metal casing of a motor or the metal sheath of a cable); also referred to simply as *ground.*

REAL ESTATE APPLICATION: Exposure of an electric circuit or electrical equipment to moisture or water increases the chance of the appearance of a ground fault. Chafing of an insulated conductor against metal (due to vibration, age, etc.) also greatly increases the chances of ground faults occurring.

ground fault circuit interrupter (GFCI)   A protective device that detects abnormal current flowing to ground and then interrupts (opens) the circuit; also called *ground fault interrupter.*

REAL ESTATE APPLICATION: A GFCI is required in electrical outlets installed in the vicinity of domestic water systems. This arrangement provides for the increased protection needed in wet environments that have increased potential of grounds. Electrical code requires the installation of GFCIs in conjunction with the installation of outlets in the vicinity of a restroom vanity.

ground fault protection   Devices (circuit breakers, relays, or ground fault circuit interrupters) that protect against short circuits produced by ground faults by instantaneously interrupting (opening) an electric circuit during a ground fault condition.

group relamping   A practice of replacing all of the lamps of a lighting system after a specific time period based on the rated life of the lamp and when the lamps were installed.

REAL ESTATE APPLICATION: Group relamping can be an effective method of lighting system maintenance, specifically with respect to cost savings associated with labor efficiencies in changing a large number of lamps at one time. Other benefits of group relamping include maintaining higher, more even light levels overall and less disruption to building occupants.

halogen lamp   An incandescent lamp that is filled with a halogen-containing gas; also called *quartz lamp* or *tungsten-halogen lamp.* This is a high-temperature, usually high-wattage lamp, typically smaller in size compared to standard lamps of similar wattage.

hardware   The tangible, physical components of a computer system—central processing unit (CPU), printer, monitor, etc. Hardware and software are the two broad categories that comprise a computer information system. (See also *software.*)

harmonic distortion   A form of interference involving the generation of unwanted signals. Harmonic distortion is often a result of power system frequencies that are multiples of the fundamental frequency (60 Hz)—e.g., 6 megahertz (MHz); 6MHz = 6,000 Hz, a multiple of 60 Hz. Harmonic distortion can cause overheating and high currents in conductors, transformers, motors, and other equipment.

header duct   In an electrical underfloor "raceway" system, the main feeder duct that provides access to interconnected distribution ducts in order to accommodate the distribution of electric wiring (cable) from an electrical (service) closet through the distribution ducts to the terminal locations (e.g., office floor receptacles).

heat tape   A long, slender, flat electrical resistance material backed by an insulating covering and connected to an electric power source via terminals or a three-prong plug.

> REAL ESTATE APPLICATION: Heat tape may be wrapped around water pipes exposed to freezing conditions in an unheated space in order to prevent the pipes from freezing.

hertz (Hz)   The international standard unit of measurement for frequency of alternating voltage and current. One Hertz is equal to 1 cycle per second (cps).

high-hat fixture   A *downlight*-type lighting fixture, usually shaped like a cylinder and recessed into the ceiling, that directs the majority of its light straight down.

high-intensity discharge (HID) lamp   A lamp that produces a significant amount of illumination, typically used in large mechanical spaces with high ceilings and obstructions, in parking garages, parking lots, etc. Metal halide and high-pressure sodium lamps are examples.

high-pressure sodium lamp   A high-intensity discharge (HID) lamp that produces a yellowish orange light, used for lighting large open spaces such as parking garages or parking lots.

homerun   Used in reference to the practice of connecting (wiring) an electrical or communication device in a straight line (i.e., point-to-point direct) from an electrical or communication service closet or other distribution area to an outlet, a computer, or other terminal location. (See the diagram at *star topology* for a representation of the homerun wiring method.)

horsepower (hp)   A unit of power (rate of doing work). One horsepower is equal to 746 watts of electricity.

> REAL ESTATE APPLICATION: The horsepower rating of a motor can be used, along with operating time and utility rate data, to calculate electricity consumption and cost. As an example, consider a 60-hp motor that drives an air handler operating 10 hours a day Monday through Friday where the local electric utility rate is $.10 per kilowatt-hour (kwh). The amount of electricity consumed and the cost to operate the motor for one year would be calculated as follows:
>
> (60 hp × 746) = 44,760 watts ÷ 1,000 = 44.76 kw rating.
> 44.76 × (10 hrs/day × 5 days/wk × 52 wks = 2,600 hrs) = 116,376 kwh/yr.
> 116,376 × $.10/kwh = $11,638 annual operating cost.

hydrometer   An instrument used to determine the condition of a battery by drawing a sample of the electrolyte solution in the battery and testing it for specific gravity. Specific gravity (density) of the solution indicates the concentration of electrolyte.

illumination   The luminous flux per unit area, usually expressed in *foot-candles* or *lumens* per square foot. The result of the conversion of electrical energy into visible light in a lamp.

impedance   The opposition to the flow of an alternating current within a circuit, cable, or component. It includes both resistance and reactance (the opposition to a change in voltage/current) and is generally expressed in *ohms*.

incandescent lamp   A light bulb in which a (usually tungsten) filament gives off light when heated by an electric current.

REAL ESTATE APPLICATION: Because incandescent lamps light instantaneously when turned on, they are energy intensive. Fluorescent lamps, which offer three to five times the efficacy of incandescent lamps, are more economical for use in general office lighting.

indicator lamp   A light that signals the operating condition of a system, control, or device or indicates a change of condition. While the lamp indicates the condition at a point in the system, it does not provide any controlling action or effect any change in the system operation.

REAL ESTATE APPLICATION: An example is a small lamp on a control panel in a remote operator control room that lights when water in a storage tank exceeds a predetermined level.

indirect lighting   Illumination via reflected (rather than direct) light, as when 90%–100% of the light distributed by a fixture is emitted upward so that illumination is by light reflected off the ceiling surface.

inductance   A property of an electrical conductor or circuit by which an electromotive force is induced in it by a change in current (similar to inertia) such that current changes lag behind voltage changes.

REAL ESTATE APPLICATION: Because the current lags behind the applied voltage, the useful (apparent) power consumed in the electrical equipment is less than the active (real or true) electric power provided to the equipment.

induction motor   A common alternating current (AC) motor having its primary winding, to which an electric power source is connected, on the stator (the stationary part of the motor set inside the casing) and a secondary winding on the rotor (the rotating part of the motor).

inductive load   An electrical load (e.g., induction motor) whose voltage and current are out of phase. True power consumption for inductive loads is calculated by multiplying the voltage, current, and power factor of the load.

inductive reactance   The opposition to the flow of an alternating current through a circuit that is due to inductance. The value of inductive reactance in any circuit depends on the inductance of the circuit and on the rate (frequency) at which the current through the circuit is changing (e.g., 60 cycles per second).

in phase   Being in the same phase; used to indicate that the voltages (phase angles) from two or more sources of electric power are synchronized (matched) with respect to one another—i.e., the peaks and valleys of the voltages of two power sources are occurring simultaneously.

REAL ESTATE APPLICATION: Two or more sources of power must be in phase with one another before they can provide power to a common circuit (share an electrical load). The diagram (next page) shows the incoming generator voltage slightly out of phase with the voltage of the "bus" (the electrical distribution conduit to which the utility is currently providing power), but over time, the voltages become synchronous (in phase). Modern electrical switching devices provide for automatic phase synchronization of two sources of electric power and switching from one power source to another.

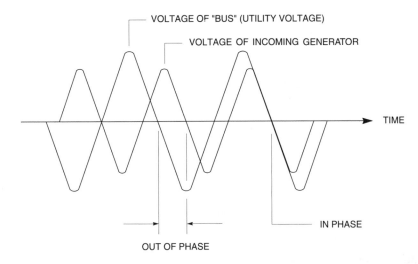

VOLTAGE OF "BUS" (UTILITY VOLTAGE)

VOLTAGE OF INCOMING GENERATOR

TIME

IN PHASE

OUT OF PHASE

instant-start fluorescent lamp An electric-discharge lamp, usually with single-pin base connections, that is started by application of a high voltage across the lamp without preheating of the electrodes. Instant start refers to the type of *ballast* (which see).

Institute of Electrical and Electronic Engineers (IEEE) An international professional society that issues its own electrical and electronic standards and is a member of the American National Standards Institute (ANSI) and the International Standards Organization (ISO).

Insulated Cable Engineers Association (ICEA) A professional society of cable manufacturing engineers who develop nationally recognized standard specifications and tests for insulated wire and cable.

insulation A nonconducting material (i.e., having good *dielectric* properties) which is used to protect and separate close electrical components and prevent the passage of current between conductors. Air, rubber, and porcelain are examples of good insulators.

insulation resistance A measure of the opposition offered to current by an insulating material. Insulation resistance is adversely affected by the presence of moisture and dirt, which can cause the insulation to deteriorate.

intercommunication system An audio communication system within a building or group of buildings with a microphone for speaking and a loudspeaker for listening at each of two or more locations; known familiarly as an *intercom*.

interference Electrical or electromagnetic disturbances that induce undesirable responses in electronic equipment, as the effect of atmospheric electrical discharges or static.

internet A loose connection of computer links which has developed into an information superhighway or network of networks—the *world wide web*.

intranet A private intercompany version of the internet that manages links between data sources.

inverter   A device that converts direct current (DC) to alternating current (AC), mechanically or electronically.

jack   A low-voltage receptacle into which a plug is inserted to make electrical contact between communications circuits.

jumper   A wire used to route a circuit by linking two cross-connect termination points; typically, the temporary rerouting and connection of an electric power source to an electrical load by bypassing a more-permanent electric circuit due to failure of a component or loss of continuity in that circuit.

junction box   A metal box inside which electric wires are connected together. The junction box serves as a common point where wiring or cables serving respective components (light fixtures, wall receptacles) can be joined and protected. Plastic junction boxes may be acceptable in some (mostly residential) applications.

> REAL ESTATE APPLICATION: In commercial applications, junction boxes are typically installed above ceilings for lighting circuits, outlets, and other 110-volt equipment circuits.

kilovolt-ampere (kva)   A unit of apparent voltage of an electric circuit equivalent to 1,000 volt-amperes; the product of the voltage of an electric circuit and the current flowing through the circuit (divided by 1,000). The formula for converting to kva is: [voltage (E) × amperage (I)] ÷ 1,000 = kilovolt-amperes (kva).

> REAL ESTATE APPLICATION: Due to the relatively high figure (product of voltage × amperage) that results when dealing with commonly used voltages, kilovolt-amperes rather than volt-amperes are used in expressing the power of a circuit. The kva of a circuit represents all of the active power provided to the circuit. This power includes useful power consumed within the circuit as well as power wasted as a result of the system's power factor. Depending on the power factor of an electrical system, the electric utility provider will bill the customer based on either kilowatt (kw) consumption or kilovolt-ampere (kva) consumption multiplied by a specified rate.

kilowatt (kw)   A unit of electric *power* equal to 1,000 watts, also equivalent to approximately 1.34 horsepower. The standard measure of electric power is watts or kilowatts. The formula for converting to kw is: voltage × amperage × power factor = watts (power consumed) ÷ 1,000 = kw.

> REAL ESTATE APPLICATION: Conversion to kilowatts is useful in computing the electricity consumption of equipment. As an example, the electric power consumed by a copier machine rated at 15 amps operating on a 110-volt circuit with a power factor (pf) of 90% would be computed as follows:
>
> 15 amps × 110 volts × .9 (pf) = 1,485 watts or 1.48 kw.

kilowatt-hour (kwh)   A unit of energy equal to 1,000 watts expended for a period of one hour; 1,000 watt-hours. Electric utility providers typically bill customers on a kilowatt-hour basis.

> REAL ESTATE APPLICATION: Real estate managers can control lighting costs if they know how much power different types of lights use. Since electricity consumption is billed in kilowatt-hours, this information can be used along with bulb wattage, time, and other factors to calculate electricity consumption and costs of operating 100 light fixtures, 10 hours a day, 5 days a week, 52 weeks a year. If each fixture consumes 65 watts of electricity, the aver-

age billing rate for the electric utility company is $.10/kwh, and the average power factor (pf) for the building is 90%, the calculations would be:

100 fixtures × 65 watts × .9 (pf) = 5,850 watts ÷ 1,000 = 5.85 kw

5.85 kw × (10 hrs/day × 5 days/wk × 52 wks/yr) =

    5.85 × 2,600 = 15,210 kwh

15,210 kwh × $.10/kwh = $1,521/year.

knockout A partially punched-out circular area in the surface of an electrical outlet, junction, or panel box which can be easily removed with a hammer or screwdriver in order to provide access for a cable.

lamp The illumination component of a light fixture in which electrical energy is converted into visible light; sometimes commonly referred to as a *light bulb*.

lens An integral component of a light fixture which serves to reduce glare and diffuse (scatter) the light emitted by the fixture's lamps. The lens also protects the lamps and other components of the light fixture from dust and other elements within the given space. A light fixture's lens is typically flush with the ceiling surface.

level A term referring to the signaling (data transmission) rate of a network, measured in bytes per second. Level 5 cable has a higher data transmission rate than level 1 cable.

light diffuser See *diffuser.*

lighting controls A system of switches, control transformers, relays, and auxiliary devices for controlling a number of lighting circuits.

lighting panel An electric panel, typically containing circuit breakers, used to protect and isolate the branch circuits serving lighting fixtures. A panel containing operable switches for controlling various lights and lighting circuits within a space could also be referred to as a lighting panel.

    REAL ESTATE APPLICATION: A lighting panel serving ceiling mounted light fixtures in a large office building would normally operate at 277 volts and would typically be located in the electrical closet on each floor.

light level A term commonly used to describe the amount of illumination (*illumination level*) within a given space. (For more technical details about light measurement, see also *footcandle; illumination; lumen.*)

light loss factor An adjustment factor for calculating the reduction in illumination levels provided by a lighting system after a set period of time and under specific conditions of temperature, voltage, and ballast variations, accounting for aging of the lamp and accumulation of dirt on lamps, light fixtures, and other room surfaces.

lightning arrester See *arrester.*

limit switch An electric switch operated by the movement of a component of a power-driven machine that controls the electric circuit associated with the machine.

    REAL ESTATE APPLICATION: As an example, a limit switch may be an integral component of an electric motor actuator in the opening or closing of a fresh-air damper such that, upon reaching a predetermined maximum opening, a lever physically connected to the damper trips (open) the limit switch, shutting off the motor that controls the actuator that was opening the damper. A limit switch might also be used to slow down or stop an elevator car automatically at or near the top or bottom terminal landing. In this case, the limit switch acts as a safety device, opening independently of the device that normally controls movement of the car.

line drop   The decrease in voltage in an electric circuit resulting from the resistance of the conductor (wiring) in the circuit; also called *voltage drop*. The resistance in an electric circuit varies directly with the length of the conductor and inversely with the diameter of the conductor.

line fault   A fault in an electrical line or circuit, such as an open circuit, short circuit, or ground.

line loss   Loss of electric energy due to heating of wires by the current passing through them. The loss of power is proportional to the square of the current flowing. For this reason it is desirable to transmit power with as low a current value as possible to keep line losses from being excessive.

REAL ESTATE APPLICATION: Nominal voltage of electrical distribution systems as it enters a property is approximately 480 volts in larger properties or 240 volts in smaller properties. This relatively higher voltage (potential difference) is conducive to the flow of current and should therefore have less line loss compared to a 110-volt circuit transmitting comparable electric power.

line noise   Sustained high-frequency voltage intrusions due to static electricity or radio frequency (RF) interference from various sources.

line side   The incoming (upstream) side of an electrical isolation or switching device (e.g., circuit breaker or main electric disconnect switch) as opposed to the load or use side; the side of a device closest to the source of current (see diagram at *load side*).

line voltage   The value of the electric potential existing on a supply or power line, used in reference to typical or nominal electric supply voltages.

link   A communications circuit or transmission path connecting two points.

live   Connected to a source of voltage (electric circuit) which has continuity to its source of power.

load   A device that consumes or converts the power delivered by another device. Light bulbs, computers, copy machines, calculators, and motors are examples of electrical loads.

load center unit substation   An electric power distribution equipment application that uses a combination of a transformer and a metal-enclosed switch gear assembled as a unit.

REAL ESTATE APPLICATION: Modern practice in power system design includes extensive use of the load-center system of power distribution. In this system, power is distributed to the point of utilization at the higher distribution voltage. In the case of a large office complex or industrial building, for example, the distribution voltage would be approximately 13,800 volts. The voltage would then be stepped down to the utilization voltage (e.g., 480 volts) by the load-center unit substation and distributed within the building by short low-voltage feeder lines.

load management   Control of electrical loads to control kilowatt demand

and kilowatt-hour consumption. Load management can be temporary or permanent. An example of the former would be shutting off a large motor for an eight-hour period while redesigning a building's lighting system is an example of the latter.

load shed   The manual or automatic disconnection (shutting off) of nonvital electrical components, devices, or equipment loads from an electric circuit in order to achieve a desired outcome, usually to reduce electrical demand; also called *load shedding.*

load side   The wiring and electrical components on the downstream (outgoing) side of an electrical isolation or switching device (circuit breaker or main electric disconnect switch)— as opposed to *line side* (which see); the side of a device electrically furthest from the current source.

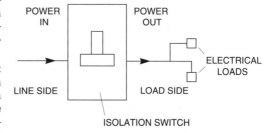

REAL ESTATE APPLICATION: When a building's main electric disconnect switch (circuit breaker) is to be opened (shut off) for inspection and maintenance of a main electrical distribution panel, the circuit breakers on the load side of the main disconnect switch should be opened first, before opening the main disconnect circuit breaker. The procedure of isolating the main electrical distribution panel in this way ensures that the main disconnect circuit breaker has a minimal flow of current through it when it is opened (i.e., no load). A malfunctioning circuit breaker of this size opened under a significant load (current flow) could cause severe arcing or, if people are present, injury or death.

local area network (LAN)   A user-owned and -operated, high-volume data transmission facility connecting a number of communicating devices (e.g., computer terminals) within an office, a building, or a complex of buildings.

local lighting   Illumination of a relatively small area without significantly illuminating the general surroundings.

loss   The portion of energy applied to an electric circuit that is dissipated and performs no useful work (i.e., wasted as heat); also called *electrical loss.*

low voltage   In accordance with the American National Standards Institute (ANSI) and the Institute of Electrical and Electronics Engineers (IEEE) standards, a nominal system voltage of 1,000 volts or less. This classification of low voltage pertains to the electric power generation, distribution, and transmission industry in general. Within electrical distribution circuits, utility providers consider 600 volts and below as low voltage. In the electric and electronic controls industry, low voltage is classified as 24 volts or less.

REAL ESTATE APPLICATION: In everyday usage one would not typically refer to a 480-volt circuit as low voltage. Low voltage is commonly used in referring to voltages low enough for domestic use, typically 120 volts or less. The term also applies generally to voltages below that required for normal operation.

lumen   The measure of light flux as a total output from a light source, used to measure total output of lamps or light fixtures. One lumen is equivalent to the light emitted from a uniform point source of one candle. Light fixture efficiency is measured in lumens/watt (lm/w).

luminaire   A complete lighting unit including lamp (bulb), reflector, fixture, and accessories.

magnetic field   The field created when current (electric charges) flows through a conductor (wire), especially a coiled conductor. The magnetic field completely surrounds the current that causes it and is perpendicular to it. Coiling a conductor (wire) around an iron material (core) increases this magnetic field effect. The measure (calculated size) of the magnetic field is referred to as *magnetic flux.*

> REAL ESTATE APPLICATION: Magnetism is a fundamental concept in the theory of electricity and electrical equipment operation. Just as two magnets repel each other (move apart) when their like magnetic poles are facing one another, movement of a rotor (the rotating element within a motor) is due to the motor's internal construction of coiled conductors, iron cores, and magnetic fields.
>
> Electricity is generated commercially by passing a metal conductor through a magnetic field. The unit is called a generator and may be driven by a steam turbine, a diesel engine, water (hydroelectric), or other means. The amount of electricity produced depends on the number and sizes of the conductors, their speed, and the strength of the magnetic field.

main disconnect   See *disconnecting switch.*

megger   A special ohmmeter for measuring very high resistance, primarily used for checking the insulation resistance of cables (electrical conductors); a *megohmmeter* (1 megohm = 1,000,000 ohms).

mercury vapor lamp   A gaseous-type lamp that emits a strong bluish-white light. A mercury vapor lamp is more efficient and has a much longer operating life than an incandescent bulb.

metal halide lamp   A high-intensity discharge (HID) lamp, similar in construction to a mercury vapor lamp but including various metallic halides in addition to mercury. These lamps have a longer rated life and are typically used in large open spaces (mechanical rooms or parking garages).

microprocessor   An ultracompact central processing unit (CPU) of a computer. Microprocessors incorporate hundreds of thousands of computer elements on a single chip. They make small computer drives work. Microprocessors are also used in numerous types of automated processes, such as *energy management systems,* handheld calculators, and automobile engine operation.

mil   A unit of measure commonly used to express the diameter of wire or the thickness of sheet metal or similar material. One mil equals one-thousandth of an inch. A 4-mil wire has a diameter of $^4/_{1000}$ in.

milliampere   One thousandth of an ampere; 0.001 ampere.

modem   A conversion device installed in pairs at each end of an analog-communications line. The modem at the transmitting end modulates digital signals received locally from a computer or terminal; the modem at the receiving end demodulates the incoming analog signal, converting it back to its original (digital) format and passes it to the destination device (computer terminal).

molded case circuit breaker   A relatively light, fast-acting, nonadjustable electric circuit breaker assembled as an integral unit in a supporting and enclosing housing of insulating materials. The molded case circuit breaker is used for circuit protection—e.g., overload protection for conductors as well as short-circuit protection for motors, control equipment, lighting circuits, heating circuits, and the like.

monitor   A *cathode-ray tube (CRT)* used for display of data or images, as a television screen or a computer terminal.

motion detector, motion sensor   See *occupancy sensor.*

motor   A machine that converts electrical energy into mechanical power by means of a rotating shaft used to drive a mechanical device (air handler, conveyor belt, machine tool, etc.).

motor control center (MCC)   A single metal-enclosed assembly that centrally consolidates and houses a number of motor controllers and sometimes other devices such as switches and control devices.

REAL ESTATE APPLICATION: The various groups of motor controllers that control the various mechanical systems (e.g., HVAC components) within a building are typically housed in a common motor control center (MCC) within the mechanical room. A building operator can control (start and stop) many building system motors from the MCC panel.

motor controller   A device that controls the electric power delivered to a motor or a group of motors.

REAL ESTATE APPLICATION: Motor controllers serve various purposes such as crisp operation (closing and opening) of motor start and stop contacts, prevention of electrical overloads, automatic reset of motor start functions, protection from low-voltage conditions, etc.

motor generator set   A device that uses an alternating current motor to drive a direct current generator; also called *MG set.* The input is typically alternating current from a building's power supply and the output is often direct current to an elevator motor.

REAL ESTATE APPLICATION: MG sets were supplied to relatively older buildings to operate elevators that required direct current. In newer buildings, rectifiers convert alternating current to direct current.

National Electrical Code (NEC)   A nationally accepted guide to the safe installation of wiring and equipment established by the National Fire Protection Association (NFPA 70). The Code is not intended to be a design specification; instead, it provides guidelines for safeguarding people and buildings and their contents from hazards arising out of the use of electricity for lighting, heating, or other purposes. In order to meet insurance and municipality requirements, wiring must conform to NEC rules, which are based on fire underwriters' requirements for interior electric wiring.

National Electrical Manufacturers Association (NEMA)   A trade association of companies that manufacture machinery and related equipment for the generation, transmission, distribution, control, and use of electricity. NEMA develops standards of product quality, electrical performance, testing, and dimensional uniformity for electric motors, distribution transformers, lamps, ballasts, light fixtures, and the like.

network   In computer terminology, a series of computer terminals (stations) connected by communications cabling. The network allows various users to share common information from each terminal. In electrical utility transmission and distribution terminology, a series of interconnected electrical conductors consisting of high-voltage feeders, step-down transformers, and protective devices.

neutral   The conductor circuit that is normally grounded or at zero voltage difference to the ground (*neutral conductor, neutral wire*). In a three-phase, three-wire electric circuit, a conductor whose voltage difference between itself and each of the other two conductors is equal in magnitude and equally spaced in phase.

noise   In a cable or circuit, any extraneous sound or signal that tends to interfere with the sound or signal normally present in or passing through the system. Electrical noise can disturb the operations of microprocessor-based equipment. (See also *line noise.*)

nominal   A standard electrical voltage rating of a given circuit. The *nominal voltage* designation is not necessarily equal to the actual voltage of the circuit, which may vary depending on many factors.

> REAL ESTATE APPLICATION: 120, 240, and 480 volts are examples of nominal voltage ratings encountered in electrical applications of various facilities.

normally closed   An electrical control (e.g. magnetic coil contactor) that is open when electric power is available to the device. In other words, the electric power provided to the device keeps the circuit open (off). Upon a loss of electric power, the device will close automatically (spring- or gravity-operated closure).

normally open   An electrical control that is closed (continuity) when electric power is available to the device. In other words, the electric power provided to the device keeps the circuit closed (on). Upon a loss of electric power, the device will open automatically (e.g. spring- or gravity-operated opener).

occupancy sensor   A device, usually mounted on a wall or ceiling, which controls the lighting in a particular space by sensing the presence or motion of occupants within the space (*motion sensor, motion detector*). The occupancy sensor activates the lights as the occupant enters the space and deactivates the lights after the occupant (or all occupants) leave the space. A timer is often integrated into the occupancy sensor to delay deactivation of the lighting circuit following the departure of occupants from the space (e.g., for 10 minutes). The delay ensures that the lights do not turn on and off frequently if the space is being occupied and vacated frequently over a relatively short period.

off peak   One of the two time periods in which electricity is consumed, the other period being peak. Off-peak hours are usually nonbusiness hours—e.g., 6:00 P.M. to 8:00 A.M. Monday through Friday and all hours on weekends. If electricity consumption in a particular area was constant during all hours and for all days, the efficiency of the utility providers would be increased. In order for the utility company to recover the costs associated with providing a relatively large amount of electricity during peak hours, and to encourage a shift of utility use from peak to off-peak hours, utility providers usually charge customers more per kwh for peak electricity consumption and less for off-peak consumption. Peak and off-peak classifications are typically associated with larger commercial (business) accounts and often do not apply to smaller commercial or residential accounts.

ohm   The unit of measure of resistance to the flow of electrons in an electric circuit.

ohmmeter   An instrument that measures the resistance of an electric circuit.

open circuit   A loss of continuity in an electric circuit such that there can be no current flow. The break could be unintentional or deliberate, as in a light switch.

outage   A complete loss of electric power lasting from several milliseconds to several hours; also called *power outage*. Outages are typically caused by power system faults, power line accidents, and transformer or generator failures.

outlet   In an electric wiring system, a point at which current is available to appliances or portable electrically operated equipment; a *receptacle* (which also see).

out of phase   The degree in which the voltages provided by two or more sources of electricity (e.g., electric generators) are out of sequence with each other. The term out of phase is specific to three-phase voltage where the voltage phase in each of the three legs or wires varies with respect to one another. Electrical equipment will not operate with two or more sources of voltage out of phase with one another.

    REAL ESTATE APPLICATION: Electrical machinery cannot operate on two sources of electric power that are out of phase with each other. An example would be the impact on a 480-volt electrically operated machine that has two sources of power (e.g., normal utility and emergency diesel generator) and is operating on emergency power during a temporary power outage. When normal power is restored, if an automatic transfer switch providing power to the machine transfers to the normal source of power instantaneously, the voltage sources may be out of phase and result in the protective tripping (shutdown) of the equipment. (Compare *in phase;* see also the accompanying diagram.)

output   The useful power or signal delivered by a circuit or device.

overcurrent protection   A device in an electric circuit that prevents damage to electrical systems and equipment resulting from excessive current; also called *overcurrent device. (Fuses* and *circuit breakers* are examples.) These devices interrupt the flow of current (open the circuit) instantaneously or over a prolonged period, depending on the degree of overcurrent.

overload   Excess voltage, current, or power in an electric circuit or device beyond that for which it was designed.

overload relay   A thermal device that protects an electric machine (e.g., motor) against overloads by automatically opening when the temperature or current exceeds a predetermined safe value; also called *overload protection* or *thermal overload relay.* After tripping, the relay protector continues to sense the heat from the motor windings and does not allow the motor to operate until it has cooled. Typically, the overload relay needs to be reset manually before restarting the motor. (See also *thermal cutout.*)

pancake molding   A flat piece of lengthwise-slotted flexible rubber material used to house electrical equipment and appliance cords or low-voltage communication or telephone cable. The pancake molding serves as a wire manager when cords or cables are laid across floor surfaces such as office carpeting.
It typically comes in rolled-up sections.

panelboard   In an electrical installation, a group of overcurrent protective
devices, buses, and in some cases switches, used to control electric circuits,
designed for assembly into a single panel or group of panels that are housed
in a cabinet and accessible only from the front; sometimes called, simply,
panel.

parabolic aluminized reflector (PAR) lamp   See *reflector lamp.*

parabolic light fixture   A very common recessed ceiling fixture (sizes 2' ×
2' or 2' × 4') used for general office
lighting applications. The parabolic fixture is comprised of one or more fluorescent lamps, a lighting ballast, and a
reflective grid whose slots run in a
crisscross pattern perpendicular to the
ceiling surface. The numerous square
openings formed by the reflective grid
are often referred to as *cubes* or *cells.*

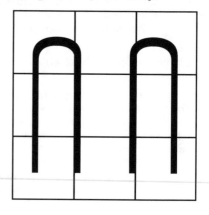

parabolic light fixture (2-U lamp, 9 cell)

parallel circuit   A circuit in which
identical voltage is presented to all
components, and the current divides
among the components according to
their resistances or impedances. In a
parallel circuit, all of the electrical
loads (equipment) are connected across the voltage source. If continuity is disrupted in one of the conductors (wires) due to tripping of a circuit breaker or
opening of a switch, the remaining conductors and their loads retain their continuity. Parallel circuits are used
almost exclusively for electrical
distribution.

parallel operation   A situation
in which two or more electric
generators operate simultan
eously at similar voltage, frequency, etc., sharing an electrical
load.

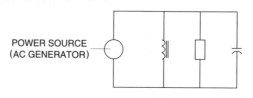

parallel circuit

peer-to-peer   A unique network architecture and operating concept in an
energy management system (EMS) or other direct digital control (DDC) system. An automated peer-to-peer network allows the various subpanels (field
panels) of a DDC system to communicate with one another directly without
communicating through a common front end (main) terminal.

phase   The position of a wave form of an alternating current in relation to
the start of a cycle, measured in *electrical degrees,* with 360° corresponding to

one complete cycle. (See *frequency* diagram; also compare *in phase* and *out of phase.*)

REAL ESTATE APPLICATION: Alternating current (AC), as opposed to direct current (DC), has more than one phase in most large electrical equipment applications. For each conductor, the applied voltage will cycle from a value of zero, to a maximum positive value, back to zero, to a maximum negative value, then back to zero (one complete cycle) for a specific time frame. At a moment in time, in a three-phase, 60-Hz commercial wiring circuit, there will be three conductors (wires) each having voltage equidistant in value with respect to one another—i.e., 120° apart (360° ÷ 3 phases = 120°).

photoelectric cell An electronic sensor that detects changes in ambient light levels or interruption of a light beam, used to activate various measuring and control devices.

REAL ESTATE APPLICATION: Photoelectric cells are used to control outdoor parking lot illumination, switching lights on and off by responding to nighttime and daytime ambient light conditions, respectively.

plenum cable Cable specifically designed for use in a plenum (the space above a suspended ceiling used to circulate air back to the heating or cooling system in a building). Also, cable or wiring that is UL-listed as having adequate fire resistance and low smoke-producing characteristics for installation without conduit in ducts, plenums, and other spaces used for ventilation air (i.e., meets requirements of UL 910-81); *plenum-rated cable.*

REAL ESTATE APPLICATION: Plenum cable has insulated conductors (wires), often jacketed with Teflon or Halar resin to give them low flame and low smoke-producing properties.

plug The male component of an electrical connection.

polarity The direction of current (electron) flow. The positive and negative sides of a terminal (electrical connection) determine the direction of current flow; current flows from the negative to the positive side of the terminal.

polarized receptacle An electrical outlet having its contacts arranged so that the plug on an electric cord can be inserted in only one orientation.

pole One of two terminals of an electric cell, battery, or dynamo which are oriented such that if connected by an external conductor (wire), a current will flow from the pole having the higher potential (negative) to the other (positive) pole. Also, a solid piece of iron affixed to the inside of a motor or generator, around which wire conductors are wrapped, creating a magnetic field—a fundamental concept of electricity. (See also *magnetic field.*)

REAL ESTATE APPLICATION: The number of poles determines the speed of the motor (based on a given frequency). Two iron cores on opposite sides of a motor represent one (set) pole.

port A computer interface capable of attaching to a modem for communicating with a remote terminal. An entrance to or exit from a network; an access point for data entry or exit.

potential difference The difference in electric potential between two points that represents the amount of work (energy released) in the transfer of a unit quantity of electricity from one point to the other. That which causes electric current (electrons) to flow, commonly referred to as *voltage.* (Its international standard unit of measurement is the *volt.*) Potential difference can be thought of as a difference in pressure within a circuit.

potentiometer   An instrument consisting of a wire-wound coil, used as a measuring controlling device in various automated control circuits, that functions by sensing small changes in electrical resistances; also referred to as a *pot.*

power   In an AC circuit, the voltage of the circuit multiplied by the current flowing through the circuit multiplied by the power factor of the circuit. (Power = voltage × current × power factor; P = E × I × pf.) Power (electrical energy) is measured in *watts* or kilowatts. (See *kilowatt* for an example of converting power consumed by an electrical component into kilowatts.)

power cable   An assembly of one or more electrical conductors in a protective covering (insulation or protective armor).

power consumption   Electricity consumed by an electrical component, measured in watts or kilowatts.

REAL ESTATE APPLICATION: Power consumption over time is expressed in kilowatt-hours. A component consuming 100 watts of electricity over a 24-hour period has a total power consumption of 2,400 watt-hours or 2.4 kilowatt-hours.

power factor (pf)   The ratio of active power (also called real power or true power) in an AC circuit, measured in watts, to the apparent power measured in volt-amperes—i.e., the electric power actually used by equipment compared to the total power provided to the circuit. (The portion of electric power that is wasted in a circuit is referred to as *reactive power.*) The pf of a circuit or system is a measure of its effectiveness in utilizing the apparent power it draws from the electrical distribution system or electric generator.

REAL ESTATE APPLICATION: The power factor of a circuit ranges from 0 to 1 or 0% to 100%. Because the higher the percentage the more efficient the circuit, 90% or .9 and higher are typically considered good target power factors to achieve in most building applications. The power factor of a circuit can be improved by installing capacitors into the circuit. The capacitors serve to release energy when inductive loads such as motors are drawing energy. They also absorb energy when inductive loads release excess energy. This concept is referred to as *power factor correction.*

With alternating current, pf = 1 only if the voltage and current are in phase (rising and falling in unison). The ballasts of fluorescent lights are a significant capacitive load (current leads the voltage). Motors constitute a major inductive load (current lags the voltage). In most buildings, the inductive effect of motor loads outweighs the capacitive effect of fluorescent lighting, resulting in the alternating current lagging the voltage. This causes an out-of-phase relationship between the current and voltage, resulting in a power factor below 1, which means part of the current performs no useful work, but instead merely builds and drains the electrical and magnetic energy fields once each cycle. A low pf is undesirable for three reasons:

1. The extra current forces the specification of a larger capacity power transmission network within the building.
2. The electric utility is also forced to use a larger-capacity power transmission network, subsequently including penalties in the electric bill for low power factors.

3. The extra current results in a direct energy drain by heat loss through-out the circuit.

power loss   The difference between the total power delivered to a circuit, cable, or device and the power delivered by that device to a load.

power supply   The voltage and current source for an electric circuit. A battery and an electric utility service are examples of power supplies.

primary power   Electric power typically provided by a local utility power company, but which could be provided by an on-site generator.

primary service   High-voltage (above 600v) service provided by the electric utility company.

primary voltage   The voltage supplied to the inlet or primary winding of an electrical transformer.

primary winding   The first coil of wire wrapped around an iron core in an electrical transformer to which electricity is supplied; also called *primary coil.* The primary winding produces a flux which is transferred to the secondary winding of the transformer. The number of turns and the ratio of turns of wire around each iron core of the primary and secondary windings of a transformer determine the output voltage of the transformer and whether it is a step-up or step-down transformer. (See also *transformer* and accompanying diagram.)

punch-down block   A two-foot piece of metal and plastic that allows the connection of telephone wiring coming from two remote points; also called *quick-connect block.*

quartz lamp   A type of bulb that provides a very bright white light almost as quickly as an incandescent lamp. Quartz is used instead of glass to permit higher temperatures, higher currents, and therefore greater light output.

raceway   A channel for holding electric wires or cables, which may be buried within the concrete substrate of a floor or an integral part of a modular floor system; also called *cellular raceway.*

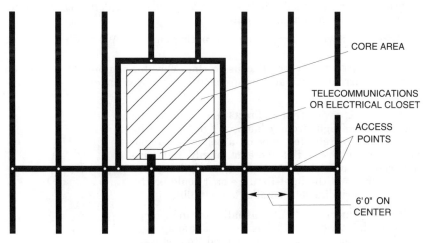

raceway (floor plan/cellular raceway)

REAL ESTATE APPLICATION: A raceway within the concrete substrate (also referred to as a *Walker duct* or underfloor raceway) allows the routing of wiring from the electrical closet on each floor to the floor outlet or other final (terminal) location. The raceway within the concrete floor will normally have strategically placed access points (e.g., cover plates) to permit routing, re-routing, and removal of the wires throughout the floor. When no access points are provided, access to the raceway requires mechanical coring of the concrete.

random access memory (RAM)   A storage device in the central processing unit (CPU) of a computer into which data can be entered (written) and read. The writing and reading of the data can be performed in any order desired.

rapid-start fluorescent lamp   A fluorescent lamp designed for operation with a ballast having a low-voltage winding for preheating the electrodes and for initiating an arc; it does not require a starter or the use of high voltage.

rated lamp life   The estimated useful life expectancy of a specific lamp in months or years. The rated lamp life can be the average life (when they cease to operate) of a large sampling of similar lamps or the average time when the light output of a large sample of lamps drops to a very low value.

reactance   The opposition offered to alternating current (electron flow) by capacitance or inductance within a circuit. The amount of such opposition varies with the frequency of the current.

read-only memory (ROM)   A storage device manufactured with predefined contents (special purpose programming) that cannot be changed by the computer.

receptacle   A device installed in an outlet box to receive a plug that will supply electric current to an appliance or other, usually portable, equipment. The permanently mounted female fitting that contains the live portion of the electric circuit connection; sometimes also called *receptacle outlet.*

recessed fixture   A lighting fixture set into a ceiling such that the lower edge of the fixture is flush with the ceiling. (See also *downlight* and its accompanying diagram and *high-hat fixture.*)

rectifier   A device for changing alternating current (AC) to direct current (DC).

REAL ESTATE APPLICATION: Because certain elevator equipment operates on direct current, rectifiers are frequently employed in elevator machine rooms.

reflector   A device that redirects and controls the distribution of light from a lamp or light fixture by reflection. The reflector may be a separate component—e.g., a 2' × 4' flat piece of highly reflective material installed between a lamp and the upper inside surface of the light fixture—or it could be the coating material inside a smaller lamp (bulb).

reflector lamp   A lamp (usually incandescent) whose back interior surface has a parabolic shape and a reflective coating, used with a lensed front surface to provide a desired spread of the light beam. Bulb

reflector lamp

types are differentiated based on their shape (e.g., PAR for *parabolic aluminized reflector*).

relay   A switch that consists of two parts (one stationary and one which moves). When a coil is energized by current passing through it, the movable part of the switch pulls in and closes the relay contacts. When the coil is de-energized, the contacts are opened by a spring. A relay is used to control a device with a high current rating from a remote point.

resistance   The opposition to the flow of electric current, measured in *ohms;* also called *resistivity*. A material that limits the magnitude of current in a conductor, converting electrical energy to heat energy. Materials of high conductivity, such as copper wire, are used in electrical applications to limit the resistance in a circuit. The greater the size (diameter and circular mil area) of a wire conductor, the lower its resistance. The standard symbol for resistance is *R*.

resistor   An electronic component designed to have a specific value of resistance that controls the flow of current. Resistors oppose the flow of current in a circuit.

resonance   A state existing in a system which is set into oscillation when a change in the frequency of electrical excitation causes a decrease in the response of the system.

rheostat   An adjustable resistor whose resistance can be changed without opening the circuit in which it is connected. A *dimmer* switch is a form of rheostat that varies the resistance of a circuit, thereby controlling the intensity (brightness) of a light.

ring topology   A cabling method (layout) whereby a cable is routed in a circuit (generally circular shape) around an office or other space. Terminal loca-

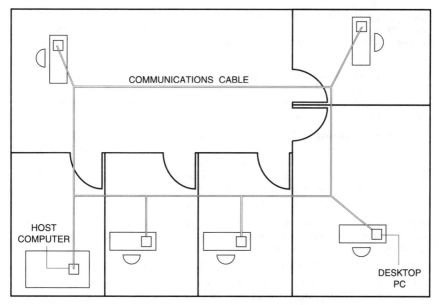

ring topology (network cabling)

tions (computers at each workstation) are connected to the ring at the shortest distance. The advantage of the ring topology method of cabling is the savings in labor and material (cable) costs during the initial installation. Its disadvantages are the lack of redundancy, which would maintain continuity in case of a break or opening in the circuit and difficulty in locating a break in the circuit. Also, the speed of data transmission in a ring topology circuit is significantly slower than that of a *star topology* (which see) having comparable components.

riser   In electric power, data, and telecommunications cabling, the main distribution cable segments that run between floors or sections of a building. An *electrical riser* extends vertically to distribute power to electric panels on the various floors of a building.

Romex   A brand of nonmetallic sheathed cable.

> REAL ESTATE APPLICATION: Romex cable is typically used in residential applications. Electrical code restricts the use of Romex cable in larger commercial applications where common return air systems are present; there, armored (metallic sheathed) cable is used almost exclusively.

rotor   The rotating element of an electric motor, which has current induced in it by the magnetic field action produced from the *stator* (stationary portion of the motor connected to the electric supply). The rotor is typically constructed of a laminated steel-and-aluminum core, with electrical conductors (wires) placed parallel to the shaft (along the length of the rotor) and embedded in the surface of the core.

secondary power source   Electric power, usually provided by an auxiliary generator, with an automatic switchover when the primary supply voltage drops below a predetermined level.

secondary service   Voltage service up to and including 600 volts. Although most voltages below 600 volts are considered to be relatively high, in electric power generation and distribution, any voltage below 600 volts is considered low voltage.

secondary voltage   The voltage supplied from the secondary (or outlet) side of an electrical transformer for use by an electrical load. Most electrical transformers are step-down type, therefore the secondary voltage is lower in value than the primary (applied) voltage.

secondary winding   The outlet or secondary coil (wire wrapped around an iron core) of an electrical transformer which provides a secondary (discharge) voltage to an electric circuit and electrical load; also called *secondary coil.* The discharge voltage is directly proportional to the number of turns of wiring around the iron core of the primary and secondary sides of the transformer. (See also *transformer* and accompanying diagram.)

semiconductor   A material having one component that acts as a conductor and another that acts as an insulator. The conductor junction offers a low resistance while the insulator junction offers a high resistance to the flow of current, thereby simulating the properties of a *rectifier* (which see).

series circuit   A circuit in which the electrical components are arranged end-to-end to form a single path for current. The current is the same throughout the circuit, but the voltage can be different across each component. In a lighting circuit wired in series, one open connection in the circuit would result in a loss of continuity in all of the lights.

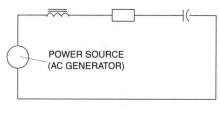

series circuit

REAL ESTATE APPLICATION: Series (single-path) circuits are not typical of electric wiring installations in buildings. Parallel circuits are the primary method of electrical distribution.

service switch One or several disconnect switches or circuit breakers whose function is to completely isolate the building from incoming electric service.

shield A sheet, screen, or braid of metal (usually copper, aluminum, or another conducting material) placed around or between electric circuits or cables or their components to contain unwanted electromagnetic radiation or to keep out interference. *Shielded twisted pair* (which see) is an example of cable that incorporates shielding material during its fabrication.

shielded twisted pair Two wires, usually loosely wound around each other to help cancel out any induced noise in balanced circuits. Multiple pairs of wires are contained in one sheath, and each wire pair is shielded by another sheath.

short In an electric circuit, a low-resistance path caused by an abnormal connection and resulting in excessive current flow and, often, damage; also called *short circuit.*

single-phase A two-wire electric circuit that provides power to relatively small electrical components and equipment loads. In a *single-phase circuit,* only a single AC power pulse is supplied. The power is pulsating in nature, cycling from positive to negative, 60 cycles per second.

REAL ESTATE APPLICATION: Most wall outlets in residential and commercial buildings are single-phase circuits.

single-phasing A condition that results when one phase of a multiphase (three-phase) motor circuit is broken or opened. When this occurs, the motor may continue to run but with lower power output and overheating.

single-pole switch In an electric circuit, a switch that has one movable and one fixed contact. (Compare *double-pole switch.*)

sodium vapor lamp An electric-discharge lamp in which electric current flowing between electrodes in an envelope containing sodium vapor produces a soft yellow-orange light; also called *sodium lamp.* Sodium lamps can contain low-pressure or high-pressure sodium vapor.

REAL ESTATE APPLICATION: Sodium vapor lamps are commonly used for lighting exterior areas or large open spaces such as parking garages. They are more efficient than mercury vapor lamps and are effective in areas where fog is a problem.

software A computer program or set of computer programs held on some type of storage medium (floppy disk, CD-ROM) and loaded into a computer's random-access memory (RAM) for execution. (See also *hardware.*)

solenoid   A usually cylindrical coil of wire which, when energized by electric current, acts as a magnet, drawing a movable core inward; such a device used to control movement of a valve or other mechanical device. (A valve controlled as an integral unit by such a coil is called a *solenoid valve.*) The valve subsequently may be repositioned by the action of a spring or other mechanism.

speed   The number of revolutions (complete turns) a motor rotor and, hence, a pump, air handler, or other motor-driven equipment, makes during a specified period of time, usually quantified in revolutions per minute (rpm). The speed of a motor is a function of the voltage frequency (cycles per second) applied to the motor.

> REAL ESTATE APPLICATION: The speed of a motor can be determined if the frequency of the voltage supplied to it and the number of poles (iron cores on the stationary part of the motor that have windings wrapped around them) are known. Sixty cycles per second (60 Hz) is a common electrical frequency. An electric circuit having a frequency of 60 Hz (60 cycles per second or 3,600 cycles per minute) will typically have a motor speed of 1,200, 1,800, or 3,600 rpm (3,600 divided by the number of pole sets).

spike   See *surge; voltage swell.*

splice   The physical connection of two or more conductors to provide electrical continuity.

spot relamping   Maintaining a lighting system by replacing lamps as they burn out. This is the most common practice, as opposed to scheduling the replacement of a group of lamps—i.e., *group relamping* (which see).

starting winding   A winding in an electric motor used for several seconds initially to provide the extra torque required to start the motor.

star topology   A cabling method (layout) whereby a cable is routed directly

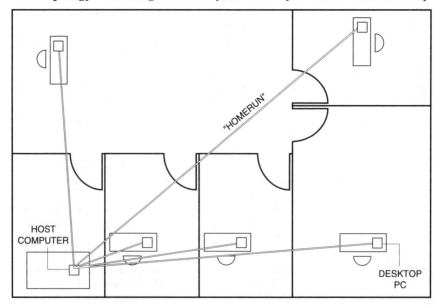

star topology (network cabling)

from the host computer *(homerun)* to each of the personal computers on the network. The advantages of this cabling method are the speed of data transmission, the redundancy of the network in case of failure of one of the cables or connections to a particular computer, and the ability to locate, isolate, and troubleshoot problems on the network. Its primary disadvantage is the higher initial cost for materials (cable) and labor to install the network system.

stator   The stationary portion of a motor that is set on the inside of the motor casing. The stator consists of iron poles (typically 1–3 sets) that are staggered in an equidistant arrangement and coiled with conductors (wires) that are connected to a power supply. Activation of the power supply to the stator coils generates the magnetic field (flux) that causes the *rotor* (rotating portion of the motor) to turn.

structured query language (SQL)   A computer industry standard method of writing and designing software that provides an economy of scale by only processing data that are requested in manageable blocks, rather than as a complete lump as in the simple client server. The SQL format allows larger data files to be manipulated more efficiently between networked stations where specific data and reports can be processed.

superconductor   A material whose resistance and magnetic permeability are virtually zero at low temperatures; a conductor that offers little or no resistance to the flow of electrons (current).

supervised   Used in referring to devices that are designed to monitor their own operations and send a signal when the condition of operation changes. Devices and components in fire alarm and sprinkler systems are often supervised. For example, a sprinkler valve that is tampered with will send a signal to its fire alarm system panel warning building operators that the position of the valve has changed. Similarly, if a wiring circuit in a fire system blows a fuse, a signal would be sent to the main fire alarm system panel warning building operators of the changed condition.

surge   A temporary and relatively large increase in the voltage or current in an electric circuit or cable; also called *spike, impulse, switching surge* or *lightning surge.* Surges typically last a microsecond to a millisecond and may be caused by lightning, switching of inductive loads (e.g., motors, transformers), short circuits, or power system faults.

surge arrester   See *arrester.*

surge protector   A device used to protect a phone system or the loads on an electric circuit from high-voltage spikes (surges) that might damage components (if a surge occurs, it is diverted to ground); also called *surge suppressor* or *voltage suppressor.*

switch   A device used to open or close an electric circuit.

switchboard   A large, single electric control panel, frame, or assembly of panels on which are mounted switches, protective devices, buses, and instruments, usually enclosed in metal and accessible from both front and rear; also called *distribution switchboard.*

switchgear   A stationary metal-enclosed switching structure containing switching, interrupting, and isolation devices and their associated controlling, regulating, metering, and protective devices; sometimes also used in referring to a *switchboard.*

REAL ESTATE APPLICATION: The switchgear for a large facility is typically located in the basement at the point of utility service entry into the building. It is recommended industry practice to take a switchgear out of service every 1–2 years for the purpose of a thorough inspection, cleaning, tightening, testing, and calibration of critical components such as circuit breakers, relays, instruments, etc.

synchronizing   The process of speeding up or slowing down a source of power (e.g., turbine or diesel generator) relative to another generator or common bus in order to run both power sources in parallel (i.e., sharing an electrical load).

system architecture   The layout of an automated system involving wiring and controls. The architecture of the system encompasses sizing and capacity of computers and panels, location of computers, field panels and components, etc. An *energy management system (EMS)* is an example of this.

task lamp   A light source positioned strategically for the specific purpose of providing light to a worker's task (work surface) area. The task light is close to the work and provides high levels of illumination with little wattage consumption.

REAL ESTATE APPLICATION: An example of a task lamp is a light that is permanently attached to the underside of a workstation overhead storage cabinet.

Telecommunications Industry Association (TIA)   A national trade organization of companies that provide information technology and communications products and services.

terminal   At the end of, as an electrically conductive element attached to the end of a conductor or a piece of equipment for connection to an external conductor. Also, any device capable of sending or receiving data over a data communications channel.

thermal cutout   An overcurrent protective device in an electric circuit, which contains a heater element and a renewable fusible member that opens when the current is abnormally high and thereby producing sufficient heat to melt it; also called *thermal overload relay.* A thermal cutout is in place to prevent overload conditions but is not designed to interrupt short-circuit currents. (See also *overload relay.)*

three-phase   An electric circuit energized by three alternating voltages (potential differences) of the same frequency but differing in phase by 120 electrical degrees. (In simplest terms, a combination of three single-phase circuits.) Three-phase machinery and control equipment is smaller, lighter in weight and more efficient than single-phase equipment of the same rated capacity. In addition, the distribution of three-phase power requires only three-fourths as much line copper as single-phase distribution of equal amounts of power.

REAL ESTATE APPLICATION: Three-phase induction motors are the universal standard of the electrical industry for running fans, pumps, and machinery of all types. A three-phase motor has three leads and a means for grounding, will start under load, and may be wired reversibly to run in either direction.

three-prong   An electric cord and attached plug with three prongs for insertion into a grounded electrical outlet designed to receive the prongs. Two of the three prongs are flat power prongs; the remaining round prong serves as the ground.

three-way switching   A wiring method that allows control of a light from two points.

three-wire distribution circuit   A common wiring method used in large buildings and facilities, this circuitry has the advantage of a higher voltage at entry (e.g., 480 and 240 volts) while still providing 120 volts at outlets for operating various equipment and systems operating on that voltage. Another advantage of this wiring method is that far less conductor material (copper wire) is required for the distribution and transmission of electric power.

transducer   Any device that receives one form of energy and converts it to another form of energy. A transducer may convert sound, force, temperature, or humidity to electrical energy, or vice versa. In other words, a device or instrument that converts an input signal to an output signal, usually of another form.

transfer switch   A device that switches an electrical conductor from one circuit (power supply) to another without interrupting the flow of current. (See also *automatic transfer switch.*)

transformer   A stationary electrical device that provides a simple means of changing an alternating current (AC voltage) from one value to another (e.g., from 240 volts to 120 volts). A transformer that receives electrical energy at a high voltage and converts it to a lower voltage is called a *step-down transformer;* similarly, one that converts a low voltage to a higher voltage is called a *step-up transformer.* The voltage is transformed by means of a *primary winding* and a *secondary winding* (which also see). The change in voltage (ratio) from the primary (incoming) side to the secondary (outgoing) side of the transformer is directly proportional to the number of turns (windings) around the primary and secondary iron cores.

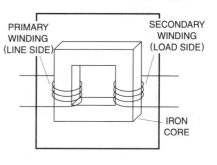

transformer

REAL ESTATE APPLICATION: Most electrical transformers are step-down type. A common example of a transformer in a building is one that steps down an incoming voltage of 480 volts to provide a power supply of 120 volts. Most relatively small transformers in buildings are air-cooled. Larger transformers that step down the electricity provided by a public or private utility to a building may be oil-cooled (immersed in oil).

transmission lines   The conductors used to carry electrical energy from one location to another. The three distinct functions of electric utility providers has historically been power generation, distribution, and transmission.

transmission loss   See *line loss.*

transmitter   In process control, a device that converts a variable into a form suitable for transmission; in a telephone, the device in the handset that converts speech (i.e., sound waves) into electrical impulses for transmission.

twisted pair   Electric cable comprising two insulated wires twisted together and having no common wrap. Also used in referring to multiple-conductor cable whose component wires are paired, twisted together, and enclosed within a single jacket. (Compare *shielded twisted pair*.)

two-breaker protection   An electrical operations and maintenance safety procedure that provides a means of ensuring the safety and physical well-being of maintenance personnel working on an electrical or electrically related system, machinery, or equipment. Two-breaker protection requires the opening or disconnecting of a minimum of two devices in an electric circuit (e.g., circuit breaker, switch, controller) for the purpose of worker protection from electric shock or mechanical harm. The two disconnecting devices should be off (open, disconnected), tagged with a colored caution, warning, or danger tag, and/or locked open with a tamper device (lock) in order to notify or prevent one from activating (closing, turning on) the device. Two-breaker protection is vital to worker protection, particularly, when an electrical system or electrically operated equipment (e.g., air handler) is controlled by a circuit breaker, switch, or controller that is in a remote location.

undercarpet power system   See *flat cable.*

underfloor duct   A type of electrical distribution system (raceway) of parallel ducts running under the floor (buried in the concrete slab). The ducts are usually spaced four to six feet on center. Cross runs and junction boxes are strategically located and run perpendicular to the parallel ducts. The underfloor duct system is similar to, but less comprehensive, than a cellular floor system. Such an arrangement will usually conform to most office requirements. (Compare *raceway*.)

undervoltage protection   An automatic device in a circuit that protects against operation under reduced voltage—i.e., when voltage in the line drops below a predetermined value—usually provided for electrically operated equipment in the form of magnetic coils and contacts. When the supply voltage falls below a predetermined value or fails completely, the magnetic coils cause the circuit to open (disconnect).

Underwriters Laboratories (UL)   A product safety certification laboratory established by the National Board of Fire Underwriters to test equipment which may affect insurance risks of fire and safety. Electric cords, fire-protection devices, and other equipment that is labeled *UL-listed* indicates that they have been tested by and meet the requirements of an Underwriters Laboratories specification for that type of device. ("UL-approved" is an incorrect usage.)

uni-block system   A type of uninterruptable power supply that is capable of providing power to vital equipment by drawing from one of three sources—the local electric utility, a battery source, or an emergency diesel generator.

uninterruptable power supply (UPS)   A system that connects office computers or other equipment to the AC power line through a device with an alternate source of power—e.g., batteries (static system) or motor generator (rotary system)—in standby mode. When the power line is weak or fails, the load is transferred to the alternate power source without any load malfunctions and without any user action. When the power is restored to normal, the load is automatically restored to the AC power line.

REAL ESTATE APPLICATION: There are several reasons to have an uninterruptable power supply system for a computer installation. A well-designed system will supply the computer with a constant voltage, frequency, harmonic content, and generally clean AC power. In addition, the UPS may be used as a buffer to prevent power loss while transfer is being made between two sources of electricity (e.g., normal utility and an emergency power source). The UPS also acts as an emergency source of power to allow for an orderly shutdown of computer equipment.

universal motor   A motor that is capable of operating on either alternating current (AC) or direct current (DC).

variable frequency drive (VFD), variable speed drive (VSD)   See *adjustable frequency drive.*

visual comfort probability (VCP)   The rating of a lighting system expressed as a percentage of people who will be expected to find the lighting system acceptable in terms of glare.

REAL ESTATE APPLICATION: The Illuminating Engineering Society of North America (IESNA) recommends a minimum VCP of 70 for office spaces and 80 where video display terminals are present.

volt (v)   The standard unit of measure of electric potential difference. One volt is equivalent to the potential difference across a resistance of one ohm when one ampere is flowing through it.

voltage   The force that causes electrons to flow through a conductor (wire)— i.e., electric potential (potential difference) or electromotive force (emf) expressed in volts. The standard symbol for voltage of a source of electromotive force is E.

voltage drop   See *line drop.*

voltage regulator   An automatic control device that uses electric sensors to detect a change in voltage in a circuit or electric generator output and then automatically adjusts the resistance in the field circuit to raise or lower the voltage. The primary purpose of the voltage regulator is to provide constant voltage to the various facilities and equipment sources consuming the power.

voltage sag   Momentary (less than two seconds) decrease in line voltage outside the normal tolerance of electronic equipment. Voltage sags can cause computers and other microprocessor-based equipment to shut down due to the lack of proper rated voltage. Sags typically are caused by the starting of heavy loads or when faults occur in the power system. They also can be attributed to utility switching or equipment failure. A similar increase is referred to as a *voltage swell* (which see).

voltage suppressor   See *surge protector.*

voltage swell   Momentary (less than two seconds) increase in line voltage outside the normal tolerance of electronic equipment. Also referred to as a *spike,* a voltage swell can damage equipment having insufficient overvoltage tolerance. Swells usually are generated by sudden load decreases, such as the de-energizing of heavy equipment.

volt-ampere (va)   A unit of electric measurement equal to the product of a volt and an ampere which is, for direct current (DC), equal to one watt, and for alternating current (AC), a measure of apparent power. (See also *kilovolt-ampere [kva].*)

voltmeter   An instrument used to measure the voltage difference between two points in a circuit (the voltmeter is connected across the two points).

Walker duct   See *raceway.*

wall washer   A ceiling-mounted light fixture located adjacent to a vertical surface onto which the light beam is directed.

> REAL ESTATE APPLICATION: Wall washers are typically utilized to illuminate artwork or signage on a wall.

watt (w)   The standard unit of measure of electric power in an electric circuit. One watt of *power* is equal to a current flow of one ampere (current) under one volt (voltage) of pressure.

> REAL ESTATE APPLICATION: The formula for conversion to watts in a direct current (DC) circuit is: Power equals volts times amperes (w = v × amps). In an alternating current (AC) circuit, the formula is: Power equals volts times amperes times power factor (w = v × amps × pf).
>
> Since power factor in an AC circuit is typically close to 0.9, the value in watts for a given electrical load in a DC or AC circuit is similar. Due to the relatively high figures that result when dealing with commonly used voltages (i.e., the product of volts × amps × power factor), the kilowatt (kw) rather than the watt is typically used in expressing the power of a circuit.

watt-hour meter   An instrument that measures electrical energy within a circuit over a given time period, used in residential and commercial applications to determine the monthly charge for electric service. The watt-hour meter has a rotating element, the speed of which at any time is proportional to the power being used at that time. The total number of revolutions over a period of time is proportional to the total energy consumed in that time period. The rotating element drives a gear train that records on a row of dials the number of *kilowatt-hours (kwh)* of electricity used.

wattmeter   An instrument used to measure the power consumed in an electric circuit, in watts.

wide area network (WAN)   A high-volume data transmission network that uses common carrier-provided lines, as opposed to dedicated user-owned lines in a *local area network (LAN).*

winding   The many conductors that are coiled around the iron poles of an electric generator or electric motor in which electricity is, respectively, generated or converted to mechanical power.

wire mold   A hollow, rigid, plastic or metal conduit, typically in the shape of a channel, used for housing electrical or communications-data conductors. The back side of the wire mold is attached to a flat surface (column, window mullion, floor baseboard) to route the conductors from point to point. Wire mold is used when routing conductors in a concealed location is not feasible (e.g., in an *underfloor duct*).

wiring diagram   A schematic drawing consisting of straight lines and symbols for electrical components which represents an electric circuit.

> REAL ESTATE APPLICATION: Wiring diagrams provide an effective means of

assisting electricians or other technicians in the investigation and troubleshooting of electric circuits and components.

Y connection   One of two methods of joining (configuring) the three wires of an alternating current (AC) generator; sometimes indicated as a *wye connection*. (See also *delta connection*.)

Elevators and Escalators

access switch   A key switch installed in designated elevator lobbies (usually at each elevator door frame) typically near or at the highest and lowest landings served by each specific elevator car; also called *elevator access switch*. Its purpose is to provide a means of automatically positioning an elevator at a predesignated landing under controlled conditions. The access switch opens the elevator doors on both hoistway and car sides when the elevator is prepositioned on the floor immediately below, permitting personnel safe access to the top of an elevator car in an emergency or for general maintenance.

annual elevator inspection   A detailed inspection of building elevator systems performed annually by an independent party (a state elevator inspector) having jurisdiction and authority in the location in which the elevator is inspected. A *certificate of inspection* (which see) is forwarded to the building owner upon satisfactory completion of the inspection.

> REAL ESTATE APPLICATION: Specific portions of an elevator inspection may have to be performed on an overtime basis (unless contractually negotiated) because the testing will disrupt elevator service to the building. An annual elevator inspection will entail numerous checks on various functions and devices, including the following: emergency stop and brakes, overspeed trip, overload trip, firemen's service, and the condition of hoist cables (traction-type elevators).

attendant operation   See *independent service*.

automatic elevator recall   See *firemen's service*.

auxiliary car operating panel   See *car operating panel (COP)*.

balustrade   The finishes on an escalator system comprising the handrails, decking or deck boards, interior side panels, and skirt boards.

beam detector   An automatic device that holds open or reopens elevator and hoistway doors upon detection of passengers entering or leaving. Beam detectors can also perform other automated functions such as initiating the closing of elevator doors after a predetermined elapsed time following the activation of the beam by passenger movement.

bottom car clearance   The vertical distance between the floor of an elevator pit and the lowest component beneath the elevator car platform when the elevator car is resting on its fully compressed buffers.

buffer   A device, usually consisting of a piston, oil, and cylinder arrangement, or a heavy coiled-spring arrangement, located at the bottom of an elevator hoistway (in the pit). The buffer is designed to stop an elevator car or counterweight from descending beyond its prescribed limit of travel.

cables   See *hoisting ropes.*

call station   See *hall call station.*

car   That part of the elevator in which passengers are transported within a building; also called *cab* or *elevator cab.*

REAL ESTATE APPLICATION: The Americans with Disabilities Act requires that elevator cars and entrances comply with specified minimum dimensions to ensure wheelchair accessibility.

car operating panel (COP)   An elevator operating panel that is mounted on a larger elevator car panel surface to the right and/or left of the elevator doors; also called *car station.* An elevator car will either have a single *(main panel)* or two (main and auxiliary) car operating panels. The *auxiliary panel* will house the same buttons and perform all of the automatic functions as the main car operating panel (e.g., floor call buttons, door open and door close buttons as well as alarm and intercom buttons). Other components might include a floor position indicator, an intercommunication system speaker, and the elevator inspection certificate holder. From an elevator passenger's perspective, the auxiliary panel will perform all of the functions that the main car operating panel performs. Additional manually activated devices and switches (e.g., the firemen's service switch, independent operation service switch, elevator power switch, elevator light switch, elevator ventilation fan switch) are located in the main car operating panel.

REAL ESTATE APPLICATION: The Americans with Disabilities Act requires the various elevator car control buttons to have raised markings, and operating panels must be positioned so they can be operated by a person in a wheelchair.

car position indicator   A numeric device that indicates the position of an elevator by displaying the number of the floor on which it is located; also called *hall position indicator.*

REAL ESTATE APPLICATION: A position indicator is located in the elevator car, usually above the doors or at the upper portion of an elevator car operating panel, to alert passengers to the floor on which the elevator is positioned.

carrying capacity   The percentage of a building's population that can be transported by all of the building's elevators in a five-minute period. Elevator carrying capacity for most office buildings averages between 12% and 17%.

car station   See *car operating panel (COP).*

certificate of inspection (elevator)   A certificate issued by the governing authority (state or municipality) upon satisfactory completion of an annual elevator inspection. The certificate is completed, dated, and signed by the elevator inspector and is typically placed in a holder or frame mounted on the surface of the elevator auxiliary car operating panel where it will be in public view.

REAL ESTATE APPLICATION: Alternatively, the original certificate of inspection may be kept in the building management office and a photocopy of the certificate posted in the elevator, or a notice may be posted indicating that the certificate is in the office.

cleated steps and risers The toothed configuration of horizontal and vertical surfaces of escalator steps. The surfaces are cleated in a male-female interlock-type arrangement so that people riding the escalators do not have their shoe surfaces drawn between the steps as they straighten out in approaching the floor landing.

coincidental stop A condition in which two elevators stop for the same hall call due to their relatively similar proximity to the floor from which the call was registered. Coincidental stopping is more common in relatively older relay-logic elevator control systems, particularly during peak traffic periods.

comb plate At the escalator landing, the section of the floor plate nearest to the escalator steps on which the comb teeth are mounted. The escalator step treads pass between the comb plate teeth with minimal clearance.

controller A vital component of electrical elevator systems designed to perform the following hoist (drive motor) operations automatically: starting, stopping, reversing, changing speed (accelerating and decelerating), etc.

REAL ESTATE APPLICATION: The elevator controller performs the power control function of elevator operation. In relatively older applications, it will control a motor generator (MG) set which, in turn, varies the voltage and speed to the elevator hoist motor. In smaller building elevator applications, a controller may be used in conjunction with a resistance-type control for deceleration instead of varying the voltage. In newer applications, a silicon control rectifier (SCR) performs the control functions of the hoist motor with more accurate elevator car motion control and increased energy efficiency.

counterweight A relatively large, heavy weight attached to the hoisting ropes (cables) of a gearless-type traction elevator (the other end of the hoisting ropes is attached to the top of the elevator car). The purpose of the counterweight is to reduce the lifting requirements of the hoist motor by counteracting the weight of the elevator car and passengers. The counterweight slides up and down its own guide rails located adjacent to the back wall of the elevator shaftway. It travels upward in the hoistway as the elevator travels downward and vice versa.

door close time The time required to fully close the doors of an elevator from a fully open position.

REAL ESTATE APPLICATION: The door close time for a standard 42-inch door opening should be just under 3 seconds. For the safety of passengers departing or entering an elevator, the door close time is usually set longer than the door open time.

door open time The time required to fully open the doors of an elevator from a fully closed position.

REAL ESTATE APPLICATION: The door open time for a standard 42-inch door opening should be approximately 2 seconds.

door operator A device that opens or closes an elevator door upon its approach to a floor, prior to departing a floor, or following a specified time period. An elevator car's inside (elevator) doors and outside (hall side or hoist-way) doors require door operators for opening and closing.

REAL ESTATE APPLICATION: Door operators are very important components for the efficient operation of elevators. Problems with elevator doors and door operators can significantly increase the response time of an elevator system.

double-deck elevator   Two elevator cars mounted one atop the other in a single car frame to provide passenger service to two floors simultaneously in order to increase capacity and efficiency without consuming more hoistway space. One car serves only even-numbered floors, the other serves only odd-numbered floors. Passengers enter the lower and upper cars from two sepa-rate lobby areas (one above the other) depending on whether their destination is an odd- or an even-numbered floor. Equal heights of lobbies, and floors throughout the building is critical to the design of this particular system.

down-peak waiting time   The average time measured from the activation of a down direction lobby call button on an upper floor (any floor other than the main lobby of the building) to the arrival of an elevator car as indicated by the start of the opening of its doors. (See also *up-peak average interval.*)

REAL ESTATE APPLICATION: The down peak waiting time will increase during peak periods of outgoing traffic, as when building occupants go to lunch or when they go home at the end of the workday. The down peak waiting time should average approximately 20–25 seconds.

drive sheave   A wheel-shaped component of an electrically driven traction-type elevator system around which the elevator hoist cables are wrapped in order to move the elevator car up and down the hoistway; the cables sit in grooves on the sheave. The drive sheave may be connected directly to the ele-vator hoist motor (gearless traction elevators) or through reducing gears (geared traction elevators). Steel cables run from the top of the elevator car up the hoistway, over the drive sheave, and down the hoistway to the counter-weight.

electromechanical control   See *relay logic control.*

elevator bank   Elevators and elevator shafts which operate as a group and are physically located in the same area of a building (adjacent shaftways).

REAL ESTATE APPLICATION: A 30-story building may have two elevator banks, one serving the lower 15 floors and the other serving the upper 15 floors. Often there is an overlap of one or two floors that facilitates movement of people between upper floors of the building without the necessity of a trip to the ground-floor lobby. Provision for such crossover is discussed under *interfloor service* (which see).

elevator cables   See *hoisting ropes.*

elevator capacity   The total weight of passengers (in a passenger elevator) or equipment and passengers (in a freight elevator) that the elevator is designed to handle.

REAL ESTATE APPLICATION: The rated capacity for an elevator car is stamped on the elevator car panels. Elevators have a built-in safety allowance with respect to maximum weight-carrying capacity—i.e., if the stamped maxi-mum weight capacity of an elevator is 2,500 pounds, the elevator might be capable of transporting 125% of this weight or 3,125 pounds before any safety devices would be activated.

elevator machine room For electrically driven, nonhydraulic elevator systems, a room on the floor above the highest floor served by the particular elevator bank, which houses the elevator operation and control equipment (hoistway motors, motor generator sets, control panels, selectors, and other elevator operating and safety devices).

elevator pit The lowermost space of an elevator hoistway (shaftway) extending up from the floor at the bottom of the hoistway to the lowest landing floor level.

REAL ESTATE APPLICATION: Personnel access to the elevator pit should be strictly controlled. (The only key to the area may be available only to the elevator service contractor.) Access may be required for routine or unscheduled maintenance of particular components or for removal of debris from the pit floor. The size and overhead dimensions of an elevator pit depend on the size and speed of the elevator. The pit must be large enough to accommodate the car frame and platform, counterweight buffer, elevator ropes, and traveling cable.

elevator recall See *firemen's service.*

Elevator Safety Code The common short form of reference to the Safety Code for Elevators and Escalators, which is published by the American Society of Mechanical Engineers (ASME 17.1-93) and prescribes standards for construction materials, emergency equipment, and safety devices to be used in elevators.

elevator speed The rate in feet per minute (fpm) at which an elevator travels through the hoistway.

REAL ESTATE APPLICATION: The speed of the elevator will vary depending on the type of elevator system. Naturally, taller buildings will have cars that travel at higher speeds than are used in small buildings. Passenger elevator speeds will vary from approximately 250 fpm in buildings of 2–5 floors to 1,800 fpm in buildings of 60 or more floors.

entrapment A situation in which passengers are trapped in an elevator as a result of a malfunction.

REAL ESTATE APPLICATION: Most entrapments occur when an elevator fails to level sufficiently to permit the safe transfer of passengers. In the case of severe misleveling, safety devices will override the door operators and not allow the elevator or hoistway doors to be opened. In most situations, entrapment is an intentional elevator system mechanism for ensuring the safety of passengers. When an entrapment occurs, an emergency call should be made to the elevator service company. Building engineers, operators, or others should not attempt to free passengers from the elevator by overriding door operators or other safety devices.

escape hatch A removable door located in the ceiling or side panel of an elevator; also called *emergency escape hatch.* An elevator escape hatch is usually well hidden.

REAL ESTATE APPLICATION: An elevator escape hatch is only used in extreme, unusual situations when elevator passengers cannot be removed through the elevator doors. (Contractors must not be allowed to open this hatch for use during construction.) The escape hatch would be accessed by an individual assisting in the removal of elevator passengers. Access through a ceiling hatch would be effected in the elevator shaft from the top of the elevator car; access through a side wall hatch would be effected from the top of an elevator car in the adjacent elevator shaft.

firemen's service   A two-phase elevator-related life safety system that renders elevators safer in the event of a building fire. *Phase I* consists of the automatic or manual recall of elevators to a designated floor (typically the first floor). The *automatic recall* of elevators is initiated by the activation of specified, predetermined fire alarm system components (e.g., elevator lobby smoke detectors). This function prevents building occupants from using elevators during a fire. It also prevents elevator cars from stopping (and opening) at a fire floor. During a fire, cars are automatically sent to the first floor (lobby level). A key switch in the main elevator lobby of the building permits fire fighters to recall elevators to the lobby level manually in an emergency if automatic recall was not initiated. (See also *firemen's key box* in Life Safety and Fire Protection Systems.) *Phase II* consists of elevator car operation by emergency personnel. A fire fighter's key switch inside the elevator on the *car operating panel* (which see) permits operation of the elevator in an independent (override) mode. The key switch gives the fire fighter independent (manual) control of the elevator and its various components (elevator doors, etc.).

floor plate   The metal plate installed level with the building floor next to (abutting) the escalator comb plate. (See also *floor plan* in Architecture, Construction, and Project Management.)

floor-to-floor time   The time it takes an elevator to travel between two contiguous floors (from one floor to the floor immediately above or below it) as measured from the release of the brake on the departure floor to the setting of the brake on the arrival floor.

freight elevator   An elevator used for carrying construction materials, tenant deliveries, and other types of freight, on which the operator and the individuals necessary for loading and unloading the freight are permitted to travel. (Compare *service elevator.*)

> REAL ESTATE APPLICATION: The capacity of a freight elevator is typically greater than the capacity of passenger elevators in the same building. Access to a building's freight elevator is typically isolated from the passenger elevators in a separate portion of the floor lobbies, and the interior is not finished (i.e., does not match building decor). While a licensed operator may be required to operate some freight elevators, most are unattended.

geared elevator   One of two general classifications of electrically driven traction elevator systems. It uses reduction gears connected to the elevator hoist motor to drive the hoisting sheave and control the speed of the elevator car. Geared-type elevator systems operate at modest speeds (e.g., between 150 and 350 feet per minute). They travel at higher speeds than cars in hydraulic elevator systems and at lower speeds than those in gearless electric elevator systems.

gearless elevator   One of two general classifications of electrically driven traction elevator systems in which the elevator hoist cable is wrapped directly around the hoist motor drive sheave without the use of any reduction gears. The gearless type of drive operation is used in higher-speed (from 250 to 1,800 feet per minute) elevator systems.

governor device   See *overspeed governor.*

group operation   The operation of a bank of elevator cars as a system; also called *group dispatching* or *group supervised*. When several elevators operate within an elevator bank, the performance of each elevator must be coordinated with the other elevators in the bank to provide effective service. Controls situated in a common elevator machine room supervising each group of elevators will dispatch elevators in a logical and efficient manner.

REAL ESTATE APPLICATION: Group dispatching is required when two or more elevators operate as a group. The system automatically coordinates the distribution of several cars to match the service of the entire group to the volume and distribution of traffic.

guide rails   Vertical steel rails permanently mounted on two opposing sides of the elevator hoistway (shaft) on which an elevator's roller guides and counterweight travel to move the elevator up and down the hoistway.

hall call station   The up and down directional buttons, finish plate, recessed wall housing, and miscellaneous contacts and electrical wiring that comprise the stationary wall-mounted device used to dispatch elevators to the lobby (floor level) from which the call was placed; also called *hall call buttons* or *lobby call station*.

REAL ESTATE APPLICATION: The Americans with Disabilities Act requires hall call buttons to include raised markings.

hall lantern   A small fixture in the shape of a circle or triangular directional arrow mounted on the wall adjacent to an elevator door frame for indicating visually when an elevator is available and the direction of car travel; also called *hall lantern/gong* when combined with an audible signal.

REAL ESTATE APPLICATION: The Americans with Disabilities Act required some changes to the location and operating characteristics of elevator hall lanterns and gongs. The lantern/gong should light up and sound one time if the elevator is traveling in the up direction. It should light up and sound two times if it is traveling in the down direction.

hall position indicator   See *car position indicator.*

hatchway   See *shaftway.*

hoisting ropes   The two sets of steel cables, attached to the elevator car at one end and to the counterweight at the other, which serve to support and drive (lift and lower) traction-type elevator cars in the shaftway; also called *elevator cables* or sometimes, simply, *cables*. Cables attached to the top of the car run up the center of the hoistway, over a grooved drum on the hoisting machine, and down the back wall of the hoistway, where they are attached to the counterweights. Cables attached to the bottom of the counterweights run down the hoistway to pulleys at the bottom of the elevator pit and back up the hoistway to the bottom of the elevator car. Each steel cable has the strength to support the elevator under full load; however, additional cables are required for the traction needed as the cables move over the motor-driven rotating drum. Most elevators have four to six cables.

REAL ESTATE APPLICATION: Elevator cables are inspected by state elevator inspectors, elevator service company technicians, and in some instances, a building insurance carrier. Inspectors look for broken strands or excessive wear. Replacement of an elevator's cables is needed approximately every six to fifteen years. Replacing these cables is relatively expensive, and the cost is often included in a building's elevator service contract if the contract is full service.

hoist motor   The electrically operated motor that drives the car up and down the elevator shaft. In addition, it serves the functions of starting, stopping, accelerating, and decelerating. The elevator car and counterweight are each connected to the hoist motor through hoisting cables and sheave or gear.

hoistway   See *shaftway.*

hoistway door   The door or doors between the elevator hoistway and the floor landing. These doors are normally closed except when the elevator is stopped at the floor for loading and unloading passengers.

hold for car call   The time elevator doors remain in the fully open position in response to a call registered from the elevator's car operating panel within the elevator.

REAL ESTATE APPLICATION: The hold for car call time to comply with ADA regulations is 3.0 seconds. The hold for car call time should be shorter than the hold for hall call time in most building elevator applications. The hold for car call time should be as close to or equal 3.0 seconds for the following reasons:

1. Three seconds is generally long enough for several people to get out of the elevator without rushing.
2. In most hold for car call scenarios, there is usually no one in the lobby where the elevator was registered, so the reaction time for an elevator passenger in the lobby should not be considered as a premise for adjusting the hold for car call time.
3. Elevator doors will reopen upon an attempt by a passenger to leave or enter the elevator car after the 3.0-second period.
4. Most importantly, increasing the hold for car call time, even for an additional one or two seconds, will adversely impact (increase) the overall elevator response time of the entire system.

hold for hall call   The time elevator doors remain in the fully open position in response to a call registered from a hall (lobby) call button. The hold for hall call duration does not include any time associated with the activation of any elevator door eye (beam), infrared, or proximity edge devices, or the time associated with any delay in actuating an elevator operating panel button by the passenger upon entering the car.

REAL ESTATE APPLICATION: The setting of the hold for hall call time should consider the number of elevators serving the hall call station. An elevator bank with six cars will require a longer hold for hall call time than one with four cars, due to the additional time required for passengers to walk from the hall call station to the two more remote (outer) elevators cars. The hall lantern device indicates which elevator is available next for the passengers, thereby giving them additional time to walk toward the selected car. A 4–5-second hold for hall call time is usually adequate for elevator banks with four to six elevators; longer times will adversely impact (increase) the overall elevator response time of the entire system.

hydraulic elevator system   One of the two general classifications of elevator systems, the other being *traction.* A type of system consisting of a relatively large steel *plunger* (piston) attached to the bottom of the elevator car, which moves the elevator car up and down in the hoistway by using a hydraulic system and associated controls. Hydraulic elevators move at speeds of 100–150 feet per minute.

REAL ESTATE APPLICATION: Hydraulic elevator systems are efficient. They are frequently used in low-rise buildings where the lack of higher speeds does not adversely impact the efficiency of transporting building occupants and visitors.

independent service   An option that removes the car from group operation and makes it available for operation from inside the elevator car (e.g., by a building attendant or operator); also called *independent operation* or *attendant operation*. Hall calls are bypassed for the car operating in the independent service mode. The switch for independent service is located inside the lockable section of the elevator car operating panel.

REAL ESTATE APPLICATION: An elevator car should be operated in the independent service mode only when absolutely necessary because it will significantly increase the response times of the remaining cars in the same elevator bank.

infrared detector   An automatic device that holds open or reopens elevator and hoistway doors upon detection of passengers entering and leaving the car; also called *infrared scanner*. Infrared detectors can also perform other automated functions such as initiating the closing of elevator doors after a predetermined elapsed time following the activation of the beam by passenger movement.

interfloor service   Elevator service for building occupants traveling from one upper floor to another.

REAL ESTATE APPLICATION: Interfloor service is not a special function of an elevator. In most buildings, interfloor service is available to occupants traveling from floor to floor in the same elevator bank. Interfloor service to floors situated on different elevator banks is more efficient if a common crossover floor is available for passenger transfer from one bank of elevators to the next, thereby eliminating the need to travel down to the main lobby. Interfloor passenger traffic is common in buildings whose tenancies include larger size companies that occupy several floors. A significant use of interfloor service can tax the elevator system and increase the response times of the elevator cars and the wait times of passengers.

landing   The floor (elevator lobby) level where an elevator rests (stops) for passenger or cargo transfer; also called *elevator landing*.

limit switch   A safety device, located near the upper and lower ends of the elevator hoistway, which protects the elevator against overtraveling. If an elevator car travels past the top or bottom landing (floor), the limit switch will trip, cutting off power to the driving machine and applying the service brakes.

load nonstop   An advanced automatic function of an elevator control system which prevents an elevator from stopping at hall calls if it is loaded beyond a specified percentage of capacity (e.g., 70%–80%); also called *load bypass*. The hall calls that are bypassed will remain registered (activated) for the next available elevator to respond to them.

lobby call station   See *hall call station*.

main car operating panel   See *car operating panel (COP)*.

misleveling   A situation during the boarding of passengers in which the elevator car floor is not level with the elevator lobby landing floor, creating an unsafe condition that could cause entering or exiting passengers to trip or fall, possibly injuring themselves.

modernization   The substantial upgrading of elevator equipment to increase system reliability and performance. The modernization can range from replacement of elevator controls to the complete replacement of elevator system components (controls, motors, car interiors, roller guides, traveling cables, etc.).

nudging   A feature of elevator door operation that causes doors to close at a reduced speed and sounds a buzzer after a predetermined time if the doors have been held open by the door open button or door edge safety device. The nudging feature prevents the holding for an excessive time period, which can increase the response time of a building's elevators.

Nudging is also used in referring to one of the elevator door safety features, which is required and available on all elevators operating with firemen's service capability. This feature permits fire fighters to control the opening and closing of the elevator doors manually. The basic concept of the nudging feature requires turning of a red key switch located on the car operating panel, which slowly opens the door; release of this switch closes the doors automatically.

overspeed governor   An elevator safety device that opens a safety switch and cuts off power to the elevator hoisting motor, initiating action that applies the service brake or other mechanism, thus stopping the car.

parking   The resting of an elevator at a specific floor while awaiting a registered call; also called *elevator car parking*. Elevator cars are often programmed to park in strategic areas to increase the efficiency of system operation and thereby decrease passenger response time.

REAL ESTATE APPLICATION: A building will often have several (or all) elevators programmed to return and park in the main lobby during up peak intervals (e.g., arrival of building occupants in the morning). At other times, elevators in a particular bank may be programmed to park on staggered floors (e.g., every third floor) to increase the efficiency of dispatching and pick up. Elevators typically park with their doors in the closed position.

pit   See *elevator pit.*

plunger   See *hydraulic elevator system.*

proximity edge   A mechanical reopening device that opens an elevator door if it comes in contact with a passenger entering or leaving the elevator car. In many buildings, these have been replaced with infrared, light beam, or other nonmechanical types of door reopening devices.

registered   The activation of a floor button on an elevator car operating panel or a call button on a hall call station, which will initiate the dispatching of an elevator.

relay logic control   A common method of elevator system control that uses electrically and mechanically actuated relays as its basis of operation; also called *electromechanical control.* As opposed to solid-state (microprocessor) control, relay logic control is characteristic of elevators built prior to the 1980s.

REAL ESTATE APPLICATION: Relay logic control systems take up more space than their solid-state counterparts. In addition, relay logic controls are not as capable of sensing and analyzing complex traffic patterns and responding with speed, precision, and dependability as are solid-state controls.

roller guide   A cylindrical bearing-type device, attached at several locations to the elevator frame (and in the case of traction elevators, to the counterweight), which makes continuous contact with and travels along the elevator and counterweight guide rails. Most roller guides consist of an automatic-adjusting spring tensioning-type system that makes minor adjustments for misalignments of the elevator's stationary guide rails to provide a relatively smooth ride.

ropes   See *hoisting ropes.*

saddle   The grooved metal plate (similar to a threshold) that forms an integral part of the door side edge of the elevator floor. The saddle provides a hard slip-resistant surface onto which passengers can step when entering and leaving the elevator.

selector   A vital controller device (system) that performs elevator group supervision functions and specific control functions of individual elevator operation. The selector or supervisory system automatically coordinates the distribution of several elevator cars in response to the demand and distribution of passenger traffic. Input signals to the various selectors include registered hall call (floor) and elevator call (car) button signals, elevator door position indicators, elevator car position indicators, etc.

service elevator   A combination passenger and freight elevator. Service elevators resemble freight elevators in use; but they can be operated with passenger elevators in group service and are readily accessible to passengers from the passenger elevator lobby area. Protective wall pads are installed for use during move-in, move-out, and construction. (Compare *freight elevator.*)

REAL ESTATE APPLICATION: Service elevators are often installed in office buildings that are not quite large enough to support a dedicated freight elevator. Service elevators are used exclusively for deliveries of construction materials and other freight. In this capacity, the service elevator will be operated independent of the building's passenger elevators rather than in group operation. In some buildings, a service elevator may be operated along with the passenger elevators during peak traffic periods. At other times, the service elevator may be operated independently.

shaftway   The floor-to-floor vertical enclosure in which the elevator car travels up and down, it contains the guide rails on which the elevator and counterweight travel, hoistway doors (lobby side elevator doors), switches, supports, other operating and safety devices, and space for traveling cables and other equipment; also called *hoistway* or *hatchway.*

shuttle service   Elevator service that provides transportation for passengers between two specific floors.

REAL ESTATE APPLICATION: Shuttle service can be temporary, as during evening hours to transport passengers to a restaurant at the top of an office building.

side panel   The interior vertical finish panels between the escalator skirt and the deck. Side panels protect passengers from the moving components at both sides of the escalator.

silicon control rectifier (SCR) motor drive   A relatively advanced form of motor control technology (introduced in the early 1970s) used in controlling an elevator hoist motor. SCR drives are an upgrade from the relatively older form of elevator control which utilizes a motor generator (MG) set and variable voltage control that provides variable direct current (DC) voltage to the elevator hoist motor. An SCR converts (rectifies) the alternating current (AC) power supply to a direct current (DC) output. An SCR drive offers superior car motion control at reduced energy consumption.

skirt boards   Vertical panels fastened to the truss adjacent to the escalator steps, running parallel to the length of the balustrade.

solid-state controls   A reliable, more-advanced form of elevator control technology used in systems of elevator automation; also called *solid-state integrated circuitry*. Solid-state control systems are capable of analyzing complex passenger traffic patterns and responding with speed, precision, and reliability. They represent the strategy for replacing the relay logic (electromechanical) controls previously in use.

> REAL ESTATE APPLICATION: Solid-state elevator controls use microprocessor components (printed circuit boards) to perform logic functions. Controllers are compact and can respond in milliseconds to complex traffic configurations that vary widely and change continuously. Programming of traffic patterns using the circuit boards and computers can increase efficiency and shorten elevator response times.

steps   The moving platforms, typically constructed of aluminum and steel, on which escalator passengers ride.

stop   Any lobby landing (specific location) where an elevator can stop for pick up or discharge of passengers or cargo; also called *elevator stop* or *floor stop*. The term is also used in referring to the number of physical stops made —e.g., elevator #3 made 58 stops during the last 20 minutes.

> REAL ESTATE APPLICATION: A floor served by six elevators has six elevator stops. A 30-story building with two banks of six elevators each, one bank serving the top 15 floors and the other bank serving the lower 15 floors, with three elevators serving the basement, has a total of 183 stops [(6 × 15) + (6 × 15) + 3 = 183].

time saver   A feature of elevator door operation that shortens the door hold open time after the beam or infrared sensing device has been broken and re-established. The time saver feature eliminates the necessity of keeping the doors open for their normal hold open times if passenger transfer is complete.

top car clearance   The vertical distance between the top of an elevator car and the nearest overhead obstruction when the elevator car is positioned at its top terminal landing (highest floor).

traction elevator system   One of the two general classifications of elevator systems, the other being *hydraulic*. These two classifications are based on the method by which the elevators are driven. Traction elevators are powered by electric motors. The term traction comes from the way in which the hoist cables are wrapped around a grooved wheel or drive sheave, which in turn is driven by the electric hoist motor, either directly (gearless elevators) or via reduction gears (geared elevators).

traveling cable   A cable comprised primarily or solely of electrical conductors (but sometimes including communication or video conductors), which provides the electrical connection between an elevator and a fixed electrical power supply in the hoistway.

truss   The welded steel structural foundation that provides a rigid support for the various components of the escalator. The truss generally consists of two or three sections (upper, lower, and sometimes intermediate) bolted together.

up-peak average interval   The average time between the departure of one elevator car from the main lobby and the next available departing elevator car, as measured during peak traffic periods—e.g., 8:00–9:00 A.M. as people arrive at work and 12:30–1:30 P.M. as people return from lunch. (Compare *down-peak waiting time.*)

variable voltage control   A standard method of elevator control for geared or gearless elevator systems. The variable voltage system controls elevator acceleration, deceleration, running speed, etc., regardless of the load. It achieves rapid starts, accurate stops, and higher operating speeds. Motor generator (MG) sets and variable voltage controls or silicon control rectifiers (SCRs) provide the means of varying the voltage to the elevator drive motor.

Architecture, Construction, and Project Management

abut   To touch or border on; in construction, to join at an end, as two pieces of base molding abutting one another.

acceptance test   A determination by an owner or owner s agent, an architect, or an engineer that the materials and services provided by a contractor conform with the contract specifications (or are otherwise acceptable).

> REAL ESTATE APPLICATION: An acceptance test would typically be conducted by a project engineer upon completion of the installation of a building *energy management system (EMS)* prior to final payment to the contractor.

access door   An operable door providing a means of inspecting and/or maintaining components housed within (e.g., water valve, sewer cleanout). Likewise, a removable tile, as an *access ceiling tile* or an *access plate.*

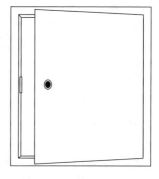

access door

> REAL ESTATE APPLICATION: In multifamily properties, such doors are usually located in common corridors for access to plumbing and other systems.

acoustical   Pertaining or related to sound; serving to aid hearing. Used in referring to an object or material that has the properties, dimensions, and physical characteristics associated with sound waves.

> REAL ESTATE APPLICATION: Acoustical ceiling tiles installed in commercial office buildings are textured such that they absorb sounds emitted by voices, ventilation fans, and other sources of noise to provide a quiet working environment.

active door   In an entrance having a pair of doors, the door to which the latching or locking device is attached; also called *active leaf.* Typically, the active door is the one capable of opening first or at all while the inactive door is held in place by a device (e.g., automatic flush bolts with a door coordinator and door closers) that must be released before the door can be opened. (See also *inactive door.*)

addendum   A supplement to the bidding documents issued to the bidders (contractors) by the owner or the owner's representative (architect or engineer or agent) prior to the submission of bids, for the purpose of clarifying, altering, adding to, or deducting from the specifications previously issued. An addendum could also be a written document issued to just one party (the bid winner or negotiated bid contractor) prior to the execution of a contract for the same purpose(s). In either case, the addendum becomes part of the contract documents. If there are multiple addendums, as may be the case for larger projects, they are typically dated and numbered sequentially.

REAL ESTATE APPLICATION: During a pre-bid demolition project walk- through of an office space, if a contractor discovered that there was 15,000 square feet of ceiling tile for demolition and removal, and the bid documents specified 1,500 square feet, an addendum would be issued to all bidders in order to clarify the amount of ceiling tile for demolition and removal.

add-on factor   See *load factor²*.

affidavit   A document completed, stamped, and signed by an authorized, competent individual (architect or engineer) and forwarded to the local municipal building code department, along with pertinent drawings and specifications, to certify that the design of a construction project complies with local and federal codes and regulations.

aggregate   Differing combinations of sand, gravel, crushed stone, vermiculite, perlite, and crushed furnace slag which, when mixed together with cement paste, form concrete or mortar.

alligatoring   Cracking of an asphalt surface (e.g., asphalt pavement, built-up roofing), paint, or other surface finish resulting in a pattern that resembles alligator hide. In the case of an asphalt surface, the cracking may be due to weather exposure of unsurfaced bitumen, poor quality base material, or inadequate drainage beneath the asphalt. In the case of a painted surface, cracking is typically due to shrinkage of a coat of paint applied over a dissimilar surface.

alternate bid   Referring to a specific portion of a project which may or may not be performed as part of the base project; also called simply *alternate*. Bidders would state in their bid submittal the dollar amount to be added to or deducted from the base bid (total bid price) if the alternate project is or is not accepted. If the amount required for the alternate work is stated *in addition to* the base bid, then the term "add alternate" is used in the bid documents. If the amount required for the alternate work is *included in the total base bid amount and will be deducted* from the base bid amount if this work is not performed, then the term "deduct alternate" is used in the bid documents.

ambient   Referring to the surrounding or background conditions (e.g., *ambient light, ambient noise.*)

REAL ESTATE APPLICATION: Ambient conditions need to be considered in the design phase of product specification and selection—e.g., the number and type of lights to use in an office space or the size and type of insulation to use in the walls of a particular room. Ambient temperature is a consideration in HVAC design.

American Institute of Architects (AIA)   A policy-making organization, founded in 1857 and headquartered in Washington, D.C., that fosters professionalism and accountability among its membership of licensed architects and promotes design excellence. The AIA also establishes guidelines for and publishes various construction related documents (e.g., AIA standard contract documents) that are universally accepted in the architecture and engineering management professions.

American National Standards Institute (ANSI)   An independent organization of trade associations and technical and professional groups that establishes and publishes recommended standards for products and materials.

> REAL ESTATE APPLICATION: ANSI publishes information regarding acceptable levels of finish, as the color requirements for painting a building's domestic water storage tank.

American Society for Testing and Materials (ASTM)   A nonprofit organization that establishes and publishes standard tests and specifications for construction, manufacturing, and other materials.

Americans with Disabilities Act (ADA)   A federal act which prohibits discrimination in employment on the basis of disability and requires places of public accommodation and commercial facilities to be designed, constructed, and altered in compliance with specified accessibility standards.

angle   An L-shaped structural steel component used for miscellaneous building construction applications such as lintels; an *angle iron* (also called *angle bar* or *angle section*).

angle of repose   The maximum angle above horizontal at which a given mass of material (e.g., soil, stockpiled aggregate) will remain without sliding; sometimes also called *angle of rest*.

angle iron

> REAL ESTATE APPLICATION: The angle of repose of the soil or other material that will be excavated at a building site must be known in advance so that building footings and retaining walls can be properly constructed to support (or be supported by) the backfill.

annealed glass   Glass that has been tempered by exposure to high heat and subsequent slow cooling as it exits the production stage. The *annealing* of glass helps to minimize and relieve internal stresses.

anodized aluminum   A common construction material used in exterior as well as interior applications. The aluminum is treated by electrolysis in order to provide a hard, noncorrosive coating on its surface. Pigments are typically added during the production process for coloring.

anticorrosive paint   Paint that is formulated with a corrosion-resistant pigment, such as zinc chromate, and a chemical- and moisture-resistant binder, used to protect iron and steel surfaces.

> REAL ESTATE APPLICATION: Anticorrosive paint can be effective when applied to a galvanized steel cooling tower, particularly since cooling towers are exposed to corrosive environments.

apex   The highest point (peak) of a structure (building).

appraisal   An estimate of the value, use, cost, or other attribute of a building and/or plot of land performed by a qualified professional appraiser.

architect   An individual who has been trained, experienced, qualified, and licensed to perform architectural services, including the design of buildings, analysis of project requirements, preparation and development of project design, drawings, specifications, and bidding requirements, and the general administration of the project contract.

architectural bronze   A metal alloy comprised primarily of copper and zinc typically used for ornamental fittings in door frame and window molding applications.

> REAL ESTATE APPLICATION: Architectural bronze is more common in upscale (high profile) areas of construction (e.g., the entrance to a building lobby).

as-built drawings   See *record drawings*.

aspect   The direction a building faces with respect to the points of a compass.

asphalt   A dark brown to black, highly viscous (thick) liquid material produced in the petroleum distillation process and used as the waterproofing agent in built-up roofing systems. In pavement systems, a similar dark brown or black cementitious solid or semisolid material mixed with an aggregate; also referred to as *blacktop*.

asphalt pavement sealer   A waterproofing surface treatment applied to asphalt pavement; also known as *asphalt seal coat*. (See also *slurry*.)

> REAL ESTATE APPLICATION: Asphalt pavement sealer is applied to pavement surfaces, especially asphaltic macadams, to protect them from deterioration caused by weather conditions (water penetration), ice- and snow-melt products, petroleum products (vehicle oils), or other damaging substances.

asphalt shingles   Shingles manufactured from roofing felts saturated with asphalt and coated with aggregate particles on the side exposed to the weather.

award   The acceptance by an owner of a bid or negotiated proposal. A bid award is usually confirmed in writing and can constitute legal obligations between the parties.

back check   The mechanism in a hydraulic-type door closer *(door check)* that controls (slows) the speed with which a door may be opened.

background noise   The irreducible noise level measured in the absence of building occupants. The noise emitted by HVAC air systems is typically the primary source contributing to a building's background noise.

balanced door   A door installed using double-pivoted hardware, which provides a partial counter-balance for ease of opening.

> REAL ESTATE APPLICATION: Oversized, heavy doors may have to be of the "balanced" type to provide easier operation.

ballast   Coarse stone or gravel used to hold down the roofing material (membrane, felt layers, insulation, etc.) on a building; the result is called a *ballasted roof*. (Use of *ballast* in lighting applications is covered in Electrical, Lighting, Data, and Telecommunications Systems.)

> REAL ESTATE APPLICATION: A ballasted roof offers the advantages of economical installation, superior tolerance of building movement, protection of the membrane from sunlight degradation and other weather conditions, and protection from debris.

base bid   The amount of money stated in a contractor's bid proposal to perform the work as stated in the owner's bidding documents or request for proposal (RFP). The base bid amount will differ from the amount actually paid on the contract if alternate work is added or deducted or if change orders are issued. (See also *alternate.*)

base plate   A metal plate used to distribute a nonuniform or concentrated load.

> REAL ESTATE APPLICATION: A base plate might be used to support and distribute the concentrated weight of a steel column installed below a machinery room as added support for a new chiller machine.

bead   See *caulking; stop.*

beam   A structural component whose primary function is to carry transverse loads. Beams are positioned horizontally as opposed to columns which are positioned vertically.

> REAL ESTATE APPLICATION: The term beam can be specific, as in describing the structural member that connects and is positioned perpendicular and horizontally between girders. The term can also be used generically to refer to various structural components (joists, girders, rafters, etc.), all of which are positioned horizontally and generally classified as beams. (See also the diagram at *skeleton construction.*)

bearing wall   A wall that is capable of providing support for the weight of a load imposed from above, as a floor, wall, or roof; also called *structural wall.*

> REAL ESTATE APPLICATION: Bearing wall construction is the most common type of single-story light-commercial construction. The ends of the beams, joists, and other structural members are supported by the walls which, in turn, transfer these loads to the foundation.

berm   A continuous bank of earth piled against a masonry wall or alongside a road. Also, an asphalt or concrete embankment used to control (contain) water.

bid   A completed, signed proposal or offer to perform work or supply goods as specified in a request for proposal (RFP), bid invitation, or contract at a specified cost. Also used in reference to the dollar amount proposed or offered by a bidder (e.g., "What was Jones Construction's bid?").

bid bond   A form of bid security executed by a bidder (contractor) and a surety (insurance company) and submitted with a bid in order to guarantee to the proposer (e.g., property owner) that the bidder, if awarded the contract, will complete the work in accordance with all of the contract documents. A certified check, cashier's check, and money order are examples of other forms of bid security.

bid documents   The various documents issued by an owner, architect, or others, all of which are considered part of the bid process. Bid documents include but are not limited to an invitation to bid, instructions to bidders, bid form, contract documents (including drawings), and addendums.

bid form   A short form, submitted to bidders as an integral part of the contract bidding documents, which is to be completed, signed, and submitted with the bidder's bid (response package).

> REAL ESTATE APPLICATION: The bid form identifies the project location and the name and address of the person to whom the bid should be submitted.

In addition, the bid price for the project is written on the bid form, including any alternate bid requests, and an authorized individual of the bidding firm signs and dates the bid form.

binder   Tar, cement, or other substance used to hold loose material together. Also, a component of an adhesive composition that provides the adhesive characteristics primarily responsible for holding two components together. (See also *insurance binder.*)

> REAL ESTATE APPLICATION: Binders are typically found in paints, plaster, caulking, and numerous other materials and products used in construction.

bitumen   A mixture of complex hydrocarbons obtained from petroleum or coal by distillation, usually in semi-solid form. Two basic bitumens are used in roofing applications—asphalt and coal-tar pitch. The bitumen is usually heated to a liquid state or dissolved in a solvent or emulsified before being applied.

blacktop   See *asphalt.*

blister   A convex, raised area occurring on a surface such as a pipe, a painted surface, or a roof.

> REAL ESTATE APPLICATION: The term blister is typically used when referring to raised areas on roofing membrane surfaces. Blisters occurring on a roof surface are raised and spongy and can vary in size. Blisters are the result of entrapped air and/or moisture (water vapor) expanding under heat from the sun.

block   See *concrete block.*

blocking   Pieces or sections of wood (or metal) used to secure, join, reinforce, or fill spaces between construction members or components (e.g., a door frame).

blueprint   A photographic process for reproducing construction drawings as dark blue lines on a light blue background; also called *blue line.* Blueprints are used by project managers, building engineering personnel, or a construction superintendent on a construction site.

boilerplate   A generically formatted document or portion thereof, often used in reference to legal documents such as contracts, requests for proposal (RFPs), leases, etc., which can be appropriately modified and issued to a company (vendor, contractor) as a matter of business.

> REAL ESTATE APPLICATION: In most cases, the legal language required in certain portions of real estate documents can be applied from one contract to another or one proposal to another. Thus, a boilerplate document is one that can be tailored to a specific contract, or client, or situation more efficiently than creating a new document for each new but similar arrangement.

bond   To join together, as with an adhesive. Also, a financial guarantee that services or work will be performed as outlined in a contract or specification—issued by a surety (usually an insurance company) to a third party as a guarantee against financial losses from nonperformance or default by a contractor or other principal. (See also *bid bond.*)

boom   A cantilevered or projecting structural member (e.g., beam) used to support, hoist (raise), or move a load. The boom is a vital component of a *crane* (which see).

borrowed light   See *light; side light.*

break   A lapse in continuity, as a gap in the surface of a wall; an abrupt change in direction.

brittle   Characteristic of a material that breaks under low stress (slight impact) and minimal deformation (bending, twisting).

broadloom   Seamless carpet woven on a wide loom, usually to 12 feet wide (range: 6–18 feet).

> REAL ESTATE APPLICATION: The term seamless refers to each roll of carpet manufactured at the mill. Naturally, there are seams in broadloom carpet that has been installed in areas where the distances between walls are greater than the width of the carpet run. Because few if any seams occur in broadloom carpet (i.e., wall-to-wall) installations, they are also referred to as "seamless" as compared to carpet tile installations which have many seams.

broken joint   Used in referring to vertical masonry joints that are staggered to provide a better bond and maximum structural strength.

broom clean   A term describing the overall condition and appearance of a room, floor, or space. It implies that the area is clear of miscellaneous equipment, tools, nails, screws, debris, construction dust, etc. (A broom clean room may have small amounts of foreign material such as might be left after a general sweeping.)

> REAL ESTATE APPLICATION: Prior to final acceptance of a construction project in a tenant space of an office building, the construction company should turn the space over to the building management or its cleaning service in broom clean condition for final cleaning. The term is also used in reference to commercial space leased in as-is condition, without additional tenant improvements.

building code   Rules and regulations adopted by authorities having appropriate jurisdiction, usually at the local (municipal) level, to control the design and construction, quality of materials, repairs, alterations, and the use and occupancy of buildings within the geographic area where the authorities have jurisdiction.

building inspector   A member of a municipal building department who inspects construction projects to determine if they comply with the requirements of the building department and the approved engineered plans and specifications. Also, a member of the building department who periodically (e.g., annually) inspects occupied buildings for violations of the building code. The term building inspector is also used in referring to an appointed government official responsible for enforcing building codes. This individual, usually called a *building official,* may review contract documents, approve issuance of building permits, inspect construction in progress, and approve issuance of certificates of occupancy.

Building Owners and Managers Association International (BOMA)
An organization of owners, investors, developers, and managers of office buildings that promotes the office building industry and establishes standards of practice and performance. BOMA publishes the *Standard Method for Measuring Floor Area in Office Buildings* (ANSI/BOMA Z65.1-1996).

building permit   See *permit.*

building skin   See *envelope.*

building standard   See *standard.*

built-up roofing (BUR) membrane   A continuous roof covering comprised of layers (plies) of felt paper alternated with thin layers of adhesive tars or asphalts and surfaced with a layer of gravel in a heavy coat of asphalt or coal-tar pitch; also referred to as a *tar-and-gravel roof.*

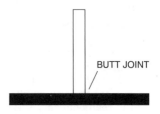

BUTT JOINT

butt joint   A joint in which the contact surfaces are cut at right angles to the faces of the components, and the two components are fitted squarely against each other.

caisson   A type of construction piling that is flared out just above the ground or other suitable stratum to give it a larger bearing area. *Caisson piles* are cast in place; a hollow tube is driven into the ground (to bedrock) and filled with concrete.

camber   A slight convex curvature of a surface, such as an intentional outward curvature of a beam to compensate for anticipated deflection and prevent sagging under a load.

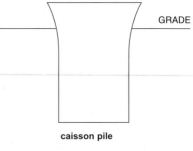

GRADE

caisson pile

REAL ESTATE APPLICATION: Paved surfaces are sometimes constructed with a camber to facilitate the runoff of water. Floors of high-rise buildings have a slight camber due to structural and loading considerations.

carpet pile   The loops or tufts (clipped ends) of yarn that stand erect from the base of the backing material and form the surface (top portion) of the carpet.

casement   A window with a sash (frame) that opens along its entire vertical length, usually on hinges fixed to the sides of the window opening.

casing   The exposed trim molding, framing, or lining around a door or window.

catch basin   A reservoir used to collect and retain surface water and typically constructed of brick or concrete with a cast iron grate.

REAL ESTATE APPLICATION: A catch basin can help to minimize problems associated with standing water. In particular, catch basins are used to divert surface water from paved parking lots.

caulking   A resilient mastic compound, often having a silicone, bituminous, or rubber base; use of such materials to seal cracks and to fill and seal joints to prevent leakage and/or provide waterproofing.

REAL ESTATE APPLICATION: Exterior caulking at the skin (facade) of buildings requires periodic maintenance. Due to exposure to weather (sun, cold, heat) and movement of the various building components, over longer periods of time, exterior building caulking will typically deteriorate and fail and need to be replaced. Caulking is also used in interior applications for waterproofing around fixtures (e.g., bathtubs) and tile (referred to as a *bead* of caulk).

ceiling suspension system   A grid-type system of metal members designed to support a suspended ceiling, usually with acoustical tiles. In some cases, the system is designed to also support light fixtures and/or HVAC diffusers.

cellulose   A naturally occurring substance found in dried woods, hemp, ramie, and various other plants and used in the manufacture of a wide variety of building construction products. (Cotton is almost 100% cellulose.)

cement   A material which, in a semi-solid to liquid state (in the drying process), possesses adhesive and cohesive properties and hardens in place; it is mixed with aggregate to form *concrete* (which see). The name cement is also applied to any compounded substance used to adhere materials to each other (e.g., asphalt, glue, gypsum, paste; also rubber cement).

cementitious   Used in referring to a material having cement-like properties or a portion of which is comprised of cement.

center line   A line representing an axis of symmetry—i.e., having equal dimensions on either side. The center line is typically shown on drawings as a broken line. Sometimes it is represented in symbol form.

ceramic tile   Tile made from clay or a mixture of clay and other inorganic materials and fired in a kiln at very high temperatures. Ceramic tile is available with either glazed or unglazed surfaces, both finishes being very hard and nonporous.

certificate for payment   A written statement from the architect (or contractor) to the building owner confirming the amount of money to be paid to the contractor for work performed and/or materials delivered.

certificate of insurance   A document issued by an authorized representative of an insurance company (i.e., an insurance agent) stating the types, amounts, and effective dates of coverages in place for an insured party (company, contractor, etc.).

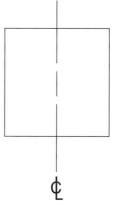

center line

REAL ESTATE APPLICATION: It is common practice for a building manager to request a certificate of insurance from a contractor prior to the contractor performing work at a property. (This should apply to subcontractors as well.)

certificate of occupancy   A document issued by a municipal building department (or other appropriate governmental authority) verifying that a building or a portion of a building (a floor, an office or other demised space) is in compliance with the applicable building, zoning, and other codes; also referred to as an *occupancy permit*. Commonly abbreviated as C of O or C.O., the certificate of occupancy permits the building or space to be occupied for its designated use.

chain fall   A tackle fitted with a chain that passes through the block continuously (an endless chain) used for hoisting a heavy load by hand; also called *chain block* or sometimes referred to as a *come along*. A chain fall is suspended from an overhead track or other support (e.g., beam).

chalk line   A cord coated with colored chalk that is stretched across a surface then pulled up slightly and snapped onto the surface to mark a straight line.

> REAL ESTATE APPLICATION: A chalk line is used during construction to lay out studs for interior walls. Chalk lines are also used to mark an intersection as a center point for beginning to lay out floor tiles. Machines that produce laser sight lines are often used today instead of chalk lines for construction layouts.

chamber test   A fire test developed by Underwriters Laboratories, Inc., that measures the flammability (speed and distance of flame spread) of floor coverings such as carpets.

change order   Issued to the contractor by the property owner and/or the architect after the execution of the contract, a written order authorizing a change in the work and, as a result (usually), a change in the original contract sum; also referred to as a *modification*. A change order is typically issued to add to the scope of work, but it can also be used to delete a portion of the originally specified work. A change order for the deduction of work is normally accompanied by a corresponding credit. It is common practice for a representative of the contractor (e.g., the project manager) to prepare and issue change orders to the owner for signature, since the contractor is usually more familiar with the on-site conditions and changes required to the original scope of the work. Properly signed, a change order is considered a legal document.

channel   A structural steel member, U-shaped in cross-section, used in miscellaneous metal applications in buildings (e.g., stringers of steel stairways); also called *channel iron* or *channel bar*.

channel

chase   A continuous, floor-to-floor recess or opening built into a wall, closet, or other enclosure to receive piping, ducts, and conduit. Usually a chase is located inside or next to a column (which provides some physical protection).

chlorinated polyvinyl chloride (CPVC)   A plastic widely used in piping applications for hot and cold water systems and in drainage systems.

> REAL ESTATE APPLICATION: CPVC piping is effectively used under conditions in which corrosion would be a potential problem.

cladding   A metal coating that is bonded to another metal, usually to impart special properties (e.g., corrosion resistance) to the core metal. Also used in referring to any covering applied to provide desirable surface properties (e.g., durability, impact resistance) to another material or substance.

clean room   An assembly room for precision products (e.g., surgical instruments) whose quality would be adversely affected by airborne contaminants such as dust, lint, and moisture. Specialized HVAC components (air precipitators, humidification systems, etc.) are often required in clean rooms to maintain the level of airborne contaminants at a specified minimum.

climbing crane   A crane used in the erection of high-rise buildings. A vertical mast is attached to the building s structural steel framing and moved up with the top level of the building as it is built. A horizontal *boom* attached to the crane is used to hoist structural steel members to the top of the structure.

code   A collection of procedural rules and materials standards established to ensure uniformity and protect the health and safety of the general public in matters such as building construction, usually adopted by a public agency (e.g., city, state, or federal government) and having the force of law within the agency s jurisdiction. (See also *building code.*)

cofferdam   A watertight temporary structure for keeping water out of an enclosed area that has been pumped dry so that a foundation or wall can be constructed.

cohesion   The molecular forces of attraction throughout the mass of an adhesive or sealant that hold it together. Also, the internal strength of an adhesive or sealant.

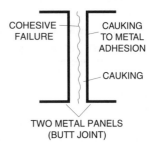

TWO METAL PANELS
(BUTT JOINT)

cohesive failure   The tearing apart of a sealant as a joint expands if the adhesive capabilities (surface attraction) of the sealant compound exceed its internal cohesive capabilities.

color retention   The ability of a material (e.g., paint, caulking compound) to retain its original color intensity and not fade with age and/or exposure to the outside elements, particularly the sun.

column   In structures, a vertical support compression member, such as steel supporting a load, which acts in the direction of its longitudinal axis. (See also *skeleton construction* and accompanying diagram.)

commissioning   Used in referring to the initial testing or putting into place of a large HVAC or other building system upon completion of delivery and installation.

common area   An area of a building intended for use by all of its occupants (lobby areas, restrooms, etc.).

> REAL ESTATE APPLICATION: In the calculation of rentable area in office buildings, the square footage that comprises the common areas may be allocated proportionately in accordance with each tenant s usable area. The *Building Owners and Managers Association International (BOMA)* publishes a standard for measuring office space. (See also *rentable area; usable area.*)

composite door   A commonly used type of door that is manufactured using a core material that is faced and edged with wood, metal, or plastic laminate.

computer-aided design (CAD)   Design, modification, and analysis of construction or other technical drawings using a computer.

> REAL ESTATE APPLICATION: Computer-aided design has gained much acceptance and popularity in the real estate and facilities space design and construction fields. CAD can save considerable time and money, particularly when modifying existing plans and drawings.

concealed spline ceiling   A ceiling in which the grid system that supports and aligns the ceiling tiles is hidden from view within an occupied space.

concrete   An artificial stone made by mixing aggregate materials with a paste comprised of cement and water as a binder. Concrete may be poured to form a floor *(slab)* in a building.

concrete block   A hollow or solid concrete masonry unit consisting of Portland cement and aggregate combined with water.

> REAL ESTATE APPLICATION: Concrete blocks are commonly used in the construction of foundation walls and interior walls of small-to-average size residential, office, industrial, and retail buildings.

connectors   The rivets, bolts, and other devices used to connect framing angles, plates, and other structural pieces. (Welds in structural steel are not considered connectors.)

contiguous   Adjoining, connected.

> REAL ESTATE APPLICATION: A tenant on a multi-tenant floor who wants to expand its leased space will almost always request that the new space be contiguous with its existing space.

contingency   An amount of budgeted funds designated to pay for unforeseen items of work or changes to the scope of the work.

> REAL ESTATE APPLICATION: A manager may consider budgeting a 7% 15% contingency for a project if he or she is not comfortable with either the price submitted by a contractor or the scope of the work to be performed.

contingency allowance   A specified amount included in the contract sum to be used at the owner s discretion (and approval) to pay for any unforeseen items or for an element or service that is desirable but not required specifically under the contract.

contract documents   All of the documents that comprise a contract (e.g., a construction contract). These documents include bidding requirements, specifications, drawings, contract forms, etc.

contractor's liability insurance   Insurance secured by a contractor to protect its company from claims that may arise as a result of the work or services performed under the contract.

control joint   See *expansion joint.*

core area   A part of a multi-story building containing a variety of service and utility functions such as elevators, stairwells, HVAC ducts, and electrical and phone/data closets.

core drill   The process of drilling through a concrete floor or ceiling or wall for the placement of piping or conduit; may also be used to access an under-floor (below slab) raceway containing phone/data cable or electrical conduit.

> REAL ESTATE APPLICATION: In an occupied facility, core drilling should normally be done during nonbusiness hours because this work can be very disruptive to occupants of floors immediately below the floor slab being drilled.

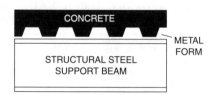

corrugated decking

corrugated decking   Steel that is preformed in the shape of peaks and valleys, used as a form for concrete poured during construction to create a floor slab (common in high-rise construction). Also used as a structural support (e.g., as a base onto which roofing materials are applied).

cost-plus-fee agreement   An arrangement in which a contractor, architect, or other service provider receives a predetermined fee (negotiated amount) for services rendered in addition to payment (reimbursement) for the direct costs (materials, labor) of the work.

counter flashing   A thin strip of material, typically sheet metal, attached or built into the building structure and turned down over the exposed edges and joints of base flashing. Counter flashing prevents water from entering the joints and exposed upturned edges of base flashing. (See also *flashing* and the accompanying diagram.)

coverage   The surface area (square footage) that can be adequately covered by a particular product (e.g., paint, roofing material, etc.).

crane   A machine for lifting or lowering a load such as heavy equipment and moving it horizontally. Cranes are classified by lifting capacity and boom configuration. (See also *boom; climbing crane.*)

crawl space   An interior space of limited height that a maintenance worker or other person can crawl through to access another area or ductwork or piping.

creep   Permanent change in the shape of a material from prolonged exposure to stress—e.g., deformation of a concrete supporting member under a sustained load. The permanent stretching or shrinkage of a roofing membrane due to changes in the environment (temperature, moisture).

cross beam   A large transverse beam—e.g., a joist or girder—that spans the distance between two sides or walls of a structure.

crushed stone   The product of artificial crushing of rock or other material used for walkway or driveway surfaces or as ballast on a roof; also called *gravel.*

cubicle   See *workstation.*

cure   To change the physical properties of an adhesive or sealant by chemical reaction; to set.

> REAL ESTATE APPLICATION: Concrete requires sufficient drying time, maintaining humidity and temperature at desired levels for a specified period, in order to ensure proper hardening *(curing)*.

curtain wall   A non-bearing exterior wall of a building, typical in high-rise construction.

cylinder   The primary component of a door lock. The cylinder assembly contains the tumbler mechanism and the keyway into which the matching key is inserted.

dead bolt   A type of door lock. The relatively large bolt component (throw) of this type of door lock is opened and closed by either a key or a turn piece. Dead bolt door locks are considered sturdier and more tamper-resistant than standard door knob locks.

dead level   Absolutely horizontal, having zero slope.

dead load   The weight of a building structure itself, including all structural steel, walls, concrete slabs, roofs, and all other permanent components such as plumbing, HVAC equipment, and ductwork. (Compare *live load.*)

deck   The flooring of a structure or the structural surface to which a roof is attached; often used in referring to the structural slab (floor) in a building.

delamination   The failure of an applied (laminated) surface or material characterized by the loss of adhesion and subsequent separation of plies, as of roofing or a glue-laminated material (e.g., a Formica desktop).

demising wall   A common wall between two adjacent commercial tenant spaces or living units. The walls defining leased (demised) premises.

demolition   The planned destruction or dismantling of a building or a portion of a building (e.g., an office space); also called *demo* for short.

density   The number of occupants per square foot area of an office, space, or building.

> REAL ESTATE APPLICATION: In many office buildings, occupant density increased in the 1990s. Previously, space planners estimated an average of 250–300 rentable square feet per person; this has been reduced to an estimated average of 150–250 rentable square feet per person.

design-build   Used in referring to the engineering design of a system and its subsequent installation or construction by the same entity.

> REAL ESTATE APPLICATION: An HVAC contractor who has the expertise required to calculate the cooling requirements of a large computer room, design a system to serve the computer room, and also install the system would be considered a design-build firm.

detail   A drawing of a part of another drawing at a larger scale in order to elaborate on the specifics of the design, measurements, location, composition, etc.

> REAL ESTATE APPLICATION: A drawing of a building's curtain wall with a scale of $\frac{1}{16}$" = 1' may have a detail of the connection of the building skin to the supporting steel drawn at a scale of $\frac{1}{2}$" = 1'.

dimension stone   One of the two principal branches of the natural-stone industry (see also *crushed stone*); blocks or slabs of stone processed to a specification of size, shape, and finish. Granite and marble are two commonly used dimension stones.

> REAL ESTATE APPLICATION: Most dimension stone today consists of slabs one to four inches in thickness that are mounted on a structure as a protective and/or aesthetic finish.

distributed load   Weight, as in computer equipment, that acts equally (is distributed evenly) over the surface or structural member that supports the load.

door contact   An electrical device having two parts, one of which is attached to the door and the other to the door frame; a *door switch.* The device activates an electric circuit when the door is opened or closed.

door jamb   See *jamb.*

door swing   The direction a door swings to open when viewed from the side of the door usually considered the outside; also referred to as *hand* in regard to the side (left or right) that is hinged. A *left-hand* door has hinges on the left side and swings away from the person opening the door. A *left-hand reverse* door has hinges on the left side but swings toward the person opening the door. A *right-hand* door has hinges on the right side and swings away from the person opening it while a *right-hand reverse* door has hinges on the right and swings toward the person opening the door.

REAL ESTATE APPLICATION: For reasons of safety and security, entrance doors to apartments, offices, and stores, as well as doors that access stairwells (fire exits), swing inward (either right hand or left hand) on hinges on the inside of the room or space. Reverse hand doors that swing outward are typically used on closets and storage areas so that the usable space and access to the contents of these usually smaller spaces can be maximized.

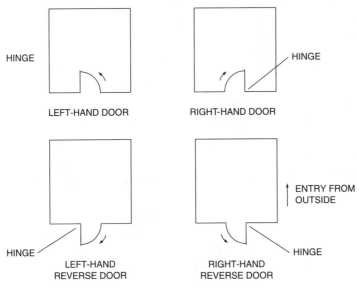

door swing

double glazing Two panes of glass set in a window with an air space between them to provide increased thermal and/or sound insulation; in certain applications, referred to as *insulating glass* (which see).

drift Side-to-side movement (lateral deflection) of a building due to wind or other loads.

REAL ESTATE APPLICATION: Drift is negligible at ground level and more pronounced at the tops of buildings, particularly in very tall high-rise structures. Large, heavy weights—e.g., a large piston-shaped device floating free in a cylinder that is filled with oil and affixed to the building structure—are sometimes located in the uppermost space of very tall buildings to counteract drift.

drop ceiling See *integrated ceiling; suspended ceiling.*

drywall Interior construction finish materials, such as gypsum board or plywood which are made and installed in sheets. (See also *wallboard.*)

REAL ESTATE APPLICATION: Drywall construction is used almost exclusively in the interior finishing of office, retail, and residential space.

dynamic load   A nonstatic (nonstationary) load (e.g., wind load, shock load due to dropping equipment, moving live load).

easement   The right, interest, or privilege one party has in the property of another.

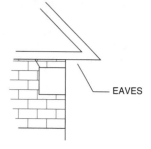

EAVES

> REAL ESTATE APPLICATION: A utility company might have an easement across another's property or through the entrance and basement of another's building in order to access a utility vault for maintenance and inspection; called specifically a *utility easement.*

eaves   The underside portion of a roof that projects beyond the wall of the building.

elastomer   A synthetic, elastic material having some of the physical properties of natural rubber; also used in referring to plastic or synthetic rubber material applied as a fluid or sheet as a roofing membrane.

elastomeric   The properties of a roofing membrane, exterior caulking, or other material that allow it to expand and contract without tearing or cracking.

elevation   A drawing showing the vertical elements of a building or object, also called *elevation view.*

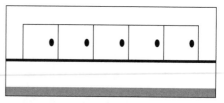

LARGE CREDENZA WORK STATION
(ELEVATION VIEW)

envelope   The outermost elements of a building (roof, exterior walls and windows, foundation, etc.); also called *building envelope, building shell,* or *building skin.*

epoxy resin   A class of synthetic, usually thermosetting, resins whose properties include excellent adhesive qualities, flexibility, and corrosion and chemical resistance; also called simply *epoxy.* Epoxy resins are commonly used in adhesives and coatings.

equal   A substitute for a material, product, or method approved for use based on a particular concern such as cost, availability, or compatibility with another component; an *equivalent.*

> REAL ESTATE APPLICATION: During a bid process, an engineer or architect might use the following language: Contractor to provide "Brand X" polished chrome door hardware or an approved equal. The equal (alternate) door hardware would typically be presented for approval by both the architect or engineer and the property owner (contracting party).

ethylene propylene diene monomer (EPDM) roof membrane system
EPDM is a fairly common type of thermoset roofing membrane consisting of a single-ply sheet composed of synthetic rubber. EPDM sheets are lapped and joined together with contact cement (not by heat welding). Applications can vary from loose laid and ballasted to fully adhered.

existing   A term referring to building components and materials already in place (e.g., sheetrock walls and ceilings, plumbing, ductwork); *existing work.*

REAL ESTATE APPLICATION: General construction drawings, particularly for rehabilitation of existing space, will identify structures and components that are in place, some of which may be protected during the project and retained for the proposed space.

expansion joint The intentional break or gap at designated intervals in concrete, masonry, and plaster construction or between adjacent parts of a building or structure that permits the movement of these materials; also called *control joint*. The free movement of these materials reduces the forces of expansion and contraction due to temperature and moisture changes, thus limiting cracks, buckling, and the like. Expansion joints are often filled with an elastic material, such as a bituminous strip.

exploded view A drawing showing each individual disassembled component part of a machine or device. An exploded view drawing displays each of the parts of the machine or device at a distance from one another but in their proper relationship with respect to their final assembled position.

exposed grid ceiling A grid system for supporting acoustical ceiling tiles in which the support components (splines) are visible in the room or space; also called *exposed suspension system*. (See also *suspended ceiling*.)

exposure The physical orientation of a structure or building; the direction in which the front entrance of a building faces. A building facing east has an east exposure.

extra Used in referring to construction or other work that is in addition to the scope of work as outlined in the drawings and specifications contained in the contract. The extra work is typically preceded by the issuance and approval of a *change order* (which see). Each specific portion of work that is in addition to the contract is referred to as an extra.

facade The exterior face of a building which is the architectural front. The facade of a building often has details that distinguish it from the other sides of the building.

fast track A building method whereby construction is begun prior to completion of all of the design details in order to shorten the time needed to design and build a structure; may be used in construction management to meet a specified or targeted deadline.

field measure Measurement of the structural components (walls, ceiling heights, etc.) at the construction site to verify the corresponding dimensions shown on a drawing.

REAL ESTATE APPLICATION: Field measurements are made to verify the accuracy of drawings in order to ensure proper construction and avoid mistakes during a construction project.

fill Soil, crushed stone, or other material used to raise the level of an existing grade.

final inspection Review and walk through of a project by an architect or engineer prior to approval of the contractor s final application for payment and project or job acceptance. Also used in referring to the inspection conducted by the (local) building inspector or building official prior to issuance of a *certificate of occupancy* (which see).

finish grade See *grade*.

fireproofing   See definition in Life Safety and Fire Protection Systems.

fixture   An item that is permanently attached to real property, as a light fixture secured to a wall or ceiling or installed plumbing fixtures (toilets, sinks).

REAL ESTATE APPLICATION: In office leases, fixtures are considered the property of the building landlord upon termination of the lease.

flashing   A thin impervious material (metal, rubber, etc.) or connecting device that seals membrane joints at expansion joints, roof drains, and other places where a membrane ends (e.g., where a roofing membrane meets a wall). The purpose of the flashing is to prevent water penetration and/or provide water drainage. *Base flashing* forms the upturned edges of a watertight membrane. (See also *counter flashing*.)

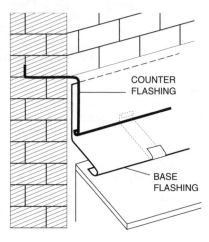

floating   Used in referring to a ceiling or other component that appears not to be attached to any other structure. Also, finishing a fresh mortar or concrete surface (e.g., floor slab) by use of a *float*.

floor closer   A door-closing device installed in a recess in the floor below a door to regulate its opening and closing.

floor plan   An architectural drawing showing the layout (outline) of a single floor (or part of a floor), including details of exterior and interior walls, doors and windows, and precise room dimensions and their interrelationships; sometimes called *floor plate*. (See also *plan view*.)

floor plate   See *floor plan*. (See also *floor plate* in Elevators and Escalators.)

floor receptacle   An electrical outlet mounted in an outlet box set flush with the floor.

floor slab   A thick, usually reinforced, structural concrete surface that serves as a floor in relatively large buildings.

flush   Having a surface that is even or level with an adjacent surface.

footing   The portion of a building foundation that transfers the load of the structure directly to the soil. The footing is part of or directly supports the foundation

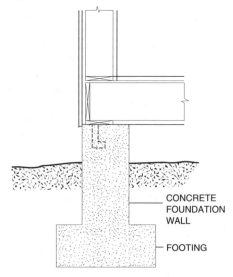

wall or column and may have a bottom surface wider than the thickness of the foundation wall or column, which will spread the load over a greater surface area and reduce settling.

form   A temporary structure made of wood, metal, or other suitable material that provides the shape and support for poured concrete or other masonry elements that are in a semi-liquid state and not yet self-supporting.

foundation   The part of a structure in direct contact with the ground that transmits the load of the structure to the ground. The foundation consists of several elements, which may include various types of beams, columns, walls, pilasters, and footings. While providing support for the building above, the foundation must distribute all of the building loads so that settlement will be either negligible or uniform under all parts of the structure.

> REAL ESTATE APPLICATION: Foundation systems can be divided into two general categories—deep systems and shallow systems. Deep systems, which involve driving long slender columns (piles) deep into the soil, are used for large high-rise buildings and when the soil close to the surface does not possess the necessary load-carrying capacity.

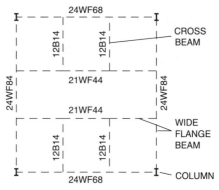

foundation wall   A part of the foundation of a building, usually made of reinforced concrete, which forms the permanent retaining wall of the structure just below grade. (See also diagram at *footing*.)

framing plan   A drawing of a building or portions of a building showing all of the structural members using a simplified system of drafting lines and symbols to show the layout and connections.

framing plan

front end   A term used by managers, engineers, architects, and others when referring to the base portion of a specification, typically situated in the front section of the specification, hence the name front end. The front end of a specification is usually formatted specifically for a building and addresses the general rules, regulations, and procedures applicable to that building (e.g., freight elevator procedures, parking procedures, environmental concerns, after hours work requirements) as opposed to the specifics of the project itself.

fully adhered roofing system   A roofing system that uses adhesives to bond the roof membrane to the structure. This type of application provides a lightweight roof with great resistance to wind lift.

general conditions   A specific part of a construction (or other work) contract that sets forth the responsibilities, requirements, and relationships of the parties involved (e.g., owner, contractor, architect).

> REAL ESTATE APPLICATION: The general conditions section of a contract is typically generic (i.e., boilerplate) and may vary locally. It outlines general responsibilities of the various entities involved in the contract. It may also

include references to things like job site cleanup and administrative fees which may apply to the way a contractor performs the work of all projects that are undertaken.

The American Institute of Architects (AIA) has published several standard general conditions documents for use by professionals in the project management industry. The specific AIA standard general conditions document selected for a project will depend on the type and size of the project.

general contractor   The lead contractor responsible for the completion of a construction project, including all of the work performed by each of the *subcontractors;* also referred to as *G.C.* The general contractor serves as the manager of the construction project, receives payment from the owner for all services rendered, and disburses payment to the subcontractors for the services they provided.

girder   A heavy steel horizontal member of steel framework construction, spanning between columns or walls and serving as the support for beams and joists; a *steel girder.* (See also *skeleton construction* and accompanying diagram.)

glazing   The process of installing glass, as in window frames, door frames, curtain walls, and the like. Also, the application of a transparent or semi-transparent (usually dark) color on top of a lighter painted surface to achieve a decorative effect.

REAL ESTATE APPLICATION: *Exterior glazed* windows are installed (set) from the outside of a building, whereas *interior glazed* windows are installed from the inside.

grade   The rate of inclination (rise or fall) of a roadway, lawn, or other surface; the ground elevation at the outside walls of a building. The top surface of an area (road, walkway, lawn) after construction has been completed is called *finish grade* or *finished grade.*

REAL ESTATE APPLICATION: When indicating the height of the top of a building, the real estate industry typically refers to a specific measurement (e.g., 385 feet 6 inches) above grade.

grandfathered   A situation in which a building or structure, or a portion thereof, does not meet the current building construction codes and requirements but is permitted to continue operating in its existing configuration because the particular codes were not in effect at the time of the original construction (or because it met the codes or requirements in force at the time of construction).

REAL ESTATE APPLICATION: Although specific building systems and configurations may be grandfathered, they may also have to be brought up to the current standards over a specified time period or during substantial renovation of the building.

grandmaster key   A master key designed to operate all the locks within several groups of locks, each of which groups has its own *master key* (which see).

granite   A silicate rock with a visible crystalline structure commonly used in building construction. Granite can have a rough surface or polished surface and is popular for use on building facades or on floors or walls in lobbies.

gravel   A course granular aggregate comprised of small, loose, rounded fragments of rock, formed either naturally or by crushing rock mechanically.

REAL ESTATE APPLICATION: Gravel is commonly used as a ballasting material for various roof coverings. It is also used as backfill to improve soil drainage and as porous fill to cover drain tiles installed next to a foundation.

green board   See *gypsum.*

grommet   A reinforced eyelet, typically made of finished metal or plastic, that fits into a sleeve flush with the working surface of a desk, credenza, or other item of furniture for the purpose of feeding phone and/or data cables from the point of access (wall, floor monument) to a personal computer, telephone, or other device.

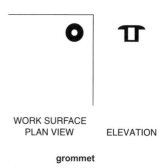

WORK SURFACE
PLAN VIEW   ELEVATION

grommet

gross area   The entire area of a building within the exterior walls; sometimes referred to as *gross square feet.* Gross area includes all core and shaft areas, stairwells, etc.

grout   A mortar containing a considerable amount of water that is applied in the joints or spaces between bricks or other masonry elements to bond them together and provide a seal.

gypsum   A soft mineral consisting of a hydrated calcium sulfate from which gypsum plaster is made by heating. Gypsum is noncombustible. *Gypsum board* is a type of wallboard fabricated of gypsum and having a paper surface. Moisture-resistant gypsum board (distinguished by having a green face paper and referred to as *green board*) is designed for use in bathrooms (as tile backing) and other areas that are often damp. (See also *drywall; wallboard.*)

hanger   A wire or rod attached to an overhead structure, such as a steel beam or the underside of a corrugated deck, to support sprinkler piping, electrical conduit, or the grid of a suspended ceiling.

hardware   Metal products used in construction (e.g., bolts or screws). Finish hardware consists of door levers, locks, hinges, and the like.

header   A horizontal framing member that supports other frames, joists, and rafters and forms the top frame of a window or door opening. (See also *jamb.*)

health code   See *code.*

heat-strengthened glass   Glass that is cut to its final size, heated to its softening point, then quickly cooled in order to place the outside surfaces and edges in compression and the interior in tension, thereby strengthening the glass.

high-rise   A building that has a relatively large number of floors (generally 6 or more stories) and is equipped with elevators.

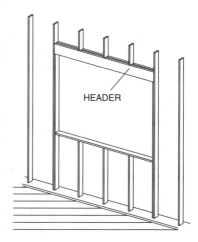

HEADER

REAL ESTATE APPLICATION: For fire protection code and compliance purposes, the NFPA classifies as a high-rise building a structure with its highest floor level 75 feet or more above grade (ground level). In some states, this height classification may be slightly different. Many six-story office buildings are high-rises because their floor-to-floor distances are 12 13 feet.

hold harmless   See *indemnification clause.*

hollow-core door   A flush-surface door that has hardwood or plywood faces applied on a skeletal framework with a hollow or honeycombed interior.

REAL ESTATE APPLICATION: Hollow-core doors are not actually hollow. The space between the outer door faces and the framing members are filled with a paper or cardboard honeycomb to give the door structural stability. The walls of the honeycomb are perpendicular to the facing surfaces (skin).

I beam   A horizontal structural steel member with a cross-section shaped like the letter I and designated by its weight per linear foot and nominal depth measurement across both flanges.

I beam
(section view)

inactive door   In a pair of doors, the one that does not contain a working door knob or lock; also called *inactive leaf.* The inactive door is normally fixed in the closed position by pins or bolts at the top and bottom of the door that slide into the floor or door frame (local codes may require other means of maintaining closure). The inactive door also houses a strike plate that receives the latch or bolt of the active door to secure it in the closed position and may also have in place nonworking (dummy) hardware. (See also *active door.*)

indemnification clause   A contractual obligation in which one party agrees to hold another party harmless in the event of loss or damage from specified causes (e.g., bodily injury due to negligence); also called *hold harmless clause.*

REAL ESTATE APPLICATION: An elevator company may ask a real estate management company to issue and sign a clause indemnifying the elevator company if a contractor retained by building management transports an over-sized piece of equipment to a construction floor on the top of the freight elevator cab and the elevator is damaged in the process.

instructions to bidders   Instructions contained and outlined in an owner's (contracting party s) bidding requirements (specifications) sent to a contractor (bidder) who will be preparing and submitting a bid proposal.

REAL ESTATE APPLICATION: Information provided in the Instructions to Bidders section of a specification might include the following: Where to pick up project drawings; location, date, and time of the pre-bid conference; date and time of the bid opening; insurance requirements; request for resumes of the proposed project supervisors; request for company names of proposed sub-contractors, and other particulars.

insulating glass   Two or more panes (lights) of glass separated by dead air space and hermetically sealed; also called *insulating glass unit.* Insulating glass provides increased resistance against the transmission of heat and sound. (See also *double glazing.*)

insurance binder   An oral or written agreement to provide immediate insurance coverage. Often used during the period between the effective date of coverage and the issuance of a formal policy, the binder states the conditions of coverage and is issued for a limited period.

integrated ceiling A suspended or *drop ceiling* system in which fire protection, lighting fixtures, HVAC components, and sound insulation are combined into a single unit or modular panel for mounting as an integral part of a ceiling grid system.

invitation to bid The portion of a bidding document that requests bids; also, a contractor s notification to selected subcontractors that a particular portion of a project is open to bids. (Compare *notice to bidders.*)

isolation joint A space or separation point between two adjacent components, as between adjoining sections of concrete, to allow for independent movement. (Compare *expansion joint.*)

jamb A vertical member or surface forming the side of an opening as for a door or window *(door jamb; window jamb)*. Sometimes the horizontal component (top head rail or *header*) is included as well.

joint The space between adjacent surfaces such as bricks, concrete blocks, or granite or metal panels.

joist One of a series of parallel horizontal structural members (beams) of steel, timber, or reinforced concrete that support floor and ceiling loads. Joists are supported by girders, bearing walls, or larger beams.

keyed-alike cylinders Door lock cylinders that are operated (locked and unlocked) by the same key. (Compare *master key.*)

key interlock A mechanism that permits operation of the key to a piece of equipment only if certain conditions have been met. A key interlock is typically used to meet specific safety requirements for equipment.

kickplate A protective plate, usually of metal, applied to the lower portion of a door to prevent scratches, gouges, and other damage.

labor and material payment bond A financial guarantee to the owner (contracting party) by a surety (usually an insurance company) that the materials and labor used in the performance of the contract will be paid for by the contractor.

laminate To manufacture by bonding together two or more layers of material, as by adhesives; a product manufactured by *lamination*. (See also *plastic laminate.*)

lap joint A seam formed by overlapping edges of two pieces of material, as wooden boards or metal plates, and fastening them in place.

latch A mechanical device installed (inset) flush with the swing side edge of a door to allow for temporary fastening to the frame (in a closed position). A simple latch does not contain a mechanism for locking (such as a dead bolt) and is typically openable from the inside or outside of the door by turning a door knob.

lath and plaster A method of wall and ceiling construction that uses sheets of stiffened wire cloth, expanded metal, or gypsum (lath) as a base that is subsequently covered with plaster.

lattice   A pattern of diagonally crisscrossed flat strips of material, typically wood, used as screening or as an ornamental design.

layout   A drawing, usually in a *plan view,* displaying the dimensions and orientation of a particular space as well as the equipment, components, and fixtures within the space.

letter of agreement   A letter outlining the basic terms of a contractual arrangement between two parties (a service contract between a building owner and a vendor, a lease between a building owner and a tenant, etc.), prepared by one of the parties and signed by the remaining party (or both parties) to indicate acceptance of the terms as legally binding.

letter of intent   A written statement of the intention to enter into a formal agreement; it often outlines the key points and general terms of the proposed agreement.

liability insurance   Insurance that protects the insured party (contractor, vendor, etc.) against a financial loss due to liability arising out of injury to a person or damage to property of another (other than the insured).

lien   A right that is enforceable against a specific property to secure payment of an obligation, as monies owed to a general contractor for a major property renovation.

light   A medium through which daylight is admitted into a building, as a pane of glass (windowpane) or alternate material (clear plastic, Plexiglas acrylic sheet); also sometimes called *lite.* A pane of glass installed in an interior partition to allow light to pass through from an adjoining room is called a *borrowed light.* (*Plexiglas* is a trademark for acrylic resin or plastic; see also *side light.*)

liquidated damages   A sum of money specified in a contract that is due an owner in the event of a breach of the contract or a portion of it.

> REAL ESTATE APPLICATION: The most common specification of liquidated damages is a fixed sum per day to be paid by the contractor to the building owner for failure to complete the specified work within the specified time period.

live load   The moving or movable load to which a building is subjected, including the weight of occupants, furniture, equipment, etc. However, *wind load* (which see) is usually not considered part of a building s live load. (Compare *dead load.*)

load   A force or combination of forces carried by a structure or a portion of it (e.g., structural beam, concrete deck, column).

load-bearing   Supporting weight imposed from above, as the ability of soil to support the load of a foundation. Also sometimes used in referring to walls. (See also *bearing wall.*)

load factor[1]   In structural design, the percentage (ratio) by which a working load is multiplied to determine the design load.

load factor[2]   The difference between rentable area and usable area in an office building, expressed as a percentage; the *R/U factor.* The difference between usable square feet (space within a tenant s demised premises) and rentable square feet (the area on which a tenant actually pays rent) is that the latter includes a portion of the common areas of a building (restrooms, corridors, utility closets, etc.). Load factor in this use is also referred to as *add-on factor.*

REAL ESTATE APPLICATION: The reciprocal of the load factor (add-on-factor) of a building or a particular floor within a building is referred to as its efficiency. A floor with a load factor of 1.19 is 84% efficient (1   1.19 = .84). High-rise buildings with multiple elevator banks will have different load factors for the groups of floors in each elevator bank. A 30-story building with two elevator banks (the lower bank serving floors 1 15 and the higher bank serving 16 30) will typically have higher load factors (less efficient space) on the floors served by the lower bank of elevators. This occurs because two banks of elevators pass through the lower 15 floors as opposed to the higher floors through which only one bank of elevators travel.

lockset   A complete door lock assembly including the locking mechanism, door knobs, strike plate, keys, and other accessories used to secure a door.

longitudinal joint   A seam created by fastening together two pieces of wood, metal plates, or the like along their length.

low-emissivity glass   See *reflective glass.*

lowest responsible qualified bidder   The bidder for a project who submits the lowest bid and is considered to be fully responsible and qualified to perform all of the work as specified in the contract documents. (An example of a low bidder who does not meet these criteria is one who submits the lowest bid for a particular project but does not have sufficient manpower available to complete the project in accordance with the contract specification.)

mantrap   A relatively short, narrow section of corridor with lockable doors at both ends, used in high-security areas such as the entrance to a money vault in a bank or to control entry to business operations kept separate from public access areas of a manufacturing facility. Access to the secured area is controlled by permitting entry through the first door into the mantrap where the visitor's credentials can be verified before being allowed to pass through the second door into the controlled space itself. A camera system is generally an integral part of a mantrap.

Masonite   Trademark for a brand of fiberboard made from steam-treated wood fiber; used as a nonstructural building material (one side has a hard, smooth surface), mostly as paneling and sometimes in insulating applications.

masonry   The art or trade of arranging and joining bricks, stones, cement block, and the like using mortar or other materials to construct walls, walkways, sidewalks, etc.

master   One who has mastered an art or trade; specifically, an individual who is licensed and authorized to install and to assume responsibility for contractual agreements pertaining to electrical *(master electrician)* or plumbing *(master plumber)* installations and to secure any permits required in order to conduct the same.

master key   A key that operates (locks and unlocks) a number of different locks, each of which is also keyed individually.

REAL ESTATE APPLICATION: Master keys are typical in buildings that have many different keys for many different locks. Master keys are typically issued only to building management and building security personnel.

mastic   A pasty adhesive compound used to permanently attach floor tiles to concrete. Mastic is also used as a sealant and protective coating on the surface of thermal insulation to prevent deterioration and moisture penetration.

means of egress   See *egress* in Life Safety and Fire Protection Systems.

measured drawing   An architectural drawing of an existing structure, commonly drawn to scale. (See also *scale drawing*.)

mechanically fastened roofing system   A roofing system that uses bars or other devices to connect the roof membrane to the building structure through the insulation. Mechanically fastened roofing systems are lightweight and easy to install.

mechanicals   The HVAC, sprinkler, and plumbing systems of a construction project. The individual who designs the HVAC, sprinkler, or plumbing system of a project is referred to as the *mechanical engineer*. The company or individual responsible for installing these systems is referred to as the *mechanical contractor*.

mechanic's lien   A claim against a property for payment of materials or labor provided that restricts clear title to the property until paid in full.

member   A single structural component such as a beam or column; also referred to as a *structural member*.

membrane   A thin, flexible, weather-resistant component of a roofing system, as elastomeric (EPDM) sheets or alternate layers of felt and bitumen.

millwork   Wood construction materials and products such as moldings, doors and door frames, wainscoting, cabinets, and countertops that are manufactured at a woodwork plant (mill) and installed at the construction site.

> REAL ESTATE APPLICATION: Millwork can add considerably to the costs of a construction project.

miter cut   An oblique (diagonal) cut across two pieces of lumber (as baseboard or molding) so they can be joined at the cut surfaces to form an angle *(miter joint)*.

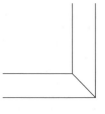

miter joint

mixed occupancy   A building that contains two or more classes of occupancy (or use), as residential and retail, office and industrial.

mock-up   A model of a structure or component, built to scale, for the purpose of evaluating its appearance, dimensions, and details or testing its performance.

model   A three-dimensional representation of a building or other structure, typically done on a small scale (e.g., miniature), for the purpose of evaluating appearance, dimensions, or details or simply for illustration or presentation.

modification   See *change order*.

modified bitumen   A type of roofing system that combines the waterproofing qualities of asphalt with the advanced polymer technology and flexibility of single-ply sheets. Modified bitumens may be used in single-ply or multi-ply applications.

modular   Being constructed or assembled from prefabricated, mass-produced components, as sections of concrete or panels. The primary advantage of modular construction is the time and cost savings realized during fabrication of the components and the labor savings in the installation process.

moisture barrier See *vapor barrier.*

molding A decorative strip used for ornamentation or finishing, usually fabricated of wood and typically installed at the base, corners, or top of walls or on door and window jambs.

moment The tendency or a measure of the tendency to produce motion, particularly about an axis. The property by which a force (weight) tends to cause a component to which it is applied (e.g., a steel beam) to rotate or bend. A moment is equal to the product of the weight times the perpendicular distance from the weight to the point of action, as measured in foot-pounds.

mortar A mixture of a cementitious material (cement, gypsum plaster, or lime) with water and a fine aggregate (sand), used in masonry construction projects to bind together bricks, stones, and the like.

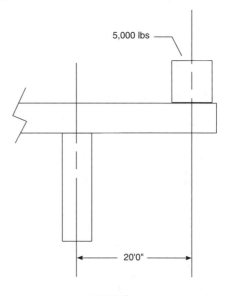

moment
(moment = 20 ft × 5,000 lbs = 100,000 ft-lbs)

REAL ESTATE APPLICATION: Mortar can withstand weathering but is porous and requires periodic maintenance, repair, and replacement (i.e., tuckpointing), particularly in geographic areas where salt and other ice-melting materials are used because they increase the freeze-thaw cycle, causing damage to the mortar.

mortise A recess cut into one member to receive a projecting component from another member, as a hole or pocket cut into a door to receive a lock.

mortise lock A lock that is installed in a recessed area (mortise) in a door rather than applied to its surface.

mullion A vertical framing member located between lights of windows, doors, or panels set in series, to separate and (often) support the glass. (Compare *muntin.*)

REAL ESTATE APPLICATION: An aesthetic cover trim piece is typically screwed or snapped in place over the interior side of structural mullions.

muntin A usually nonstructural horizontal or vertical member used to subdivide an open area in a frame or door; the strip placed between panes of glass in windows and doors. Muntins are secondary, nonsupporting members, as opposed to *mullions,* which are primary and supportive. (See also diagram at *stile.*)

negotiated bid A process in which an owner (contracting party) selects a contractor for a particular project and negotiates a price for the work rather than inviting several contractors to bid competitively on the project.

REAL ESTATE APPLICATION: The bid price for a construction project may be negotiated due, among other things, to a time constraint for completion of the project, specific expertise of a contractor, or past experience and trust in an individual or company.

neoprene   A synthetic rubber (polymerized chloroprene) with a high resistance to petroleum products and sunlight, used in sheet form as a roof membrane or flashing. In roofing applications, a *neoprene roof membrane system* is installed as a single-ply and ballasted or fully adhered; also called *polychloroprene roof membrane system*.

noise-reduction coefficient   The average of sound absorption coefficients of a specific acoustical material (e.g., ceiling tile) at various testing frequencies. Determination of the noise-reduction coefficient of a particular material would ensure that it could be used for the specified application.

non-bearing wall   A wall that does not provide vertical support to other building elements and components such as a roof or floor. A *curtain wall* is an example; also, most sheetrock walls in offices are non-bearing.

notice to bidders   A notice from an owner or owner's representative informing prospective bidders (contractors) of the opportunity to submit bids for a particular project. The document usually sets forth the procedures for submitting a bid e.g., where to send it, to whom, and when the bid is due. (Compare *invitation to bid.*)

notice to proceed   A written document (letter) issued by an owner authorizing a contractor to proceed with the work.

occupancy   The type of use (residential, office, retail, industrial) to which a building or part of a building is put.

occupancy permit   See *certificate of occupancy.*

occupant load   The total number of persons that may occupy a building, restaurant, elevator, or other defined space as specified on a *certificate of occupancy* or per local building construction codes.

on center (OC)   The distance between the center line of a component (structural frame, stud) and the center line of the next similar component; also referred to as *center to center*. The dimensioning of framing members equally spaced four feet apart would be referred to on a drawing as "framing members, 4' OC."

one-line diagram   A representation (drawing) of an electrical or plumbing system displaying a layout of the system and its major components by means of single lines and symbols. A one-line diagram provides a quick effective way for the reader of the plan to grasp the layout of a particular system.

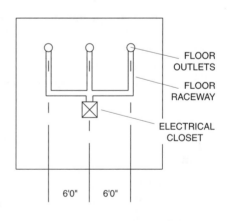

FLOOR OUTLETS

FLOOR RACEWAY

ELECTRICAL CLOSET

6'0"   6'0"

on center
(floor outlets 6'0" on center)

opaque   Impervious to the transmission of visible light (e.g., opaque glass); not translucent or transparent.

open bidding   A procedure in which bids are accepted from all interested and qualified contractors.

> REAL ESTATE APPLICATION: Due to the time required for an owner to analyze the numerous bids submitted, and because the owner may have little or no experience with the many contractors submitting bids, open bidding is not very common in private sector contracts.

operable window   A window that can be opened for ventilation purposes.

> REAL ESTATE APPLICATION: Newly constructed large commercial buildings typically do not have operable windows; instead they have fixed lights (panes of glass).

ordinance   A law or regulation enacted by a city council or other similar local governmental authority.

> REAL ESTATE APPLICATION: A city may adopt an ordinance restricting lighted signage on buildings at night. Zoning of land for commercial or residential use and requirements regarding security deposits under residential leases are other examples.

organic soil   Characteristic of soil that has a high content of plant material and, being very compressible, has poor load-sustaining properties (as required for building foundations).

overdesign   Adherence to structural design requirements that are more stringent than the expected service demands as a way of allowing for unknown deficiencies.

overhead door   Any of various doors that typically roll up and down, either lifted by hand or raised mechanically via an electric motor and associated controls, often used for parking garages and loading docks; also applied to the grilles used as retail shop entrances in malls.

pan construction   A type of construction that employs a prefabricated metal or wood form (pan) to receive the poured concrete; used in constructing floors, roofs, decks, and other flat areas.

panel construction   A type of building construction that uses prefabricated panels as the primary components; also called *panelized construction.*

panic exit device   A locking device on exit doors that unlatches when a horizontal *panic bar* across the inside of the door is pushed; also called *panic hardware.* The design of the bar is such that the action of a body leaning or being forced against it will release the latch and open the door.

parapet   A low wall or barrier positioned to denote the edge of a platform or other sudden drop—e.g., the edge of a roof, where the parapet wall is usually an upward extension of the exterior curtain wall of the building.

particleboard   A composition board comprised of small pieces of wood bonded together with an adhesive (often a synthetic resin). Particleboard sheets, often with a veneer face (surface), are commonly used in construction applications. A thicker, heavier (denser) version, stained or with a veneer surface finish, is used in furniture manufacture. (Compare *Masonite.*)

partition   An interior wall that divides one space from another in a building, usually constructed of drywall or plasterboard.

passage set   A door knob or lever assembly comprising a latching mechanism and associated components that are attached to and used for opening and closing a door. A passage set is not capable of locking a door as is a *lockset* (which see).

paving brick   A vitrified clay brick particularly suitable for use in pavement construction due to its abrasion-resistance characteristics.

penalty clause   A contract provision setting forth the damages a party must pay in the event that the contract is breached, often specifically stating *liquidated damages* a contractor must pay if a project is not completed by a set date.

penetrations   Any openings in the exterior walls or roof of a building (exclusive of window or door openings) for the installation and housing of vents, air-conditioning units, piping, etc. Also, openings within a building for similar purposes—e.g., holes in phone closet floor slabs for routing conduit.

percolation test   A determination of the rate at which a particular soil absorbs effluent (wastewater). The test is conducted by digging a hole in the soil, filling it with water, and measuring the rate at which the water level drops.

> REAL ESTATE APPLICATION: A perc test is typically conducted prior to development of a residential property and its septic system.

performance bond   A bond procured by a contractor in which a surety (insurance company) guarantees to the property owner that the specified work will be performed in accordance with the contract documents (usually stipulated as a requirement of working with governmental agencies).

> REAL ESTATE APPLICATION: A performance bond may be required if there is likely to be a monetary loss for the owner if the contractor performing the construction project failed to complete the contracted work as specified.

perimeter   The defining boundary of a property; the exterior of a building, near the curtain wall in a high- rise.

permanent load   The total load that is permanently supported by a structure, including concrete slabs, steel, major HVAC equipment, elevator equipment, etc. (See also *dead load; live load.*)

permit   A document issued by a governmental agency (e.g., city building department) authorizing work for a specific project at the request of a property owner or contractor. More specifically, a form issued by state or local governments that allows construction of a building or of improvements to a permanent structure *(building permit)*. Usually there is a fee for a building permit, and regular inspections of the work in progress and/or at completion may also be required as noted on the permit.

perspective drawing   A graphic representation of a structure or component as it would appear three-dimensionally.

pile   Structural members of a building foundation which are driven into the soil to support the weight of the building and transmit the weight to the underlying soil and rock. Piles (columns) may be made of steel, concrete, or wood or some combination of those materials.

pitch   A dark, viscous, distillate of tar used in paving and built-up roofing because of its waterproofing properties; also called *coal-tar pitch.* (For the definition of pitch with respect to angle or incline, see *slope.*)

pitch pocket   A metal flange placed around the base of a roof-penetrating component (structural column, HVAC condensing unit piping, etc.) that is filled with flashing cement or bitumen (pitch) to provide a seal.

plan view   A two-dimensional graphic representation (drawing) of a particular location (e.g., floor or structure), sometimes simply called a *plan.* More specifically, in architectural drawings, a top view of a horizontal section of a floor, including symbols representing details of materials used for construction; a *floor plan* (which also see).

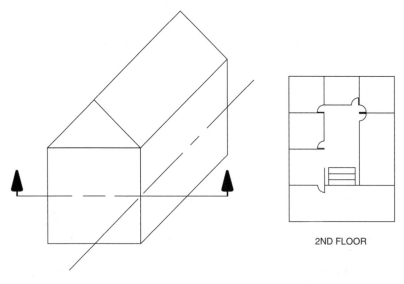

2ND FLOOR

plan view

plaster   A plastic material of paste-like consistency used for interior and exterior finishing, usually consisting of a mixture of Portland cement, lime, or gypsum with water and sand; fiber is sometimes added as a binder. There are many types of plasters. Plaster is applied to wall and ceiling surfaces in a plastic (semi-solid) state, and it sets to form a hard surface.

plastic laminate   A surface finishing material composed of a decorative sheet and kraft paper impregnated with resins. Manufactured in sheet form, plastic laminate provides a hard, nonporous surface that can be adhered to wood or particleboard as a *veneer*-type finish.

REAL ESTATE APPLICATION: Formica is a brand of *high-pressure plastic laminate* (subjected to 1,200 2,000 psi pressure in manufacturing) used for surfacing countertops, tabletops, and cabinets. *Low-pressure plastic laminate* materials (cured at 400 psi max) are used for low-wear surfaces and vertical (e.g., cabinet facing) applications.

plate glass   A common, high-quality glass manufactured in large sheets by a rolling process.

platform   See *stair platform*.

plot plan   See *site plan*.

plumb   Exactly vertical. Also, a metal weight (usually lead or another heavy material) attached to and suspended from a string or line used to indicate the vertical direction; a *plumb bob*.

ply   A single thickness of a material (usually thin sheets) that is applied in layers. Built-up roofing (BUR) membrane felts and plywood are examples.

pocket door   A door that slides into a hollow wall adjacent to the doorway.

point   To remove mortar from between bricks, cement blocks, and other masonry components and replace the joints with new mortar; sometimes also called *point up* or *repoint*. Mortar is porous and subject to deterioration thereby requiring periodic pointing. The term is also used in referring to the process of finishing a masonry wall by filling the joints with mortar. Application of a narrow ridge of fine lime mortar or putty as an additional decorative finish is called *tuckpointing*.

polished finish   A smooth, mirror-like (i.e., reflective) finish that is formed by prolonged mechanical buffing and/or chemical treatment of a material such as granite.

polyethylene (PE)   A flexible plastic material, available in sheet form (rolled up), used frequently in various waterproofing applications.

> REAL ESTATE APPLICATION: Polyethylene sheeting is used as a vapor barrier and to protect walls and equipment during asbestos abatement projects.

polyvinyl chloride (PVC)   A plastic material that is chemically inert, highly corrosion resistant, nonconductive, and heat resistant, often used as an insulating spacer in window and curtain wall applications as well as piping for domestic water systems, sewage and waste lines, and water treatment systems.

polyvinyl chloride (PVC) roof membrane system   Roofing membranes composed of single-ply sheets of a thermoplastic polymer synthesized from vinyl chloride, which can be applied loose and ballasted, fully adhered, or mechanically fastened.

ponding   The accumulation (pooling) of rainwater in a surface depression, as on a flat roof.

post-tensioning   A method of prestressing reinforced concrete in which steel cables are housed in a plastic raceway embedded in the poured concrete. The cables are stretched (tensioned) *after* the concrete has set, which puts the entire structure in tension. Combining the high compressive strength of concrete with the high tensile strength of steel creates a strong structure overall. (See also *prestressed concrete*.)

precast concrete   Standardized concrete units (sections of walls, floors, etc.) that are cast, hardened, and cured in a form or mold under controlled conditions off site, then transported to a construction site and lifted into place.

> REAL ESTATE APPLICATION: Precast concrete construction can be an efficient process, particularly if the number of standardized precast units is sufficiently large. While precast concrete can be used in many types of structures, it is more common in the construction of parking garages.

prefabricate   To construct parts of a building as modules that will be joined together to form the final structure. *Manufactured housing,* for example, is prefabricated under controlled conditions in a factory and transported to the site where it can be assembled quickly.

preliminary drawings   Drawings (blueprints) prepared during the early design stages of a construction project.

prestressed concrete   A form of reinforced concrete in which initial stresses opposite of those caused by the applied loads are induced by applying tension to high-strength steel cables embedded in the concrete. Prestressed concrete is constructed in such a way as to counteract the anticipated load.

primer   A liquid material (e.g., paint) applied to a surface to improve the adhesion of subsequent (finish) coats. In roofing, a coating of thin liquid bituminous solvent applied to the roof surface to improve the adhesion of heavier applications of bitumen materials.

progress payments   Periodic partial payments from the owner (contracting party) to the contractor for materials provided and services performed during a construction project. The specifics regarding the number and timing of progress payments are usually delineated in the contract documents. The owner makes a progress payment after the contractor files an application for payment upon completion of a specified percentage of work.

punch list   The architect's or owner's list of deficient items requiring correction by the contractor. The punch list is normally compiled upon *substantial completion* of a construction project.

quarry tile   A type of machine-made unglazed ceramic floor tile made of extruded clay. The most common size is 6" × 6" square and ½ to ¾ inch thick.

   REAL ESTATE APPLICATION: Because quarry tile performs well in the presence of oil, grease, and moisture, it is commonly used in cafeteria and kitchen spaces. It is also used in building entrances and lobbies and in bathrooms. When a rough finish is applied to the surface of the tile, it provides excellent slip resistance.

ready-mixed concrete   Concrete in an unhardened state mixed at a batch plant and ready for delivery and immediate use.

rebar   See *reinforcing bar.*

record drawings   Construction drawings that are revised to document the various changes made during the construction project; also called *as-built drawings.*

reflected plan   A drawing of an upper surface (as a ceiling) projected downward.

   REAL ESTATE APPLICATION: A reflected plan of a ceiling may be developed during the design phase of interior construction such as tenant improvement projects.

reflective glass   Window glass that has been treated on the outside surface with a transparent metallic coating in order to reflect light and radiant (solar) heat; *low-emissivity glass.*

reflective insulation   Material in sheet form that limits the transmission of heat through use of reflective backing material (e.g., aluminum foil) or by having applied on one or both surfaces a metallic coating. Reflective insulation is used in building construction, typically placed to face an air space (gap) in order to be more effective.

regulation   A rule issued by an administrative agency under authority granted to it by legislation—e.g., environmental regulations issued by the U.S. EPA under the Environmental Protection Act. Regulations are not issued by governmental entities themselves. (Compare *code*.)

reinforced concrete   Concrete in which steel rods, bars, or wire mesh or other reinforcing components are embedded to increase its load-carrying capacity. Concrete slab is an example. Some of the advantages of reinforced concrete are relatively low cost, weather resistance, fire resistance, good compressive strength, and high tensile strength.

reinforcing bar   Steel rod, round in cross-section, sometimes with a rough or deformed surface, used in construction of concrete beams and floor slabs to provide additional strength; also called *rebar*.

release of lien   A document executed by a provider of contract services (materials and labor) whereby the contractor gives up the claim imposed against the property where the services are being performed. (See also *waiver of lien*.)

rendering   A perspective-type drawing of a project as it will look on completion, showing building and landscaping with delineation of materials, shapes, shades of color, etc.

   REAL ESTATE APPLICATION: Renderings are usually produced prior to the execution of a project for display and presentation purposes.

rentable area   The total floor area for which a tenant in an office building pays rent. Rentable area may be defined to include the usable area that the tenant occupies plus a pro-rata share of *common areas* utilized by other building tenants—e.g., lobby areas, restrooms, portions of mechanical areas, electrical and phone closets. (See also *load factor*[2].)

reproducible drawing   A drawing capable of being reproduced to the same quality, identical scale, etc. Drawings made with sepia (dark brown) ink and those produced on Mylar polyester film and vellum (translucent parchment paper) are examples of reproducible drawings. Although blue line drawings can be copied, they are not considered to be truly reproducible.

request for proposal (RFP)   Written specifications that describe the goods and/or services to be provided by the bidder. These may include details related to design, use, power requirements, location (delivery point or work site), and the like and ask for specifics regarding materials, pricing, timing (delivery), payment, etc. An RFP is used to ensure that bids address the same issues so that the decision-maker is comparing the same kinds of things. (See also *bid*.)

residential occupancy   A use classification of a building in which sleeping accommodations are provided, with the exception of those buildings classified under institutional occupancy.

resilient flooring   An interior floor covering, either in tile or sheet form, that is made of plastic and has the ability to return to its original shape or condition—i.e., resists deformation. (See also *vinyl tile*.)

REAL ESTATE APPLICATION: Resilient flooring is used in applications where primary considerations are durability and low maintenance. Vinyl composition tile and vinyl sheet goods are considered resilient flooring materials.

responsible bidder   See *lowest responsible qualified bidder.*

retainage   A pre-determined sum of money withheld from *progress payments* to the contractor in accordance with the project contract documents (owner-contractor agreement). The retainage amount usually represents a percentage of the total sum of the costs of the project completed to date. The concept of retainage is that the contractor should not receive the entire compensation for materials and services provided to date in case there are a few incidental work requirements or corrective measures to be performed. The portion of money withheld for retainage (usually 10%) is released at the end of the project following acceptance of the work.

retaining wall   A wall made of brick, concrete block, cement, or other material designed to resist lateral pressure and contain the fill material (soil or water) behind it.

retrofit   The replacement or significant alteration of an existing building element, component, or system in order to increase performance or efficiency or both.

return   The continuation of a molding, wall-covering, or other material on another surface (i.e., a change in direction).

reverse-swing door   See *door swing.*

revolving door   An outer door having two or more leaves that rotate about a common vertical axis within a cylindrical-shaped vestibule. Revolving doors typically have four leaves at right angles to each other.

REAL ESTATE APPLICATION: Revolving doors are very common in large buildings where they minimize the passage of air into or out of the building through the vestibule, thereby saving energy and decreasing a property's heating and cooling costs. Revolving doors are also easier for building occupants to operate because larger buildings require higher grade construction (heavyweight) doors due to frequent use and pressure differences between indoor and outdoor air.

rigid insulation   A building construction insulation material in preformed sections that will stand upright due to its composition.

riser   See *stair riser.*

riser diagram   An elevation-type two-dimensional drawing that shows the layout of piping or electrical conduit and major components of a plumbing or electrical distribution system. Riser diagrams provide a clear snapshot view of the general layout of a system. A *one-line diagram* (which see) is an example.

REAL ESTATE APPLICATION: Mounting a framed riser diagram of the electrical distribution system on the wall in a building's electrical vault (distribution center) is an effective way of providing accessible information to building engineers, electrical service technicians, and Building Emergency Re-sponse Teams.

rivet   A short metal cylinder or rod, with a head at one end, used to join two metal plates. The rivet is passed through a hole in each plate, and the protruding end is hammered to flatten it and secure the connection.

roof drain   A drain designed to receive rainwater collecting on a roof and discharge it to a drain pipe or downspout.

REAL ESTATE APPLICATION: Roof drains should be installed at the low points of a roof in order to minimize accumulation of rain water *(ponding)* on the roof surface. Roof drains should be inspected periodically to ensure they are intact and clear of leaves, trash, and other debris.

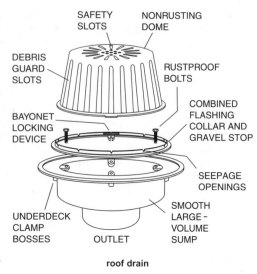

roof drain

roof hatch   A weather-tight hinged-panel assembly, usually at the top of a built-in ladder, which provides a means of access to a roof.

roof pitch   See *slope.*

roof vent   A device installed in or on a roof for the purpose of ventilating an attic or roof cavity (space); sometimes called *roof ventilator.*

rough floor   In wood frame construction, a layer of boards or plywood nailed to the floor joists which serves as a base for the finish floor; a *subfloor.*

roughing in   The preliminary or rough work in any phase of construction. An example would be the installation of plumbing piping from a basement to the point of connection to a plumbing fixture at the bathroom wall. *Finish work* naturally follows the rough work.

rough opening   An opening in the building framework or an interior wall into which a window or door frame is to be fitted.

run   See *stair run.*

R value   See *thermal resistance.*

sandblast   To use sand driven by a blast of compressed air to remove paint or graffiti or otherwise generally clean concrete, metal, or other surfaces by a process of abrasion.

sash   The framework into which panes of glass (lights) are set in a window or door. The sash may be fixed or movable, or it may be pivoted, as in a casement window.

scaffold   A temporary platform and its supporting structure, assembled in pieces and sections, in order to support workers and materials at the face of a structure at elevated levels; sometimes also called *staging.* Scaffolding is also erected in order to provide a temporary protective shelter for pedestrians walking at the perimeter of a building when work is being performed overhead (e.g., roof repairs or upper story facade work).

scale drawing   A drawing of a structure, site, or space in which dimensions are reduced proportionately using a specified ratio or scale—e.g., $\frac{1}{4}$" = 1' or $\frac{1}{8}$" = 1' or 1" = 10'. (See also *measured drawing.*)

REAL ESTATE APPLICATION: Construction drawings are almost always drawn to a specific scale, which is indicated in the lower right hand corner of the drawing. A scaled ruler is the simplest method of calculating distances and dimensions from a scaled drawing. One simply needs to choose the scale on the ruler that matches the scale indicated on the drawing (e.g., $\frac{1}{8}$" = 1'), and the actual dimensions in feet and inches can then be read directly from the ruler. *Engineering scale* is in tenths, and drawings may be scaled in multiples of ten feet (e.g., 1" = 20'0").

schedule   A detailed listing of equipment, components, and finishing materials to be furnished as part of a project.

REAL ESTATE APPLICATION: Architects typically provide a separate drawing (blueprint) detailing the schedule of doors, light fixtures, and other components for a construction project. These schedules provide a clear, concise reference for contractors to use for ordering and pricing.

Sample Door Schedule Information

Room	Door Material	Hardware Finish
101	Solid Wood	Polished Chrome
102	Solid Wood	Polished Chrome
103	Hollow Metal	Stainless Steel
104	Solid Wood	Polished Chrome

sealant   A liquid substance that seals the surfaces of wood, concrete, and other, usually porous, materials. Also called *sealers,* these coating materials protect against moisture damage and prevent surfaces from absorbing paint and other finishes.

section drawing   A diagrammatic representation of a building, machine, or other object showing the internal structure as it would appear if cut through by an intersecting plane.

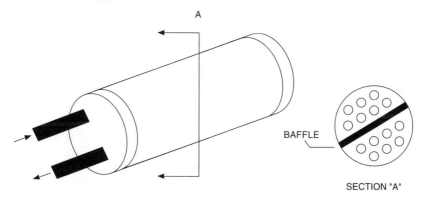

TWO-PASS SHELL AND TUBE HEAT EXCHANGER

section view

seismic load   The assumed force that might be applied to a building during an earthquake or due to vibrations caused by equipment, traffic, trains, or other means. Seismic loads vary from one geographic region to another and should be considered during the building design process.

seismic protection   The design and construction of buildings and installation of systems and components in order to ensure continuance of water and sewer, electricity, gas, and other services during and after an earthquake.

shaft wall   A fire-rated wall that isolates a shaft area (elevator core, emergency stairwell core, plumbing shaft) in high-rise construction.

shall   A word meaning is required to do or mandatory. Shall is the correct recognized term to indicate mandatory requirements in specifications and other contract documents.

shear load   The stress or force created as a result of two contiguous parts of a building (members) sliding relative to each other in a direction parallel to their plane of contact.
  REAL ESTATE APPLICATION: The shear load due to the presence of wind can be a major factor in the designing of structural frames, particularly for high-rise buildings.

shell   See *envelope.*

shock load   A suddenly applied load, as the dropping of equipment or material or the cycling (starting or stopping) of heavy equipment or machinery. A trash container dropped on a loading dock located above a vault is an example of a substantial shock load.

shop drawings   Drawings, schedules, performance charts, and other information prepared by a contractor, supplier, or manufacturer that illustrate how specific portions of a project are to be fabricated or installed.
  REAL ESTATE APPLICATION: Shop drawings are generated by the particular trade or supplier (e.g,. HVAC contractor, curtain wall component/glass manufacturer) selected for the project. Shop drawings are produced (taken off) from the architectural drawings.

side light   A framed, fixed glass adjacent to a door or window opening on an interior wall; also called *borrowed light.* (See also *light.*)

site plan   A drawing of a construction site showing the position, orientation, and dimensions of the building to be erected and the dimensions and contours of the lot.

site visit   A planned (or unplanned) visit to a construction site by a project manager, a contractor, or an owner s representative to examine existing conditions of the project.

skeleton construction   A type of construction in which concrete floor slabs, partitions and exterior walls are all supported by a framework of steel beams and columns; also called *beam and column construction, skeletal steel construction,* and *steel-frame construction.* This type of structure, which can be erected to substantial heights, is typical for high-rise buildings. In skeletal construction, columns are typically spaced 20, 25, or 30 feet apart with girders and beams connected to them from both directions at each floor level. Girders are positioned in the longer direction between the columns, and the beams are positioned between the girders in the shorter direction. The exterior wall *(skin)* of a skeletal steel building is supported by the steel frame and is non-bearing; it is typically referred to as a *curtain wall*.

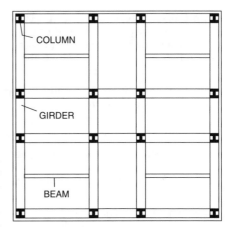

skeleton construction
(structural steel, plan view)

slab The upper part of a reinforced concrete floor which is supported by beams below; also called *concrete slab*. In this form of construction, concrete is often poured into a metal decking or pan that serves as a form and sometimes as a structural component. (See also *pan construction*.) The term slab is also used in reference to the first pour—concrete that is poured on grade (i.e., directly on soil).

slope The ratio of vertical rise to horizontal run; also called *pitch*. In a stairwell, the slope of the stair flight. In roofing, the slope of the inclined roof in relation to the horizontal.

> REAL ESTATE APPLICATION: Slope is usually measured in inches of vertical height per foot of horizontal distance expressed as inches per foot. The Asphalt Roofing Manufacturers Association classifies roofing as follows:
> 1. Level—One inch per foot maximum slope.
> 2. Low slope—From ½ inch to 1½ inches per foot.
> 3. Steep slope—Greater than 1½ inches per foot.

slurry A mixture of finely divided insoluble material suspended in water.

> REAL ESTATE APPLICATION: Portland cement in a slurry dries to form a solid concrete mixture. It is typically used to fill abandoned underground fuel oil storage tanks. Likewise, asphalt emulsion applied as a sealcoat to blacktop or other paved surfaces is called *slurry seal*. (See also *asphalt pavement sealer*.)

snow load The load on a structure caused by the weight of snow, sleet, or ice, which is a form of a roof *live load*. Accumulation of snow on a roof can act as a substantial load for extended periods of time.

> REAL ESTATE APPLICATION: The slope of a roof surface, the type of insulation, and subsequent heat loss through a roof can influence the impact of snow load.

soil strength The quality of a soil and its ability to support a foundation based on its composition.

soil survey A detailed investigation performed at a construction site that describes the soil's composition; results are presented in a written report. The process includes taking soil samples (borings) and testing for strength, compressibility, and other characteristics of soil substructure that can impact project design; also called *surface investigation*.

solid-core door A door with a core of solid wood or mineral composition, as opposed to a *hollow-core door* (which see).

sound absorption coefficient   The fraction of sound energy that is absorbed by the surface of a material or component (e.g., ceiling tile), as opposed to being reflected. A material that absorbs a high percentage of sound would be designated with a higher sound absorption coefficient than a material that absorbs a low percentage of sound.

sound attenuation   The reduction in the intensity of sound waves transmitted from one point to another.

> REAL ESTATE APPLICATION: An HVAC duct silencer attenuates sound, thus providing a quieter environment near the duct.

sound-insulating glass   A glass unit which efficiently insulates the interior of a building from outside noises. A sound-insulating glass typically consists of two panes of glass (lights) fixed and sealed in a resilient mounting and separated by an air space (gap).

soundproofing   The design and construction of a building using materials and assemblies that make it impervious to sound transmitted from the outside to the inside of the building or from one point to another within a building.

sound transmission   The transfer of sound from one point to another.

sound transmission class (STC) rating   The level which indicates how well construction components (walls, ceilings, doors) reduce sound. Construction with a high rating (STC 40-45) reduces sound more than construction with a lower rating (STC 20).

spalling   The separation or flaking of material from the face of stone or concrete.

> REAL ESTATE APPLICATION: Usually a result of prolonged exposure to the elements (rain and moisture, ice melt materials, oil deposits from vehicles, etc.), spalling of concrete walkways and parking surfaces is a common problem. Continued spalling can lead to structural degradation, particularly if concrete reinforcing components (e.g., rebars) are exposed to the corrosive elements. Excessive spalling may also result when there is excess air or water in the cement mixture at installation.

span   The horizontal distance between two components; the linear distance in feet and inches between two beams or two columns.

specification   A written document describing in detail the scope of work, materials, methods of installation, and operating parameters for a particular contract. A project specification, abbreviated *spec*, is a critical component of the contract documents.

splash block   A small masonry block strategically positioned on the ground below a downspout, to direct roof drainage away from the perimeter of a building and prevent puddling and soil erosion.

splashboard   A board set against a wall to protect it from water damage due to splashing (carelessness), particularly behind a sink.

sprayed acoustical plaster   A sound-absorbing plaster applied to a surface (e.g., a ceiling) using a spray gun such that the resulting plaster coating has an irregular (rough) surface.

sprayed fireproofing   A heat-insulating material that is applied directly to structural members (beams, girders, columns, steel decking) with a spray gun to increase resistance to fire.

spreading rate The area covered by a gallon of paint or other liquid or semiliquid material, expressed in square feet or square yards per gallon.

square Unit of measure of roofing or siding materials equal to 100 square feet.

staging A method of running a *fast track* job. (See also *scaffold.*)

stainless steel A high-strength steel alloy containing approximately 4%–25% chromium that is highly resistant to corrosion and rust.

REAL ESTATE APPLICATION: Stainless steel is frequently used in the fabrication of kitchen appliances and food preparation and storage surfaces.

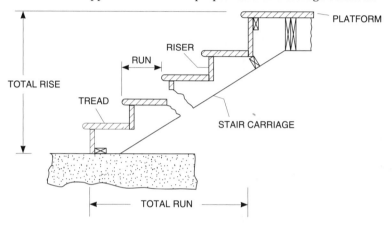

stair nomenclature

stair platform A landing in a stairway that breaks a continuous run of stairs; also, an extended landing at the uppermost part of a staircase (see diagram).

stair riser The vertical face of a stair step. The total vertical distance from the lowest point of the lowermost stair to the top of the platform level is referred to as the *total rise* (see diagram).

stair run The horizontal width (front to back) of a single stair tread. The total horizontal distance covered by a flight of steps is referred to as the *total run* (see diagram).

stair tread The horizontal portion of a step (see diagram).

stairwell The enclosed vertical shaft in a building that contains a staircase.

standard A defined level or degree of quality that is adequate and appropriate to the intended purpose or use. That which is established by authority, custom, or general consent as an example or model to be followed. Established criteria for composition, size, and other physical characteristics of specific materials (e.g., wood and steel structural members).

REAL ESTATE APPLICATION: Real estate management personnel usually establish "building standard" requirements for each property in order to maintain consistent appearance, streamline or preserve current building operating practices, and control costs.

static load A load on a structure that is constant—i.e., it does not change in magnitude or position over time.

steel and concrete framing   A very common method of construction of small to mid-size buildings using reinforced concrete and structural steel; also called *combination steel and concrete framing*. The steel column shapes surrounded by and bonded to reinforced concrete are referred to as combination columns.

steel-frame construction   See *skeleton construction*.

stiffener   A secondary structural member (angle iron or channel) attached to a plate to increase its stiffness and prevent buckling.

stile   One of the vertical structural members (the upright edge) of a window or door frame. A wood door with a stile type of construction can add a decorative touch to a finished space.

stone dust   Pulverized stone (fine particles) used to fill the spaces between bricks or stones in the construction of exterior walkways or driveways.

stop   The trim piece on the inside of a door frame against which the door closes (a *door stop*); the molding on the inside of a double-hung window frame (a *window stop* or *sash stop*); sometimes also called *bead*.

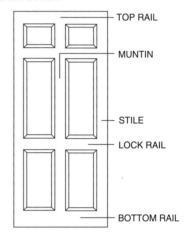

stile and rail door

story   The space in a building between floor levels; specifically, the part of a building between the upper surface of one floor and the upper surface of the floor above; synonymous with *floor*.

>   REAL ESTATE APPLICATION: The term story is often used in a general sense when describing the height of a high-rise structure: a 50-story building.

structural drawings   Plan drawings of the design, layout, and other specifics of a building s structural components (beams, girders, columns) prepared by structural engineers.

structural engineering   The branch of engineering concerned with the design and construction of buildings to withstand anticipated physical forces (loads) without danger of failure or loss of function.

structural failure   Inability of a building or structural member to support the design loads; a collapse of an essential component of a structure.

structural steel   Steel rolled into a variety of shapes and sizes (beams, angles, plates, etc.) and fabricated for use as structural members in load-bearing applications.

structural tee   A structural steel member in the shape of the letter T, produced by flame-cutting one of the flanges from a standard I beam or wide-flange beam; *T-shaped structural steel*.

structural wall   See *bearing wall*.

stucco   An exterior surface finish, usually textured, using a plaster material composed of Portland cement, lime, sand, and water.

stud One of a series of vertical (upright) framing members to which sheathing or paneling is attached to form walls or partitions. Studs may be made of wood, steel, and composite materials.

REAL ESTATE APPLICATION: Wood studs are typically used in residential construction while metal studs are used primarily in commercial or industrial construction.

subbasement The level of a building (story) immediately below the basement. There may be more than one such underground story.

REAL ESTATE APPLICATION: The various utilities of a high-rise typically enter the building at the subbasement level.

subcontractor A company or individual having a contract with the prime (general) contractor for a project to perform a specific portion of the work for which the prime contractor is responsible (e.g., concrete, electrical, painting); also abbreviated *sub.*

substantial completion Condition of the work when the project is substantially complete as specified in the contract documents (i.e., ready for owner acceptance and occupancy); any items remaining to be finished at this point would be noted in writing *(punch list).* Substantial completion is typically certified by the architect prior to final payment by the owner.

substrate An underlying material to which a surface finish is attached or bonded. (See also *underlayment.*)

supplementary conditions Part of the contract documents that is in addition to the general conditions of the agreement. Typically placed in the contract documents immediately following the general conditions, the supplementary conditions are specific to the job for which the contract has been written. (See also *general conditions.*)

supply bond A guarantee provided by a surety that materials will be delivered in accordance with the contract document (i.e., quantity and quality as required). This bond is secured by a subcontractor as a protection for the general contractor on a project. It differs from a *labor bond,* which guarantees the workmanship of the job. (See also *labor and material payment bond.*)

suspended ceiling An acoustical ceiling that is hung by wires or other means from the structural framing members (e.g., metal decking) above; also called *drop ceiling.* The method is typically used in office buildings.

swatch A relatively small sample of a material (carpet, plastic laminate, etc.) that is representative of the whole.

swinging scaffold A temporary platform suspended by ropes or cables from a roof parapet or other element on top of a structure, which can be raised or lowered in order to service the building; used for window washing and exterior surface cleaning and tuckpointing.

tape joint A flat (abutting) joint between two pieces of sheetrock wall that is sealed with a joint compound and reinforcing tape in order to cover the joint (a more aesthetic final finish) and provide added strength.

tar-and-gravel roofing See *built-up roofing (BUR) membrane.*

tempered glass Glass that is significantly stronger (2–4 times) than ordinary glass due to prestressing (heating and rapidly cooling) during the manufacturing process. The rapid cooling (quenching) produces a compressively stressed surface layer.

template   A pattern, typically of sheet material (e.g., flat, rigid cardboard), used as a guide for laying out and dimensioning work.

temporary electrical service   Electrical service used for a limited time, as during a construction project on a vacant floor or during an asbestos abatement project, to power electrically operated equipment and machinery.

tensile strength   The resistance of a material against the forces of tension (pulling apart). The forces of tension along a structural component are opposite in action to the forces of compression. (*Compressive strength* is resistance to crushing under pressure.)

terrazzo   A marble-aggregate concrete surface that is usually cast in place and ground smooth. Terrazzo floor surfaces are extremely hard, durable, and easy to maintain.

thermal barrier   A material with low conductivity (e.g., vinyl or polyurethane insulation) used as a spacer in an assembly of conductive materials to reduce the flow of heat; also called *thermal break*. Thermal barriers are typically used in colder climates and in curtain walls and windows.

thermal conductivity   See *thermal transmittance*.

thermal insulation   The process of insulating against heat transmission; also applied to materials that are effective in retarding heat flow. A good thermal insulator has a high *thermal resistance* (which see).

thermal resistance   Ability of materials to resist the transfer of heat; the opposite of *thermal conductance*. Measurement of the resistance of heat transfer through a material when there is a 1°F difference in air temperature from one side to the other is called *R value*. Thermal resistance (thermal resistivity) is the reciprocal of thermal conductance (thermal conductivity). A high R value indicates that a material is a good insulator.

thermal transmittance   The rate of transfer of heat through a material of a specified thickness when the air temperature is 1°F different from one side to the other, measured in Btu per hour per square foot; also called *U value* (the opposite of R value).

thermoplastic   A material that softens when heated and hardens again when cooled. Thermoplastics never cure; they retain their thermoplastic properties throughout their use life. The seals of thermoplastic materials are fused by the use of heat (e.g., thermal welding) or adhesives.

REAL ESTATE APPLICATION: Thermoplastics are used in roofing membrane applications, where they are repeatedly softened by heat and hardened by cooling. Polyvinyl chloride (PVC) and its numerous variations are the most common examples. Others are thermoplastic olefins (TPOs) based on polypropylene and ethylene propylene polymers.

thermoset   A type of polymer that is cured (set) by heat. The curing process is not reversible. Once cured, thermosets are relatively incapable of softening when heated and may decompose. Thermoset materials are sealed by the use of adhesives.

REAL ESTATE APPLICATION: Thermosets are used as roofing membrane materials, the most common being *ethylene propylene diene monomer (EPDM)*, a synthetic rubber. Polyisobutylene (PIB) is another example. Thermoset membranes may be installed in fully adhered, mechanically fastened, and ballasted applications. They may also be reinforced or nonreinforced and are available in a variety of colors (black, gray, white, etc.).

tinted glass   Glass that has been darkened in color by incorporation of additives in the manufacturing process in order to filter out solar energy and light. There are many variations in glass tinting.

> REAL ESTATE APPLICATION: Use of tinted glass will reduce solar heat gain through windows, thereby reducing the load on a building air-conditioning system.

tongue-and-groove joint   A joint formed by the insertion of the protruding tongue of one component into the corresponding depressed groove of another, as floor boards machined with a tongue on one edge and a groove on the other.

GROOVE   TONGUE

tongue-and-groove joint

topsoil   The surface or upper layer of soil, which usually contains organic material and is not conducive to building foundation support.

translucent   Characteristic of a material that admits light but diffuses it so that objects are not clearly visible through the material.

> REAL ESTATE APPLICATION: Translucent glass is sometimes used in office partitions to admit light but provide some measure of privacy. A more common application is in shower and bathtub enclosures.

transom   A horizontal component across the top of a window or door, usually hinged and used for ventilation.

transparent   Allowing light to pass through with minimal scattering so that objects on the other side are clearly visible.

travertine   A variety of limestone, usually containing bands of various colors, used as a building stone for interior flooring and facing of walls, particularly in highly visible construction fit-up areas (building entrance lobbies, commercial bank space).

tread   See *stair tread.*

trim   Millwork and metal finishing elements of a room, such as the visible woodwork and moldings that serve as ornaments or protective edges.

truss   A structural component comprised of a combination of members typically configured to form a rigid triangular framework and often used to support a roof. Trusses may be made of wood or steel or a combination of the two.

> REAL ESTATE APPLICATION: Trusses are common in the construction of large single-story industrial buildings and warehouses.

tuckpointing   See *pointing.*

tunnel test   The common name for the official NFPA test method for determining the surface burning characteristics of building materials.

turnbuckle A device for connecting and tightening (shortening) a cable, rod, or stay. A turnbuckle has right-handed threads on one end and left-handed threads on the other, with a link connecting the two. It can normally be hand turned for tightening.

underlayment Plywood, hardboard, or other smooth materials laid onto and adhered to the subfloor *(substrate)* to provide an even surface for attachment of the finish floor (e.g.,vinyl tiles, hardwood flooring, carpeting).

unit price A price per unit of a specified material or service. Examples include: $20.00 per man hour–straight time, $30.00 per man hour–overtime, or $185.00 per 100 square feet of ceiling tile installed (material and labor).

uplift The upward pressure on a structure, component, or surface due to a force such as water freezing and thawing underneath brick pavers or wind blowing across a roof membrane.

upset price An amount agreed to by an owner and contractor as the maximum cost of specific work performed; also called *upset fee* or *guaranteed maximum cost.*

usable area The net floor area of a building or a tenant's space after deducting the *common* (shared) *areas* in the core of the building, which include public corridors, restrooms, elevators, emergency stairwells, and other service areas (electrical closets, phone closets, janitorial closets).

U value See *thermal transmittance.*

vapor barrier Impervious material applied to restrict the passage of water vapor through a wall, roof, or other structural component; also called *moisture barrier.*

variance Written authorization from the city building department or other responsible agency allowing construction in a manner that deviates from the standard building code or ordinance.

veneer A thin sheet of wood used as a facing material on a less-attractive wood base or as one of several plies in plywood in order to strengthen its composition. A masonry (brick, stone) facing applied to the exterior of a structure. Metal and plastic may also be applied as veneers (a Formica countertop is an example of the latter).

verdigris The greenish colored film that forms naturally on copper and copper-containing metals as they weather in the open air; a form of corrosion, also called *patina.*

vinyl tile A resilient floor covering which is composed of vinyl chloride (binder) mixed with fillers, pigment (for coloration), and plasticizers. *Vinyl composition tile (VCT)* has glass fibers added for reinforcement.

> REAL ESTATE APPLICATION: Vinyl tile is frequently used as a floor covering in kitchen areas, office copy rooms, service areas, and other areas with heavy foot traffic. (See also *resilient flooring.*)

wainscot Use of a different, often decorative, facing material on the lower three to four feet of an interior wall; more specifically, decorative wood paneling applied to a wall from the floor base to approximately 30–32 inches above the finished floor.

waiver of lien A voluntary relinquishing by subcontractors of *mechanic's lien* rights to make a claim against a property for payment of materials or labor provided; a requirement so the general contractor or the property owner can receive a draw against a construction loan.

wallboard An interior surface finishing material comprising a gypsum core encased in heavy paper and applied to framing members using dry methods; sometimes also referred to as *gypsum drywall* or *sheetrock*. (See also *drywall*.)

wallguard A protective resilient strip, with two surfaces typically at right angles to one another, applied to the corner of a wall to protect it from being damaged by carts or other movable conveyors; also, a protective strip of resilient material (a type of bumper) mounted on a wall to protect the surface from damage.

waterproof Impervious to water. *Waterproofing* refers to the application of a material (rubber membrane, sealer compound) to a building surface (e.g., foundation) to prevent the infiltration of water.

water-resistant Capable of withstanding (resisting) limited amounts of water or water vapor, used in referring to materials that resist the action or entry of water (but do not wholly prevent it). A caulking product is an example of a water-resistant material.

weatherproof To protect a material or component (e.g., electric wiring) or construct a building so that it can withstand exposure to the weather without damage or loss of function.

weatherstrip A strip of metal, plastic, or other material applied to abutting edges to seal the joint between an exterior door and the threshold or between a window and the sill or casing. *Weatherstripping* is done to prevent cold air, snow, and rain from entering a building.

weathertight Properly sealed against the intrusion of rain, snow, and cold and warm air.

weep hole A small opening in a window or wall system to allow accumulated moisture from condensation or water penetration to drain to the outside of the building.

REAL ESTATE APPLICATION: Effective design and placement of weep holes during construction is an important part of preventing water damage to building components.

wide-flange (WF) beam A large structural steel member that is almost square in cross section, resembling the letter H but with a wider flange than an I beam. Wide-flange beams are used for large building columns.

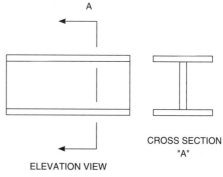

wide-flange beam

wind guard A component constructed and/or applied to a structure to provide protection against the wind.

wind load   The horizontal force exerted on a building or structure by the pressure of the wind. Wind load calculations are an important factor in the design and subsequent construction of a building.

window jamb   See *jamb.*

wood-frame construction   A very common type of construction in which the floors and roof as well as exterior bearing walls are made of wood. Wood is universally available and possesses many properties that make it suitable for various complex uses in construction (e.g., high strength relative to its weight). Overall, wood provides a very economical way to build, particularly single-family homes and small commercial and retail structures.

working drawings   Drawings that contain the necessary information to manufacture or construct a building or component thereof. Working drawings are part of the contract documents and are used by the architect, contractor, subcontractors, and others.

workstation   A series of strategically positioned panels, free-standing as a group in place, used to create individual work spaces for employees; also called *cubicle.* Workstation panels vary in height, dimensions, and surface finishes (materials, colors) and can be configured in a variety of ways. The various other components of a workstation, in addition to the panels, include work surfaces, task lighting, built-in electrical outlets, overhead storage compartments, and file cabinets.

REAL ESTATE APPLICATION: Work stations are commonly used in office space applications, particularly in the interior floor areas of office buildings. (The tendency is to build separate spaces for office and other use along the perimeter walls.) The primary advantage of such pre-fabricated workstations is flexibility of location and configuration and ease and speed of installation. Workstations also reduce the need (and, therefore, the cost) to modify support systems such as HVAC ductwork, general office lighting, and sprinkler systems when workstation location and configuration changes are made.

wrought iron   Nearly pure iron, fibrous in composition with low carbon content, that is ductile and resists corrosion; used in decorative outdoor applications as railings, fences, lamp posts, etc.

Environmental Management and Indoor Air Quality

abatement Reduction of the degree or intensity of pollution; reduction of the amount or concentration or outright removal of a hazardous substance. (See also *remediation*.)

acid rain See *nitrogen oxide (NO$_x$)*.

acute Having a short, relatively severe course, as a disease or condition of sudden onset and short duration; used to characterize symptoms resulting from one-time or short-term exposure to an environmental contaminant. (Compare *chronic*.)

airborne Carried in or by the air; used to refer to the presence of solid (particulate) or gaseous contaminants in the air. (See also *particulate; volatile organic compounds [VOCs]*.)

air cleaning The process of removing airborne particulates and/or gases by filtration, electrostatic precipitation, gas sorption, or other means.

> REAL ESTATE APPLICATION: Filtration accomplished by strategically positioned filters in the air supply stream is the most common form of air cleaning in typical HVAC applications in general occupancy situations.

air monitoring The process of collecting representative samples of air within a prescribed space and testing them for specific contaminants.

> REAL ESTATE APPLICATION: Air may be monitored to ensure acceptable air quality for building occupants or to protect workers performing abatement of asbestos or other contaminants (e.g., lead, PCBs). Airborne asbestos fibers are monitored using an *air pump* (which see).

air pump A type of vacuum pump; in the environmental field, an electrically operated centrifugal pump used to pull air from a room or other space through a confined restricted opening that contains a filter of sufficient fineness to trap asbestos fibers. (The air pump is not used to remove asbestos fibers from the space, but rather to determine the concentration of fibers within the space; see also *fiber concentration*.)

air sample A representative amount of air obtained from a specific area, usually by means of a specialized vacuum pump, to be tested for specific contaminants.

asbestos   Six naturally occurring minerals   *chrysotile, tremolite, actinolite, amosite, crocidolite, anthophyllite*   which separate into long flexible fibers suitable for uses requiring materials that are incombustible, nonconducting, or chemical resistant. When mined and processed, asbestos separates into very thin fibers that are usually invisible to the naked eye.

REAL ESTATE APPLICATION: Asbestos fibers are a known health hazard. Workers directly exposed to asbestos (mining and manufacturing, especially without respiratory protective devices) are likely to develop *asbestosis* (a fibrous scarring of the lungs that causes difficulty breathing due to reduced lung capacity and may lead to death). Asbestos has also been found to cause lung cancer, particularly when prolonged exposure to asbestos is combined with tobacco smoking, and *mesothelioma* (a malignant growth of the lining of the chest or abdominal cavity).

The U.S. Environmental Protection Agency (EPA) and Occupational Safety and Health Administration (OSHA) have joint regulatory responsibility for asbestos management. The EPA stance on how to deal with asbestos in the workplace is more conservative than that of the National Institute for Occupational Safety and Health (NIOSH). EPA considers the health risk to most building occupants to be very low and, therefore, prefers to be proactive in the management of asbestos in place rather than aggressively removing it. Two important EPA documents specific to the management of asbestos are *Managing Asbestos in Place: A Building Owner's Guide to O&M Programs for ACM* (the "Green Book") and *Guidance for Controlling ACM in Buildings* (the "Purple Book").

State and local compliance requirements regarding asbestos abatement, including disposal (i.e., as a hazardous waste), may be more stringent than the federal regulations. It is important to know and comply with all regulations that apply to asbestos. Consultation with local health officials regarding potential hazards of various forms of asbestos is also advisable.

asbestos abatement   The encapsulation, enclosure, or removal of asbestos-containing material (ACM) under controlled conditions.

asbestos-containing material (ACM)   By regulatory definition (prior to 1990), material containing more than 1% by weight of asbestos. More current regulations specify other methods of determining asbestos content.

REAL ESTATE APPLICATION: Prior to and into the early 1970s, asbestos-containing materials were frequently used in fireproofing and insulation and as a component of floor tiles, roofing felt and shingles, ceiling tiles, etc. Asbestos-containing fireproof material covering the structural steel is very common in buildings of that period. Asbestos-containing pipe insulation and boiler lagging is also common in steam heating applications.

The presence of ACM can significantly impact the operation or sale of real property. Asbestos fibers released from ACM may remain in the air for many hours and may be inhaled during this time. Because of the potential health hazard, removal of asbestos is often the preferred method of abatement.

Asbestos Hazard Emergency Response Act (AHERA)   A federal law passed in 1986 to amend the *Toxic Substances Control Act* that focuses primarily on identification and abatement of asbestos in public schools. Administered by the U.S. Environmental Protection Agency (EPA), AHERA requires schools to retain qualified individuals to inventory all asbestos materials. The Act also requires training for school employees whose job activities may result in asbestos disturbances.

barrier   A material or structure used to prevent or delay the movement of contaminants into the accessible environment. A physical separation of one defined space from another to isolate areas undergoing environmental remediation. An impermeable material such as polyethylene sheeting is often used for this purpose.

bioaerosol   Airborne material that is or was living (e.g., mold, bacteria, insect body parts, animal feces).

biological contaminants   Living organisms such as viruses, bacteria, and fungi (also called *microbes*) and agents derived from living organisms (mammal and bird antigens) which, when inhaled, can cause allergic reactions, respiratory and hypersensitivity disorders, infectious diseases, and other health effects. (See also *bacteria, fungi, microbes* in Water Treatment, Water Chemistry.)

REAL ESTATE APPLICATION: Indoor airborne microbial contaminants are typically related to water contamination. Some potential sources are stagnant water in HVAC system mechanical components (e.g., drain pans), humidifiers, porous insulation in air-handling units, cooling towers, and excessive relative humidity (greater than 70%) in occupied spaces. In almost all cases, contamination can be controlled by restricting the water or nutrients required for growth of microbes and proper chemical treatment.

building-related illness   A discrete, identifiable disease or illness that can be traced to a specific pollutant or source within a building. (Contrast *sick building syndrome.*)

bulk sample   A sample of a material suspected of containing a contaminant, which sample is then tested for the contaminant. In the case of a suspected asbestos-containing material (ACM), results of testing a bulk sample would indicate whether and how much asbestos is present in the material itself. (Compare *air sample.*)

carbon dioxide (CO_2)   A colorless, odorless gas exhaled by animals and humans during breathing. (See also *design conditions, exfiltration, infiltration, occupied load* in Heating, Ventilation, Air Conditioning [HVAC] and Refrigeration Systems.)

REAL ESTATE APPLICATION: Carbon dioxide levels, measured in parts per million (ppm), are the primary indicator of the effectiveness with which air is being exchanged in a given space. CO_2 levels in a typical facility will vary depending on the occupant load and the degree to which fresh air is exchanged in the space via HVAC systems, infiltration, exfiltration, available operable windows, etc. Peak CO_2 concentrations above 1,000 ppm indicate inadequate ventilation. Given moderate to full occupancy, CO_2 levels tend to be higher during design heating and cooling conditions as less outside fresh air is typically introduced into the building during these extreme conditions since it is inefficient and costly to heat or cool relatively cold or hot, humid outside air.

CO_2 levels can be measured as required either within a specific space using portable instruments or continuously using an instrument mounted permanently in a common HVAC return air duct. In the accompanying diagram (see next page), CO_2 levels, as measured in the building, increase over time with occupancy by people. The building HVAC system appears to have adequately stabilized the CO_2 levels after they peaked at 2:00 P.M.

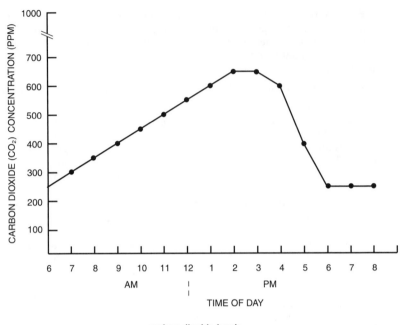

carbon dioxide levels

Also, the CO_2 level decreased noticeably after 4:00 P.M. as the occupancy of the building decreased.

carbon monoxide (CO)   A colorless, odorless, highly toxic gas; a product of the incomplete combustion (burning) of carbon. Accumulation of carbon monoxide in the blood may result in disruption of the transportation of oxygen. Individuals with cardiovascular and pulmonary diseases, the elderly, and the unborn fetus are particularly sensitive to elevated CO levels.

> REAL ESTATE APPLICATION: Carbon monoxide gas kills very quickly and is often difficult to detect in enclosed spaces, as when people warm up vehicles inside garages without opening the doors during cold weather. CO levels above several parts per million indicate an inappropriate presence of combustion by-products. CO may enter a building in the form of entrained vehicle exhaust (e.g., from the loading dock area or an in-building parking facility) due to the proximity of an HVAC air intake or to building and outside air pressure differentials accentuated by cracks or openings near the source of exhaust fumes.

chemical sensitivity   Development of symptoms (e.g., tightness of the chest, dizziness, nasal congestion, eye and throat irritations) upon being exposed to certain chemicals. People may react to trace amounts of chemicals to which they have become sensitized previously even though such prior exposure (one-time, repeated, continuous) may have been without incident.

chlorofluorocarbons (CFCs)   A group of inert halogenated organic compounds used as refrigerants, solvents, and aerosol propellants. CFCs are synthesized by replacing one element of a hydrocarbon molecule (i.e., hydrogen) with another element (e.g., fluorine, bromine, and especially chlorine).

Because of their chlorine content, CFCs are thought to contribute to ozone depletion when released to the atmosphere, and they have been increasingly regulated since the mid-1970s. By international agreement—the *Montreal Protocol,* to which the United States is one of 49 signatories—and under the federal Clean Air Act Amendments of 1990, CFCs are scheduled to be phased out and replaced by compounds that contain fewer or no atoms of chlorine. The two leading alternative refrigerants currently accepted under the Clean Air Act and targeted to replace specific chlorofluorocarbons (CFC-11, CFC-12, CFC-114, and CFC-500) are HCFC-123, a *hydrochlorofluorocarbon,* and HFC-134a, a *hydrofluorocarbon.* (See also *refrigerant* in Heating, Ventilation, Air Conditioning [HVAC] and Refrigeration Systems and *Halon* in Life Safety and Fire Protection Systems.)

chronic Of long duration; used to characterize symptoms resulting from repeated long-term exposure to environmental contaminants, which do not go away. (Compare *acute.*)

class of activity The classification of various asbestos-related activities, as defined by OSHA, which calls for specific actions regardless of the anticipated asbestos levels. *Class I* activities include the removal of asbestos-containing material (ACM) in thermal insulation and surface materials. *Class II* activities include the removal of other types of ACM (e.g., roofing and floor tile). *Class III* activities involve maintenance and repair work where ACM is disturbed. *Class IV* activities involve custodial activities in which workers have minimal contact with ACM.

Clean Air Act A federal law, enacted in 1970 and amended in 1977 and 1990, that establishes air quality standards and mechanisms for administering those standards. The *Clean Air Act Amendments* (1990) gave the U.S. Environmental Protection Agency (EPA) new broad powers to reduce airborne pollutants, particularly those emitted by boilers—e.g., nitrogen oxides (NO_x).

Clean Water Act A federal law that establishes standards for water quality and mechanisms for administering those standards. Originally enacted in 1972 as the Federal Water Pollution Control Act (FWPCA), the Act was renamed in 1977 and amended extensively in 1987.

clearance test See *final air clearance.*

Comprehensive Environmental Response, Compensation, and Liability Act (CERCLA) A law promulgated in 1980 and amended in 1986 by the Superfund Amendments and Reauthorization Act (SARA). Collectively known as *Superfund,* they provide funding and enforcement authority for cleaning up hazardous waste sites. (See also *Superfund Amendments and Reauthorization Act [SARA].*)

> REAL ESTATE APPLICATION: Under CERCLA, any and all owners of a property, past and present, can be held liable for cleanup of a hazardous waste site, which is one reason Phase I site assessments are requested with increasing frequency.

concentration Percentage or degree of potency of a particular substance, usually measured in parts per million (ppm).

containment The complete isolation of an environmental remediation site through the effective use of physical barriers and air pressurization and exhaust systems.

contaminant   Something that pollutes or otherwise renders a desired thing unfit for use, as a solid, liquid, or gaseous material that may cause adverse health effects if present, say, in air or water in a significant concentration.

decontaminate   To remove contaminants. The process of removing asbestos-containing material or other substances considered environmentally contaminating from an object, surface, person, or space, usually through mechanical or other means—e.g., chemical treatment. (See also *high-efficiency particulate air [HEPA] filter.*)

decontamination unit   Usually a three-section, temporary structure consisting of an equipment room, a shower room, and a *clean room.*

REAL ESTATE APPLICATION: The decontamination (decon) unit separates the environmental remediation site from the adjacent staging area. All personnel who enter and leave the remediation site must do so through the decon unit, which is the only pathway into and out of the area. In asbestos remediation, the decon unit normally comprises 2' × 4' rooms constructed of wood frames and polyethylene sheeting.

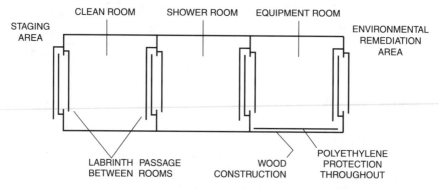

decontamination unit

Department of Environmental Protection (DEP)   One way in which state or local agencies responsible for environmental regulatory compliance may be named. Some states configure this entity as a state EPA (e.g., Illinois Environmental Protection Agency) while others subsume this function under a Department of Natural Resources.

diagnostic testing   Strategically conducted tests in which location, frequency, timing, and the method of sample collection are considered with the purpose of developing a pattern or an observation in order to determine means of resolving an indoor air quality problem or other environmental concern.

dioxin   A family of chemical compounds (known as dibenzo-*p*-dioxins) that are by-products of paper bleaching and the manufacturing of pesticides, refined oil products, and other chlorinated hydrocarbon compounds. Because dioxin is a by-product as opposed to an active ingredient, it is rarely listed on warning labels for pesticides and other materials. Dioxin is considered by the EPA to be a carcinogen, a hazardous waste, and a priority toxic pollutant.

REAL ESTATE APPLICATION: In order to control and minimize the use of chemicals containing dioxins, real estate managers should require landscaping and exterminating contractors to take precautions in the use of pest control substances.

disinfectant A chemical that destroys or inactivates infectious agents (pathogenic microbes) or other undesirable organisms but not necessarily their spores.

disposal bags Lightweight plastic containers of specified thickness, size, color, markings, etc., used to hold abated asbestos-containing material for subsequent removal from the job site and proper disposal.

disturbance Disruption; interference. Specifically, the physical disruption of asbestos-containing material (ACM) resulting in a release into the air of asbestos fibers, which could pose a potential health risk to building occupants. Friable ACM is at greater risk of disturbance than *nonfriable* (intact, undisturbed) ACM, which poses no health risk. (See also *friable.*)

dose An amount of a substance to which an individual is exposed; specifically, the amount of contaminated solid, liquid, or vapor ingested or inhaled by an individual. Also, the cumulative amount of radiation to which an individual is exposed over a given period of time.

double bag To use two bags. A common procedure specified by environmental industry consultants and used by environmental contractors whereby asbestos-containing material removed from a building is put in a bag for storage and disposal, and that bag is then placed in a second bag to minimize the potential release or spill of hazardous material.

effluent Wastewater that is discharged into the environment.

electromagnetic field (EMF) A field of force (energy) associated with an electric charge in motion having both electric and magnetic components and containing a definite amount of energy. Electromagnetic fields always exist whenever electricity flows. Electromagnetic fields (particularly high-level EMFs) can cause functional problems with electric circuits and equipment. Although some scientific data are suggestive, there is no conclusive evidence of a link between EMFs and adverse health effects in humans.

emission A discharge, especially to the atmosphere, of a substance (particulates; vapor or gas) which may be a potential air pollutant. The term is also applied to discharges that affect indoor air quality.

encapsulation Surrounded or encased, as in a capsule. Specifically, the application of a liquid coating agent to asbestos-containing material in order to isolate it and prevent future disturbance or release.

environmental impact statement (EIS) A document that reports the findings of a comprehensive analysis performed to determine the environmental effects of a proposed action. An EIS may be required for federal actions, especially when the habitat of an endangered species may be affected, or by the EPA on an as-needed basis for any other proposed action.

environmental management plan See *operation and maintenance (O&M) plan.*

Environmental Protection Agency (EPA) An independent agency of the U.S. government established in 1970 to consolidate the various federal entities involved with pollution abatement and control. The entity responsible for administering a wide array of laws that set air and water quality standards, regulate the manufacture and use of pesticides and other chemicals, and control discharges to waterways and disposal in landfills. It also conducts non-regulatory indoor air quality programs that emphasize research, information dissemination, technical guidance, and training. (Non-federal regulatory agencies are discussed under *Department of Environmental Protection [DEP];* see also specific environmental laws.)

environmental site assessment   An environmental study from which a report is created that documents the environmental status of the investigated site—i.e., a determination by environmental specialists of the presence or potential presence of contamination.

Environmental site assessments are typically conducted in phases that vary in the level of scrutiny of a property. A *Preliminary Site Assessment (PSA)* is a general environmental investigation that does not involve any on-site testing; it is comparable to and often conducted in lieu of a phase I site assessment. A *Phase I* assessment is slightly more detailed and includes some on-site testing. A *Phase II* assessment examines specific problems or potential problems identified in the PSA or Phase I assessment and may include the formation and testing of specific plans for cleanup or remediation. A *Phase III* program of cleanup or remediation is conducted on sites requiring such action.

environmental stressors   Conditions other than indoor air contaminants (e.g., humidity extremes, drafts, lack of air circulation, noise, vibration, overcrowding, light glare) that cause stress, comfort, or health problems.

environmental tobacco smoke (ETS)   An indoor air pollutant and source of indoor air contaminants; also called *secondhand smoke*. ETS is a combination of sidestream smoke from the burning end of the cigarette, pipe, or cigar and the exhaled mainstream smoke from the smoker. ETS contains over 4,000 chemicals, several of which are known carcinogens, and is believed to be a cause of lung cancer in healthy nonsmokers.

> REAL ESTATE APPLICATION: The optimum solution to the potential health concerns associated with ETS in an indoor environment is to prohibit smoking in the indoor environment. If smoking areas are established indoors, they should be separately ventilated, negatively pressurized in relation to surrounding interior spaces, and supplied with much more ventilation air than nonsmoking areas. The air from the smoking area should be exhausted directly outdoors, not recirculated in the building or vented with the general exhaust of the building.

ergonomics   An applied science that investigates the impact of the physical environment on people's health and comfort—things like the proper chair height for computer operators.

exhaust fumes   Combustion by-products emitted by automobiles and other internal combustion engines. Exhaust fumes pose an indoor air quality health concern if they are of substantial volume and in close proximity to building air pathways.

exposure   Contact with a potentially hazardous substance, whether intentional or not. An actual *exposure level* as measured by an industrial hygienist is the measurable amount of material to which an individual was exposed in the area of concern. The maximum permissible exposure level is the upper limit of a particular substance to which one could be exposed over a specified time period without any expectation of raising health concerns. (See also *permissible exposure limit [PEL].*)

failed test   The results of an air test (e.g., an asbestos fiber concentration test) that exceed the prescribed maximum limit set by the appropriate (local or federal) authority.

fiber   Thread-like in form; specifically, the form of airborne particles of asbestos. Asbestosis and other long-term health effects can result when human lungs are exposed to substantial concentrations of airborne asbestos fibers for prolonged periods.

fiber concentration   The number of fibers (specifically, asbestos) per unit volume, usually expressed as fibers per cubic centimeter. Fiber concentration is normally determined using a vacuum pump to draw a given volume of air through a filter over a set period of time. The fiber concentration is determined visually by placing the filter under the lens of a microscope and counting the number of fibers in a measured portion of the filter surface. This count is then converted from fibers per millimeter (area) to fibers per cubic centimeter (volume).

fiber release   Disturbance of a material such that component fibers are released into the air; normally associated with unintentional disruption of asbestos-containing material (ACM) that is *friable* in nature (i.e., crumbling).

REAL ESTATE APPLICATION: Release of asbestos fibers, as from friable ACM, could be caused by vibration of equipment in use nearby (e.g., mechanical coring of an overhead concrete floor), deterioration of ACM due to water penetration, or unintentional disruption by a contractor working on a nearby system component such as a ceiling grid or sprinkler support.

final air clearance   An air test (as required by local and federal agencies for occupancy) to determine and ensure a minimum acceptable threshold level of specific contaminants, typically performed immediately after completion of remediation of the subject space; also called *clearance test.*

floor tile   See *vinyl asbestos tile (VAT).*

formaldehyde   A *volatile organic compound* (VOC) used in the manufacture of some construction and interior finishing materials—insulation, particle board, and masonite sheeting are examples. New materials containing formaldehyde may emit vapors for some time after installation. Such materials can be particularly hazardous in the event of a fire as they generate toxic smoke.

REAL ESTATE APPLICATION: Formaldehyde (chemically, HCHO) is present in relatively low concentrations in most office environments. The most likely sources when higher concentrations are present is new office furnishings and materials (carpeting, fabric surfaces in so-called systems furniture, insulation, etc.) People experiencing such symptoms as itching of the eyes, nose, and throat may indicate an elevated concentration of formaldehyde.

friable   Easily crumbled; used to describe asbestos-containing material that is in poor physical condition—i.e., can easily be crumbled and, if physically disturbed, may release asbestos fibers into the air. (Asbestos-containing material in good condition is typically referred to as *nonfriable.*)

full-face respirator   See *personal air purifying respirator (PAPR).*

gas sorption   A method of air cleaning that controls compounds that behave as gases rather than as particles (gaseous contaminants such as formaldehyde vapor, sulfur dioxide, etc.), using activated carbon, chemical reaction, binding, or diffusion to remove or substantially dilute the contaminant. (Operating expenses of gas sorption units are comparatively high.)

generator   As defined by the EPA, a person, facility, or mobile source that emits pollutants into the air or releases hazardous substances into water or soil.

REAL ESTATE APPLICATION: A licensed environmental contractor who disposes of hazardous substances removed in a remediation procedure (e.g., asbestos-containing material) will require the property owner or manager to sign a hazardous waste manifest document as the hazardous waste generator.

glove bag method   A method of containment that utilizes a length of polyethylene sheeting which has gloves completely attached to it.

REAL ESTATE APPLICATION: The glove bag method is utilized in the removal of asbestos-containing material (ACM) used as pipe insulation. The polyethylene sheet is wrapped loosely around the pipe insulation and sealed with duct tape to form a mini-enclosure. The asbestos-containing insulation is removed by the worker using the internally attached gloves. This localized approach to asbestos removal, which is specific for smaller applications such as pipe insulation, significantly reduces the scope of preparation and the size of the containment area.

good condition   Not subject to crumbling; *nonfriable.* Used in referring to asbestos-containing material (ACM) that poses no short-term concern of fiber release unless it is physically disturbed. In the long term, however, the material should be inspected periodically to determine its condition (friability).

groundwater   Water located below the earth s surface in porous rock strata and springs; a major source of drinking water.

half-face respirator   A respirator that covers a worker s nose and mouth areas and has cartridge-type filters attached to its sides. The half-face respirator, which is used when working in or near an asbestos environment such as above a ceiling that contains asbestos on the overhead structural steel, does not provide the protection required during large asbestos abatement projects.

hazardous material   Any substance that exhibits one or more characteristic hazards as determined by standardized tests. More broadly, any substance which is classifiable as combustible, flammable, explosive, reactive, toxic, corrosive (either to metal or to skin), carcinogenic, infectious, radioactive, or a skin or eye irritant.

hazardous waste   As defined in the *Resource Conservation and Recovery Act (RCRA)* of 1976, a solid waste or combination of solid wastes which, because of its quantity, concentration, or physical, chemical, or infectious characteristics, may (1) cause or significantly contribute to an increase in mortality or irreversible illness, or (2) pose a substantial present or potential hazard to human health or the environment when improperly treated, stored, transported, or disposed.

REAL ESTATE APPLICATION: Many common products and materials used in operating and maintaining managed real estate or by residents or tenants in their daily activities are considered hazardous wastes when disposed. The following are a few of the types of wastes that are subject to regulation under RCRA:

    Waste oils and automotive fluids
    Cleaning chemicals
    Used batteries (flashlight, automotive, etc.)
    Liquid and powdered chlorine and bleach
    Dry cleaning and laundry cleaning fluids
    Machinery lubricants
    Roofing materials
    Concrete and masonry cleansers and sealants
    Water treatment chemicals
    Freons and HVAC charging chemicals
    Copier toner and inks
    Dyes, paints, and thinners
    Pesticides
    Asbestos
    Used cooking oils
    Medical wastes

heavy metals   Any of several metallic elements having a high specific gravity and potentially harmful to humans at low concentrations; specifically, arsenic, cadmium, chromium, lead, and mercury, which accumulate in the food chain and are known to be toxic to humans.

high-efficiency particulate air (HEPA) filter   A mechanical air-cleaning device that is capable of removing particles of submicron size; also called *high-efficiency particulate arrestance.*

REAL ESTATE APPLICATION: A HEPA filter resembles a high-powered vacuum. In an asbestos abatement project, portable HEPA devices may be used for localized removal of small amounts of asbestos debris while more-permanent models may be used for the day-to-day, week-to-week removal of airborne asbestos fibers.

homogenous sample   A representative sample of similar material common to several areas.

REAL ESTATE APPLICATION: In order to eliminate redundancy as well as time and costs in trying to determine the type and percentage of asbestos fibers contained in the insulation applied to the steel structure of a 20-story building, representative samples from three of the floors may be tested if it can be determined that the insulation on the structural steel of all 20 floors is reasonably similar in nature (i.e., homogenous).

hydrochlorofluorocarbons (HCFCs)   Halogenated hydrocarbons created by adding hydrogen to *chlorofluorocarbons* (which also see). Because they decompose more readily than CFCs, they have been used as alternative refrigerants.

hydrofluorocarbons (HFCs)   Halogenated hydrocarbons that do not contain chlorine but are used for the same purposes as *chlorofluorocarbons* (which also see).

incident log   An IAQ-related document maintained by building operators or building management personnel that documents all known indoor air quality concerns, including concerns generated by building occupants or the building management team. The incident log assigns the IAQ problem a file number and tracks and organizes the other IAQ documents (complaint form, occupant interview, occupant diary, log of activities, etc.) that should be used in resolving the particular concern.

indicator   A chemical compound whose presence at certain concentrations may be used to estimate certain building conditions (e.g., adequacy of airflow, the presence of pollution sources).

> REAL ESTATE APPLICATION: Carbon dioxide (CO_2) levels measured in a particular space are normally a primary indicator of the amount of fresh air being introduced to that particular space.

indoor air quality (IAQ)   The state or condition of the air available to occupants in a building or a particular room within a building. The quality of indoor air is affected by outdoor pollution sources (vehicle exhaust), indoor pollution sources (tobacco smoke, office furnishings and equipment), and the effectiveness of HVAC system maintenance and operation, among other things. Although legislation has been proposed at the federal level, indoor air quality is not officially regulated at this time.

indoor air quality (IAQ) manager   One who manages the indoor air quality concerns of a building or group of buildings.

> REAL ESTATE APPLICATION: Designating a specific IAQ manager ensures consistency in the management of IAQ complaints, response, and remediation. The IAQ manager maintains all documents and records pertaining to IAQ issues in a building. In a larger facility, the IAQ manager might be the chief engineer or operations manager.

indoor air quality (IAQ) profile   A base-line description of the characteristics of a building that impact indoor air quality (i.e., structure, function, and occupancy). Upon completion of an IAQ profile, one should have an understanding of the current status of air quality in the building and information on the systems that are potential causes of problems in the future.

industrial hygiene   A technical occupation that generally deals with the safety and health of employees in the work environment. More specifically, an industrial hygienist may be employed by an environmental engineering firm to ensure that workers removing asbestos are wearing proper protective equipment and that airborne concentrations of asbestos fibers are within the specified limits.

intermittent problem   An indoor air quality (IAQ) problem that is not continuous or consistent in occurrence; one that occurs irregularly.

> REAL ESTATE APPLICATION: An effective method of resolving an intermittent IAQ problem is to maintain an occupant diary, an incident log, and a log of activities and systems operations. One or more of these records can provide building operators and management personnel essential information about the timing of systems operation, occupant complaints, weather conditions, and outside activities adjacent to the perimeter of the building, which can help resolve an intermittent IAQ problem.

landfill   A designated waste disposal site where solid wastes are spread, compacted, and covered with specified materials. Under RCRA, a disposal facility where hazardous waste is placed in or on the land.

leaching   The process by which contaminants are dissolved and carried away by water or moved into a lower layer of soil. Leaching of hazardous wastes into groundwater is a specific environmental concern.

lead   A heavy metal which can cause a variety of adverse health effects in humans. Lead poisoning has been widely publicized in regard to ingestion of flaking lead paint by infants and small children who reside in relatively older apartment buildings or houses. Other potential sources of toxic lead exposure are gasoline additives (e.g., tetra-ethyl lead), lead-based paints, and lead solder used to join copper pipe fittings. There are health screening, management (e.g., encapsulation), and removal requirements for lead, and persons who work with lead, similar in nature to the requirements for asbestos.

REAL ESTATE APPLICATION: The *Residential Lead-Based Paint Hazard Reduction Act* of 1992 became effective in late 1996. Under this law, sellers or landlords of housing built before 1978 are required to give the purchaser or tenant a lead hazard information pamphlet, disclose the presence of any known lead-based paint in the housing and give a copy of any available evaluation report, and give the purchaser a 10-day period to conduct a risk assessment or inspection for the presence of lead-based paint hazards (unless a different period is agreed to by the parties).

Legionnaires' disease   A lobar pneumonia caused by the bacterium *Legionella pneumophila,* so-named because its first recognized occurrence was during the 1976 American Legion convention. It is transmitted to individuals who inhale water mists (e.g., from fouled cooling towers, showerheads, drinking fountains, etc.) that contain levels of bacteria sufficient to cause infection.

REAL ESTATE APPLICATION: Routine maintenance of water-containing equipment and periodic testing for *Legionella* species should be part of a routine maintenance program.

mastic   A heavy-bodied adhesive compound often used in floor tile installation. Mastic used in the installation of vinyl asbestos tile (VAT) usually contains a small percentage of asbestos fibers. It is therefore normally considered an asbestos-containing material and should be treated as such.

material safety data sheet (MSDS)   An informational document, typically one to two pages in length, that outlines the specific characteristics of a substance. In addition to physical properties, a variety of hazard-specific information is included, not only hazardous ingredients, but flammability, explosion potential, toxicity and other health hazard data, and chemical reactivity are cataloged along with spill and leak procedures, recommended protective devices, and special precautions.

REAL ESTATE APPLICATION: It is the responsibility of the manufacturer of a product to make the MSDS available to the user of a particular material. (Product hazard labeling serves this purpose at the consumer level.) MSDSs should be filed in a safe place but readily accessible for future use. Specific product hazard information as detailed on an MSDS should be read by all personnel who will handle or work with the product before it is used.

maximum contaminant level (MCL)   The highest permissible level of a contaminant in a water supply intended for human consumption.

medical screening   An OSHA requirement, the physical examination (usually annual) conducted by a qualified physician for the purpose of periodically testing the health of an individual who works in an asbestos-containing environment or an asbestos-related industry. The same type of requirement applies to individuals who work with lead or lead-containing products.

> REAL ESTATE APPLICATION: A maintenance worker who is involved with repair and maintenance of equipment where asbestos-containing material is likely to be disturbed is required to receive an annual medical screening. OSHA requires that the medical screening be performed by or under the supervision of a licensed physician and provided by the employer at no cost to the employee.

mercury   A heavy metal whose use has been regulated under federal law but which may still be present in small quantities in various products (e.g., mercury vapor lamps).

microbiological contaminants   See *biological contaminants.*

microscopy   A method of examining materials that are or have components which are not visible to the unassisted eye. More specifically, a method of determining the quantity of asbestos fibers in a sample by using a microscope. Two common methods of microscopy are *phase-contrast microscopy (PCM)* and *transmission electron microscopy (TEM);* they offer different types of imaging characteristics.

mildew   Growth of a fungus on the surfaces of objects, within pores, or in deteriorated materials; such growth is also called *mold.* The conditions necessary for mold to grow on surfaces are temperature range above 40°F and below 100°F and the presence of mold spores, nutrient base, and moisture.

> REAL ESTATE APPLICATION: Mildew or mold can cause discoloration and odor problems, deteriorate building materials, and lead to allergic reactions and other health problems in susceptible individuals, especially those who have asthma or other lung diseases. Since temperature in most buildings ranges between 40°F and 100°F, mold spores are always present in outdoor and indoor air, and most surfaces contain nutrients that can support mold growth, moisture control is an important strategy in preventing or reducing mold growth.

mitigation   The reduction or elimination of a hazardous substance by a specific course of action. Asbestos abatement is an example.

monitoring   See *air monitoring.*

Montreal Protocol   An international agreement made in 1987 that establishes a comprehensive schedule for phasing out the production and use of *chlorofluorocarbons* (which see) and other ozone-depleting chemicals.

multiple chemical sensitivity   A condition in which a person is considered to be sensitive to a number of chemicals at very low concentrations.

> REAL ESTATE APPLICATION: An individual with multiple chemical sensitivity may have a physical reaction to chemicals emitted by a number of sources (e.g., a laser printer, a photocopier, a fax machine) while another individual may react similarly to only one source or experience no symptoms whatsoever.

National Emission Standards for Hazardous Air Pollutants (NESHAP)
An EPA document that defines acceptable practices for renovation and demolition activities where asbestos-containing material (ACM) is involved. The 1990 revision of this document requires public and commercial buildings facing major renovations or demolition to be inspected for the presence of ACM.

National Environmental Balancing Bureau (NEBB) An organization of qualified HVAC contractors who specialize among other things in air balancing, testing of HVAC systems, and testing of clean rooms. They establish standards and procedures for Testing, Adjusting, and Balancing (TAB) work and establish qualifications for TAB supervisors.

National Institute for Occupational Safety and Health (NIOSH) Conducts research, recommends standards to the U.S. Department of Labor, and conducts training in various subject areas, including indoor air quality, to promote safe and healthful workplaces. NIOSH undertakes investigations at the request of employees, employers, other federal agencies, and state and local agencies to identify and mitigate workplace problems. NIOSH also recommends guidelines for the management of asbestos-containing material (ACM) in buildings; its position on asbestos in the workplace has traditionally been more proactive than the EPA with respect to removal of ACM.

National Pollutant Discharge Elimination System (NPDES) A national permitting program under the Clean Water Act that imposes and enforces pretreatment requirements for wastewater and regulates the discharges of wastewater into U.S. waterways.

National Priorities List (NPL) The EPA listing of the most serious uncontrolled or abandoned hazardous waste sites identified for long-term remedial action under CERCLA.

negative pressure The intentional reduction (or absence) of air pressure within a given space, used to facilitate abatement procedures; also called *negative air.*

REAL ESTATE APPLICATION: The air pressure within a space or floor of a building undergoing asbestos abatement is typically negative while the adjacent spaces or floors are usually under positive air pressure. This pressure differential ensures the containment of any asbestos fibers that become airborne during the abatement process. Negative air pressure is usually achieved by using HEPA fans and filtration systems to exhaust air from the inside to the outside of the abatement space or to the outdoors.

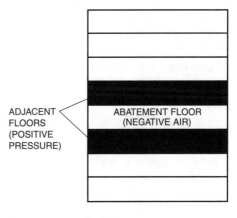

negative pressure

nitrogen oxide (NO$_x$) One of the two primary gases that reacts with water and moisture to form acids, the other being *sulfur dioxide (SO$_2$)*. Respectively, they form nitric acid (H_2NO_3) and sulfuric acid (H_2SO_4). These gases, which are emitted during the burning of heating oil and other petroleum products (gasoline, diesel fuel), combine with the water in normal precipitation to form *acid rain*. Both gases also react with volatile organic compounds (VOCs) to form ozone.

nonfriable   See *friable.*

occupant diary   An indoor air quality document maintained by an affected occupant for recording incidents or symptoms and associated observations as they occur. The occupant diary provides an excellent source of information relative to the frequency and severity of the symptoms which can be very helpful when evaluated in conjunction with the activities and operation of the building and the space itself.

occupant interview   A discussion process and a subsequent document pertaining to indoor air quality that records the observations of a building occupant in relation to symptoms experienced and conditions in the building.

> REAL ESTATE APPLICATION: The occupant interview would typically be conducted by the building IAQ manager. Potential issues for discussion would include the occupant's health history and questions about possible recent relocation of the occupant or other personnel, relocation of office equipment into the space, recent construction, floor or wall finishing or systems furniture installations conducted, etc. Relevant facts acquired from the occupant's physician may also provide important information to building personnel which could possibly narrow the field of potential sources of indoor air quality concerns.

Occupational Safety and Health Administration (OSHA)   The federal agency that promulgates safety and health standards (including requirements for surveillance, medical screening, analytical methods, and methods of control), facilitates training and consultation, and enforces regulations to ensure that workers are provided with safe and healthful working conditions. OSHA also promulgates occupational standards for preventing asbestos-related diseases and sets *permissible exposure limits (PELs)* for workers in an asbestos environment. OSHA regulations also provide guidance on day-to-day activities that may bring workers in contact with asbestos-containing material.

off-gassing   A term used to describe the process by which newly installed carpets, furniture, wall coverings, and other materials emit vapors and chemicals to the air, specifically *volatile organic compounds (VOCs);* also called *outgassing.*

> REAL ESTATE APPLICATION: Low levels of volatile compounds are emitted from many of the building materials and furnishings in an office for an extended period after installation, but the concentrations of contaminants emitted from newer products may be high enough to cause indoor air quality problems. Several solutions to off-gassing are removal of the contaminant using appropriate cleaning methods, encapsulation of the contaminant by sealing the surfaces, reducing the source by scheduling installation of furnishings during unoccupied periods, or storing new furnishings in a clean, dry, well-ventilated area for a period of time prior to installation.

operation and maintenance (O&M) plan   A written strategic plan to manage and control contaminants present at a property. Specifically, a plan which ensures that day-to-day management of a building is carried out in a manner that minimizes the release of asbestos fibers into the air and, when asbestos fibers are released either accidentally or intentionally, that proper control and clean-up procedures are implemented.

REAL ESTATE APPLICATION: An O&M plan for a property should be developed by an accredited individual in the environmental consulting field with assistance from the on-site management staff. The first step is to identify asbestos-containing materials (ACMs) and document their location, amount, and condition. As ACM is removed, the plan should be updated. An O&M plan in an asbestos environment (e.g., a building containing asbestos) should always address three primary areas of concern—abatement (removal) procedures, repair and maintenance procedures, and janitorial activities.

ozone   Triatomic oxygen (O_3) formed naturally in the upper atmosphere by the action of solar ultraviolet (UV) radiation on oxygen gas (O_2). Ozone is a powerful oxidizing agent, chemically unstable, and a respiratory and eye irritant.

At the earth's surface, ozone occurs as a by-product of such chemical processes as the manufacture of hypochlorite bleaches for textiles and paper and the chlorination treatment of water supplies. It is also produced by a natural photochemical reaction that takes place when nitrogen oxides are exposed to sunlight. Combined with smoke (including automobile exhaust), ozone is a component of smog. Within the lower atmosphere, ozone is a major pollutant; in the upper atmosphere, the ozone layer acts as a shield that protects humans, in particular, from UV radiation. (See also *ozone* application in Water Treatment, Water Chemistry.)

ozone depletion   Reduction or destruction of the ozone shield in the upper atmosphere, primarily caused *by nitrogen oxides (NO_x), carbon dioxide (CO_2),* and *chlorofluorocarbons (CFCs)*.

particulate   Microscopic in size; used in the plural to refer to dust, tobacco smoke, and other airborne particles that can be distributed throughout building spaces if the proper systems, maintenance procedures, and controls are not in place *(respirable particulates)*. Particulates may be effectively controlled through HVAC regulation (proper filtration, air changes, etc.).

peppermint oil   A fragrant liquid, with a smell similar to that of toothpaste, often used to investigate air movement in order to disclose or confirm suspected pathways of contaminants. It may also be used in resolving concerns about building pressurization, which may prohibit effective ventilation.

permissible exposure limit (PEL)   The maximum allowable human dose *(time-weighted average [TWA])* of a specified contaminant, usually set by OSHA.

personal air purifying respirator (PAPR)   A breathing device that protects a worker's facial areas (eyes, nose, mouth) and lungs. Specifically, a *full-face respirator* worn by personnel conducting asbestos-abatement activities to protect them from airborne asbestos fibers and other particulates.

phase-contrast microscopy (PCM)   A method of determining the concentration of fibers (fibers per cubic centimeter) in a given volume of air . (See also *transmission electron microscopy [TEM]*.)

REAL ESTATE APPLICATION: PCM does not distinguish between asbestos fibers and non-asbestos fibers. It is less costly than transmission electron microscopy (TEM) and would typically be used when there is no need to distinguish between asbestos fibers and non-asbestos fibers, as when it is anticipated that the total fiber count of a space is well below acceptable standards.

phase I assessment (also phase II, phase III)   See *environmental site assessment.*

picocurie (pCi)   One-trillionth of a curie, which is a unit of radioactivity. Radon gas levels are measured in picocuries.

polarized light microscopy (PLM)   The uniformly specified and accepted method (by EPA and OSHA) of determining the percentage of asbestos fibers in a given material. Language was adopted in 1990 specifying this method; prior to 1990, other methods of determining the percentage of asbestos fibers in a material were used.

pollutant   A contaminant that could potentially result in indoor air quality problems if building occupants are exposed to it. Potential sources of pollutants in a building include bathrooms, food-preparation areas, print rooms, smoking lounges, spaces being painted, loading dock areas, etc.

polychlorinated biphenyl (PCB)   A class of stable, nonflammable, oily compounds that serve, among other uses, as heat-transfer agents. They are known to cause health problems in humans if inhaled, ingested, or absorbed through the skin. PCBs can also contaminate water and soil, as they were once widely used as hydraulic fluids and in transformers.

>REAL ESTATE APPLICATION: PCBs are often contained in older electrical equipment or components (transformers, capacitors, light ballasts) that contain an oil to absorb heat. Electrical transformers in a building or on a property may contain PCBs (so-called wet transformers), particularly if they were manufactured before 1976. A malfunctioning transformer could emit smoke and vapors containing hazardous levels of PCBs.

polyethylene   A plastic material, impermeable to water (and selected other substances), which can be extruded in large-size sheets. Polyethylene sheeting is used for the containment and protection of floor, wall, and overhead surfaces and equipment or other objects during asbestos abatement. It is the preferred containment material in asbestos abatement because (1) it is impermeable to water, therefore protecting the work area and adjacent spaces during asbestos removal; (2) it is impermeable to asbestos fibers, therefore containing any ACM; and (3) it can be readily cut into sections with a utility knife and taped to the surfaces being protected.

preliminary site assessment (PSA)   See *enviromental site assesment.*

protective clothing   Disposable apparel items—typically lightweight coveralls (usually white in color), gloves, and foot coverings—worn during environmental remediation activities. More specifically, clothing donned by asbestos workers, along with respiratory protective devices, during abatement or remediation of ACM.

psychological stressors   Organizational (company, environment) and personal factors causing mental strains, which could produce symptoms similar to those caused by poor indoor air quality.

publicly owned treatment works (POTW)   A facility for treating sewage or industrial wastes that is owned by a state, municipality, or similar agency.

radon   A colorless, odorless, chemically inert, radioactive gas produced by the decay of radium that occurs naturally in almost all soil and rock. Its decay products can cause lung cancer.

REAL ESTATE APPLICATION: Radon migrates through soil and groundwater and can enter buildings through cracks or other openings in their foundations. The introduction of radon gas from the soil into a building is typically more prevalent during colder weather conditions when the heating system, in use, causes the radon gas to be pulled into the building because of the temperature difference between the soil and the basement area (natural draft effect). Based on early data, the EPA concentrated its radon reduction efforts on one- and two-family homes where basement accessibility and proximity to residents is greater. Radon is not usually considered a problem in commercial buildings because they have a smaller percentage of underground area per square foot of occupied space, and their internal air-flow requirements are more stringent.

regulated activities   A term specific to any work around asbestos-containing material (ACM) which is regulated by OSHA or the EPA. The regulations require different responses and procedures for their varying levels of impact in the workplace. EPA regulations generally depend on the amount of ACM being disturbed and the type of work being performed. OSHA regulations generally depend on the risk of exposure or the degree of potential exposure (fiber concentration in the air).

remediation   The removal of hazardous substances from a site, building, or other area under controlled conditions, often specific to removal of asbestos-containing material (ACM); also called *environmental remediation*.

Residential Lead-Based Paint Hazard Reduction Act   See *lead.*

Resource Conservation and Recovery Act (RCRA)   See *hazardous waste.*

Safe Drinking Water Act (SDWA)   A law enacted in 1974 and amended in 1986 that authorized federal regulation of drinking water systems and required EPA to establish standards for levels of contaminants in drinking water.

sample   A representative portion of a substance (air, water, soil, or other material) collected for testing, usually to determine the presence and concentration of a suspected contaminant. Examples of types of samples are air samples, swipe samples, bulk samples, and water samples. Air sampling methodologies include use of an *air pump* (which see), a direct-reading meter, detector tube kits, or a personal monitoring device (also referred to as a dosimeter). The method chosen will vary, depending on such factors as the level of contaminant concentration, the time available for sampling, the degree of accuracy required, and the costs involved.

sanitary sewer   A large pipe used to carry liquid-borne waste from plumbing fixtures and to which storm and surface water and groundwater are not admitted intentionally.

sanitizer   An antimicrobial agent that significantly reduces but does not necessarily eliminate all the microorganisms on a treated surface.

secondhand smoke   See *environmental tobacco smoke (ETS).*

septic tank A watertight receptacle, buried in the soil, designed and constructed to receive discharged sewage from a property sewage pipe, separate solids from the liquid, digest organic matter, store digested solids, and allow the liquids to discharge for final disposal.

sewage Any liquid-borne waste containing animal or vegetable matter in suspension or in solution.

sewage pump A specially designed centrifugal pump that can move liquid and pieces of solid matter without clogging.

> REAL ESTATE APPLICATION: Sewage pumps are required in buildings where the sewage drainage pit is located below the street sewer (i.e., when gravity drainage is not feasible). Most sewage systems are provided with high-water alarms to warn building operators of a pump or system failure.

sewage treatment An artificial process applied to wastewater in order to remove materials or alter its composition, rendering it less hazardous to human health.

sewer A channel that carries wastewater (sanitary sewer) or runoff rain water or melted snow (storm sewer), or both.

sewerage The effluent carried by sewers and the system used for collection, treatment, and disposal of liquid wastes.

sick building syndrome (SBS) Acute health and comfort effects experienced by building occupants, which are apparently linked to the time they spend in the building but for which no specific illness or cause can be identified. Symptoms such as respiratory complaints, irritation, and fatigue have been associated with SBS, and complaints may be localized in a particular room or zone or widespread throughout the building. Analysis of air samples often fails to detect high concentrations of specific contaminants. Symptoms of SBS may be caused by any or all of the following:
1. Combined effects of multiple pollutants at low concentrations.
2. Other environmental stressors (e.g., overheating, poor lighting, noise, vibration).
3. Ergonomic stressors.
4. Job-related psychosocial stressors (e.g., overcrowding).
5. Unknown factors.

> REAL ESTATE APPLICATION: The term sick building syndrome has been prominently publicized. Incidents seem to occur more frequently following initial construction in new buildings or during a major retrofit of a system (e.g., HVAC) in existing buildings. SBS is often related to emissions of vapors associated with new construction materials or components.

smoke test A method of evaluating the effectiveness of HVAC systems, in particular tracking potential contaminant movement and identifying pressure differentials, using chemical smoke, which will move from areas of higher pressure to areas of lower pressure if there is an opening between them (a door, cracks, elevator shaft, etc.); also called *chemical smoke test.*

soil gases Gases that enter a building from the surrounding soil (e.g., radon).

spray-on insulation An acoustical insulating material typically applied to ceilings by means of a spray gun. The spray-on material yields an irregular coating with rough patterns and uneven surfaces that serves as a sound absorption barrier. Prior to the restrictions on the use of ACMs, spray-on insulation often contained asbestos fibers.

standing water   Water or moisture which remains on a surface for an extended period. Its continued presence can result in mold growth, insect activity (e.g., breed mosquitoes), and other biological consequences which can pose a threat to air quality, particularly if the standing water is in close proximity to the fresh air intakes in a building.

sterilizer   An antimicrobial agent that destroys or eliminates all forms of bacteria, fungi, viruses, and their spores. Because spores are considered the most difficult form of a microorganism to destroy, EPA considers the term *sporicide* to be synonymous with sterilizer.

storm sewer   See *sewer.*

sulfur dioxide (SO₂)   See *nitrogen oxide (NOx).*

Superfund Amendments and Reauthorization Act (SARA)   The 1986 law that amended the *Comprehensive Environmental Response, Compensation, and Liability Act (CERCLA)* of 1980, together known as *Superfund,* which has four primary objectives:

1. Monitoring and regulation of "inactive" disposal facilities, dump sites, landfills, and spill sites;
2. Providing regulations and requirements for the remediation and cleanup of these sites;
3. Increasing the reporting and response requirements for spills and releases (to local, state, and federal agencies); and
4. The issue of "absolute liability" (the assignment of liability for remediation or cleanup costs of contaminated sites, regardless of fault).

swipe test   A test in which a suspected contaminant is collected by means of passing or wiping a small, circular white cloth filter across the exposed surface (also called *surface test*). The filter is then placed under a microscope for examination.

time-weighted average (TWA)   The amount of material to which a person is exposed in a given period, usually a work day. The accepted procedure for determining the concentration of an airborne contaminant by obtaining a representative sample of air over a specified time period and extrapolating the results. OSHA often establishes time-weighted average concentrations for specific contaminants such as lead and asbestos.

toxicity   The quality of being poisonous; in the environmental milieu, the degree of danger posed by a substance to living organisms. On material safety data sheets, toxicity is expressed as the median lethal dose (LD_{50})—the amount of the material that is lethal to (kills) 50% of the animals exposed to it.

Toxic Substances Control Act (TSCA)   A law enacted in 1976 that authorizes the EPA to require testing of chemicals and to regulate hazardous substances. TSCA addresses issues such as control of and restrictions on the use of polychlorinated biphenyls (PCBs) and the issuance of material safety data sheets (MSDSs).

transite   A cementitious asbestos-containing board used on building facades as a thermal insulating barrier and for decoration.

transmission electron microscopy (TEM)   A method of determining the quantity of asbestos fibers in a given air sample. (See also *phase-contrast microscopy [PCM]*.)

> REAL ESTATE APPLICATION: TEM differs from phase-contrast microscopy (PCM) in that it can differentiate between asbestos fibers and non-asbestos fibers. Being more comprehensive, TEM also costs more to perform.

treatment   A process designed to change the chemical or biological character or composition of a substance; specifically, such a process applied to a hazardous waste.

underground storage tank (UST)   A large container located partially or completely underground that is designed to store fuel oil or other petroleum products, liquid chemicals, etc. Prior to the 1980s, USTs were often constructed of steel and therefore subject to corrosion, particularly in wet soil conditions. If a UST developed a leak, the fuel or other contents could seep into the soil and enter local drinking water supplies (groundwater, lakes, streams, etc.). A *leaking underground storage tank (LUST)* can be an environmental hazard.

underventilation   A condition of insufficient air changes, typically associated with an HVAC system in which the number of times the air in the building is changed is too low.

> REAL ESTATE APPLICATION: The potential causes of underventilation are numerous. Underventilation could result from malfunctioning of central HVAC equipment (central air handler, dampers, etc.) or local HVAC devices (e.g., variable air volume dampers). It could also be due to pressure relationships within various spaces—in some instances, the HVAC equipment may be functioning properly, but the area may have a heavily loaded occupancy. In this case, the HVAC system may have to be adjusted or upgraded in capacity in order to perform adequately.

vinyl asbestos tile (VAT)   A resilient floor covering material that contains small amounts of asbestos (usually 2%-5%) and could pose a health concern for occupants if tiles are damaged or disturbed and occupants are exposed to that condition for a prolonged period.

> REAL ESTATE APPLICATION: *Floor tiles* are typically 12" × 12" squares and approximately ⅛" thick, but they are also made in 9" × 9" squares, and it is mostly these smaller size tiles that contain asbestos. Vinyl asbestos tile was installed in many commercial and residential buildings through the late 1970s into 1981; in good condition, it poses no threat to occupants' health. *Vinyl composition tile (VCT)* does not contain asbestos fibers. (See also *vinyl tile* in Architecture, Construction, and Project Management.)

volatile organic compounds (VOCs)   Carbon-containing chemicals that are typically found in indoor air at trace levels. VOCs evaporate from the many housekeeping products and building materials at a property. Many hundreds of these chemicals are typically found in an indoor environment; they may present an IAQ problem when individual compounds or mixtures of different compounds exceed normal background concentrations. In sufficient quantities, VOCs can cause eye, nose, and throat irritations, headaches, dizziness, nausea, and other symptoms. Formaldehyde is one of the most common VOCs and one of the few indoor air pollutants that can be readily measured.

REAL ESTATE APPLICATION: A few examples of the thousands of VOC-containing sources in a building are:

1. Personal items such as hair sprays and scents.
2. Photocopy machines and laser printers.
3. Office products such as correction fluid and copy paper.
4. Other chemicals such as glues or adhesives, photographic solutions, and permanent markers.

wet method   A method of abatement in which the source of contamination is saturated with "amended" water or, in the case of dusting, using a wet rag and misting. Wet methods are almost always used in the abatement of asbestos-containing material in order to limit the release of fibers.

Additional Resources

Additional information can be obtained from the organizations listed here, many of which have also been described or cited in the glossaries. Detailed information about these and other related trade associations and professional organizations can be found in the *Encyclopedia of Associations* published annually by Gale Research, Inc. Also listed are sources for specialized technical publications as well as selected individual publications related to subjects of the glossaries.

Organizations

American Institute of Architects (AIA), 1735 New York Avenue, N.W., Washington, DC 20006 (phone: 202-626-7300; fax: 202-626-7587; web page: www.aiaonline.com).
>   Organization of professional licensed architects; developer of *Architectural Graphic Standards* (9th ed.; 1994) published by John Wiley & Sons, Inc.

American Insurance Association (AIA), 1130 Connecticut Avenue, N.W., Suite 1000, Washington, DC 20036 (phone: 202-828-7100; fax: 202-293-1219; web page: www.aiadc.org).
>   Formed by merger of National Board of Fire Underwriters, Association of Casualty and Surety Companies, and American Insurance Association; publishes *Summary of States Regulations and Laws Affecting General Contractors.*

American National Metric Council (ANMC), 1735 North Lynn Street, Suite 950, Arlington, VA 22209 (phone: 703-524-2007; fax: 703-524-2303).
>   Publishes *Metric Reporter* newsletter covering metric transition in the United States and elsewhere.

American National Standards Institute (ANSI), 11 West 42nd Street, 13th floor, New York, NY 10036 (phone: 212-642-4900; fax: 212-398-0023; web page: www.ansi.org).
>   Clearinghouse for nationally coordinated voluntary standards for building construction, methods of testing and analysis, measurements, etc.

American Society for Testing and Materials (ASTM), 100 Barr Harbor Drive, West Conshohocken, PA 19428 (phone: 610-832-9585; fax: 610-832-9555; web page: www.astm.org).
>   Establishes and publishes standards for materials, products, systems, and services, including test methods to verify compliance with those standards.

American Society of Heating, Refrigerating and Air-Conditioning Engineers (ASHRAE), 1791 Tullie Circle, N.E., Atlanta, GA 30329 (phone: 404-636-8400; fax: 404-321-5478; web page: www.ashrae.org).
>   Technical society of HVAC and refrigerating engineers that conducts research and publishes reference materials on HVAC systems, equipment, and applications, including engineering standards.

American Society of Mechanical Engineers, ASME International, Three Park Avenue, New York, NY 10016 (phone: 212-591-7000; fax: 212-591-7674; web page: www.asme.org).
  Develops boiler, pressure vessel, and power test codes as well as safety codes and standards for equipment, including *Safety Code for Elevators and Escalators* (ASME 17.1-93).

American Society of Plumbing Engineers (ASPE), 3617 Thousand Oaks Boulevard, No. 210, Westlake, CA 91362 (phone: 805-495-7120; fax: 805-495-4861).
  Organization of consulting engineers involved in design and specification of plumbing systems; its code committees review existing industry codes and propose revisions to code writing authorities.

Asphalt Roofing Manufacturers Association (ARMA), 4041 Powder Mill Road, Suite 404, Calverton, MD 20705 (phone: 301-231-9050; fax: 301-881-6572; web page: www.asphaltroofing.org).
  Organization of manufacturers of asphalt shingles and built-up roofing (BUR) and modified bitumen roofing systems.

Association of Facilities Engineers (AFE), 8180 Corporate Park Drive, Suite 305, Cincinnati, OH 45242 (phone: 513-489-2473; fax: 513-247-7422; web page: www.afe.org).
  Formerly (1996) American Institute of Plant Engineers (AIPE); professional society of plant engineers and facilities managers; publishes *AFE Facilities Journal.*

Association of Major City Building Officials (AMCBO), 505 Huntmar Park Drive, Suite 210, Herndon, VA 22070 (phone: 703-481-2020; fax: 703-481-3596).
  Organization of city and county building officials that focuses on issues of public safety in buildings and building codes; publishes *Directory of Building Codes and Regulations* (every 2 years).

Building Officials and Code Administrators International (BOCA), 4051 West Flossmoor Road, Country Club Hills, IL 60478 (phone: 708-799-2300; fax: 708-799-4981; web page: www.bocai.org).
  Organization of entities concerned with building, fire, mechanical, plumbing, zoning, and housing regulations; publishes *BOCA® National Building Code* (every 3 years), one of several model building codes recognized in the United States and Canada; also publishes mechanical, plumbing, and maintenance codes.

Building Owners and Managers Association International (BOMA), 1201 New York Avenue, N.W., Suite 300, Washington, DC 20005 (phone: 202-408-2662; fax: 202-371-0181; web page: www.boma.org).
  Publishes *Standard Method for Measuring Floor Area in Office Buildings* (ANSI/BOMA Z65.1-1996).

Building Owners and Managers Institute International (BOMI), 1521 Ritchie Highway, Arnold, MD 21012 (phone: 410-974-1410; fax: 410-974-1935; www.bomi-edu.org).
  Offers classroom and home study courses leading to the Real Property Administrator (RPA), Facilities Management Administrator (FMA), Systems Maintenance Technician (SMT), and Systems Maintenance Administrator (SMA) designations.

Construction Metrication Council, National Institute of Building Sciences, 1090 Vermont Avenue, N.W., Suite 700, Washington, DC 20005 (phone: 202-289-7800; fax: 202-289-1092; web page: www.nibs.org/cmchome.htm).
  Supports metrication of federal construction and promotes use of the metric system of measurement in the U.S. construction industry; publishes *Construction Metrication* newsletter.

Electronic Industries Alliance (EIA), 2500 Wilson Boulevard, Arlington, VA 22201 (phone: 703-907-7500; fax: 202-457-4985; web page: www.eia.org).
  Organization of electronic component manufacturers; affiliated with the Telecommunications Industry Association.

Illuminating Engineering Society of North America (IESNA), 120 Wall Street, 17th floor, New York, NY 10005 (phone: 212-248-5000; fax: 212-248-5017; web page: www.iesna.org).
   Organization of engineers, architects, designers, contractors, and others who deal with illumination; publishes lighting standards.

Institute of Electrical and Electronics Engineers (IEEE), 345 East 47th Street, New York, NY 10017 (phone: 212-705-7900; fax: 212-705-4929; web page: www.ieee.org).
   Organization of engineers and scientists in electrical engineering, electronics, and allied fields; publishes standards related to these fields.

Insulated Cable Engineers Association (ICEA), P.O. Box 440, South Yarmouth, MA 02664 (phone: 508-394-4424; fax; 508-394-1194).
   Develops standards for insulated wire and cable.

International Conference of Building Officials (ICBO), 5360 Workman Mill Road, Whittier, CA 90601 (phone: 562-699-0541; fax: 562-692-3853; web page: www.icbo.org).
   Publishes *The Uniform Building Code* (every 3 years), one of several model building codes recognized in the United States and Canada.

International Facility Management Association (IFMA), 1 East Greenway Plaza, Suite 1100, Houston, TX 77046 (phone: 713-623-4362; fax: 713-623-6124; web page: www.ifma.org).
   Organization of persons involved with facility management—the planning, designing, and managing of workplaces; certifies facility managers; publishes *Facility Management Journal.*

International Organization for Standardization (ISO), 1, rue de Varembé, Case postale 56, CH-1211 Genèva 20, Switzerland (phone: 22 749 01 11; fax: 22 733 34 30; web page: www.iso.ch).
   Proper name: Organisation Internationale de Normalisation; federation of national standards bodies united to promote standardization worldwide; affiliated with American National Standards Institute (ANSI).

National Association of Women in Construction, 327 South Adams Street, Fort Worth, TX 76104 (phone: 817-877-5551; fax: 817-877-0324; web page: www.nawic.org).
   Promotes the construction industry and supports the advancement of women within it; Greater Phoenix (Arizona) Chapter publishes *Construction Dictionary* (9th ed.; 1997).

National Conference of States on Building Codes and Standards (NCSBCS), 505 Huntmar Park Drive, Suite 210, Herndon, VA 22070 (phone: 703-437-0100; fax: 703-481-3596; web page: www.nasbcs.org).
   Organization of state building code officials and others entities interested in building code administration; publishes annual *Directory of Building Codes and Regulations.*

National Electrical Manufacturers Association (NEMA), 1300 North 17th Street, Suite 1847, Rosslyn, VA 22209 (phone: 703-841-3200; fax: 703-841-3300; web page: www.nema.org).
   Develops product standards covering nomenclature, ratings, performance, testing, and dimensions for equipment used in generating and distributing electricity; participates in developing the National Electrical Code and National Electrical Safety Codes.

National Environmental Balancing Bureau (NEBB), 8575 Grovemont Circle, Gaithersburg, MD 20877 (phone: 301-977-3698; fax: 301-977-9589; web page: www.nebb.org).
   Publishes *Procedural Standards* for building systems commissioning, certified testing of clean rooms, and testing, adjusting, and balancing environmental systems.

National Fire Protection Association (NFPA), 1 Batterymarch Park, Quincy, MA 02269 (phone: 617-770-3000; fax: 617-770-0700; web page: www.nfpa.org).

NFPA develops and publishes fire protection standards (*Fire Protection Handbook* and *The Life Safety Code® Handbook*); publishes annual compilation of more than 270 fire codes, standards, recommended practices, manuals, and guides on fire protection (*National Fire Codes*).

National Lighting Bureau, 831 Colesville Road, Suite G106, Silver Spring, MD 20910 (phone: 301-587-9572; fax: 301-589-2017; web page: www.nlb.org).
    Organization of companies involved in lighting; develops guidelines for interior and exterior lighting requirements; provides comparison data on types of lights, illumination they provide, and related costs.

Southern Building Code Congress, International (SBCCI), 900 Montclair Road, Birmingham, AL 35213 (phone: 205-591-1853; fax: 205-591-0775; web page: sbcci.org).
    Publishes *Standard Building Code* (every 3 years), one of several model building codes recognized in the United States and Canada.

Telecommunications Industry Association (TIA), 1300 Pennsylvania Avenue, Suite 350, Washington, DC 20004 (phone: 202-383-1480; fax: 202-383-1495; web page: www.tiaonline.org).
    Organization of manufacturers of products for and providers of services to the telecommunications industry; affiliated with Electronic Industries Alliance.

Underwriters Laboratories (UL), Inc., 333 Pfingsten Road, Northbrook, IL 60062 (phone: 847-272-8800; fax: 847-272-8129; web page: www.ul.com).
    Establishes product safety specifications for electrical, fire protection, and other equipment and devices and conducts tests to verify that those specifications are met.

U.S. Metric Association (USMA), 10245 Andasol Avenue, Northridge, CA 91325 (phone: 818-363-5606; fax: 818-368-7443).
    Promotes greater use of the metric system of measurement; publishes *Metric Today* newsletter.

Publishers

R. S. Means Company, Inc., 100 Construction Plaza, Kingston, MA 02364 (phone: 617-585-7880; fax: 617-585-7466; web page: www.rsmeans.com).
    Publishes construction cost information and reference books, including *The Building Professional's Guide to Contract Documents* (rev. ed.; 1990), *Means Graphic Construction Standards* (1986), and *Means Illustrated Construction Dictionary: New Unabridged Edition* (1991); web page includes links to related resources.

Government Institutes, Inc., 4 Research Place, Suite 200, Rockville, MD 20850 (phone: 301-921-2300; fax: 301-921-0373; web page: www.govinst.com).
    Publishes information on government regulatory topics in environmental, health and safety, and telecommunications fields, including the current *Code of Federal Regulations*. Environmental titles include *Building Air Quality* (1990), *Directory of Environmental Information Sources* (5th ed.; 1995), *Environmental Audits* (7th ed.; 1996), *Environmental Engineering Dictionary* (2d ed.; 1992), *Environmental Law Handbook* (14th ed.; 1997), *Environmental Laws and Real Estate Handbook* (3d ed.; 1992), and *Environmental Statutes* (annual compilation of environmental regulations).

Publications

Air-Conditioning and Refrigeration Institute: *Refrigeration and Air-Conditioning* (Englewood Cliffs, N.J.: Prentice-Hall, Inc., 1979).

Anixter Wiring System Catalog (Skokie, Ill.: Anixter Brothers, Inc.).

Carrier System Design Manual (Syracuse, N.Y.: Carrier Corporation, 1972).

Harris, Cyril M. (ed.): *Dictionary of Architecture and Construction* (2d ed.; New York: McGraw-Hill, Inc., 1993).

Parks, David C.: *Environmental Management for Real Estate Professionals* (Chicago: Institute of Real Estate Management, 1992).

Periodicals

Architecture magazine (web page: www.architecturemag.com)

Building Design and Construction (web page: www.bdcmag.com)

Building Operating Management (web page: www.tradepress.com)

Buildings: The Facilities Construction and Management Magazine (web page: www.buildings.com)

Professional Builder (web page: www.probuilder.com).

Index

drying agent, 71
dry lay-up, 114
dry pipe sprinkler system, 44
dry pipe system, 44
dry pipe valve, 44
dry powder fire extinguisher, 44
drywall, 191, 197, 223
dual-duct system, 73
duct, 73
duct silencer, 73
duct smoke detector, 44
ductwork, 73
duplex receptacle, 129
duty cycling, 14
dynamic load, 192

E
easement, 182
eaves, 192
economizer, 73–74, 104–105
economy cycle, 73–74
eddy current test, 14
eductor, 15
effective area, 74
effective temperature, 74
effective value, 129
effluent, 231
egress, 45
ejector, 15
elastomer, 192
elastomeric, 192
elbow, 15
electrical degree, 146–147
electrical grid, 133
electrical loss, 141
electrically supervised, 129
electrical metallic conduit, 129
electrical metallic tubing, 125, 129
electrical non-metallic tubing, 129
electrical riser, 152
electrical service, temporary, 220
electric circuit, 129–130
  dedicated, 126–127
  distribution, 128, 157
  open, 145
  parallel, 146
  series, 152–153
  short, 153
  single-phase, 153
  three-phase, 156
  three-wire distribution, 157
electric current, 130, 131
electric heater, 74–75
electric heating element, 130
electric heat lamp, 130
electricity, 130
electric lock, 130
electric-pneumatic switch, 75
electric-release strike, 130

electric resistance heater, 74–75
electric space heater, 130
electric strike, 130
electric water heater, 130
electrolyte, 130
electromagnetic field (EMF), 231
electromechanical control, 172–173
electromotive force (emf), 130
electron, 131
Electronic Industries Alliance (EIA), 131, 251
electrostatic filter, 75
elevation, 192
elevation view, 192
elevator(s)
  beam detector, 163
  buffer, 164
  carrying capacity, 164
  certificate of inspection, 164–165
  counterweight, 165
  double-deck, 166
  drive sheave, 166
  entrapment, 167
  firemen's service, 168
  group operation, 169
  guide rails, 169
  hoisting ropes, 169–170
  independent service, 171
  interfloor service, 171
elevator access switch, 163
elevator bank, 166, 171
elevator cab, 164
elevator cables, 169–170
elevator capacity, 166
elevator car
  bottom clearance, 164
  escape hatch, 167–168
  operating panel, 164
  position indicator, 164
  top clearance, 174
elevator car parking, 172
elevator door(s)
  close time, 165
  nudging, 172
  open time, 165
  operator, 165–166
  proximity edge, 172
elevator landing, 171
elevator machine room, 167
elevator pit, 167
Elevator Safety Code, 167
elevator speed, 167
elevator stop, 174
eliminator, 75
emergency egress, 45
emergency escape hatch, 167–168
emergency generator, 45
emergency lighting, 45

emergency power generator, 45
emergency stairwell, 45
emergency stairwell pressurization, 56
emission, 231
encapsulation, 231
end bell, 131
energy, 15
energy audit, 15
energy management system (components), 27, 31, 38, 87, 94, 96–97, 127, 142, 146, 156, 177
engineering scale, 213
enthalpy, 15
entrainment, 75
entrapment, 167
envelope, 192
environmental impact statement (EIS), 231
Environmental Protection Agency (EPA), 231–232
environmental remediation, 243
environmental site assessment, 232
environmental stressors, 232
environmental tobacco smoke (ETS), 232
epoxy, 192
epoxy resin, 192
equal, 192
equalizer, 15
  tube, 15
  valve, 15
equivalent, 192
ergonomics, 232
escalator(s)
  balustrade, 163
  cleated steps and risers, 165
  comb plate, 165
  floor plate, 168
  side panel, 174
  skirt boards, 174
  steps, 174
  truss, 174
escape hatch, 167–168
ethernet, 131
ethylene propylene diene monomer (EPDM), 220–221
ethylene propylene diene monomer roof membrane system , 192
evacuation signal, 45–46
evacuation tone, 45–46
evaporation, 15
evaporation loss, 75
evaporation phase, 75
evaporative condenser, 76
evaporator section, 76
excess air, 105

packaged, 99
perimeter, 87–88
variable air volume, 99
water-cooled, 100
hydraulic accumulator, 1
hydraulically calculated
sprinkler system, 51
hydraulically designed
sprinkler system, 51
hydraulic elevator system,
170–171
hydrochlorofluorocarbons
(HCFCs), 229, 235
hydrofluorocarbons (HFCs),
229, 235
hydrometer, 33, 135
hydronic system, 83
hydrostatic test, 21
boiler, 106
hygrometer, 83
hygrostat, 82–83

I
I beam, 198
ice storage, 98
ignition temperature, 21
Illuminating Engineering Society of North America
(IESNA), 159, 251
illumination, 135
illumination level, 139
impairment, 51
impedance, 135–136
impeller, 21
impulse, 155
inactive door, 198
inactive leaf, 198
incandescent lamp, 136
inches of mercury column, 21
inches of water column, 21
incident log, 236
incomplete combustion, 106
indemnification clause, 198
independent operation, 171
independent service, 171
indicator, 21
chemical, 236
litmus paper, 114
indicator lamp, 136
indirect lighting, 136
indoor air quality (IAQ),
236, 240
diagnostic testing, 230
emission, 231
Environmental Protection
Agency (EPA), 231–232
exhaust fumes, 232
incident log, 236
indicator, 236
intermittent problem, 236
Legionnaires' disease, 237
National Institute for Occupational Safety and
Health (NIOSH), 239
occupant diary, 240

occupant interview, 240
off-gassing, 240
pollutant, 242
psychological stressors,
242
radon, 243
volatile organic compounds
(VOCs), 246–247
indoor air quality manager,
236
indoor air quality profile, 236
inductance, 136
induction motor, 136
induction system, 83–84
induction unit, 83–84
inductive load, 136
inductive reactance, 136
industrial hygiene, 236
infiltration, 84
inflammable, 49
infrared (IR), 21
detector, 171
radiation, 21
scanner, 171
inhibitor, 114
inlet dampers, 69–70
in phase, 136–137
instantaneous load, 21
instantaneous water heater,
21
instant-start fluorescent
lamp, 138
Institute of Electrical and
Electronic Engineers
(IEEE), 137, 141, 251
instructions to bidders, 198
instrument, 21
Insulated Cable Engineers
Association (ICEA), 137,
251
insulating glass, 198
sound, 216
insulating glass unit, 198
insulation
acoustical duct lining, 60
electrical, 137
spray-on, 244–245
thermal, 22
insulation resistance, 137
insurance, contractor's liability, 188
insurance binder, 198–199
integrated ceiling, 199
intercom, 137
intercommunication system,
137
interference, 137
interfloor service, 171
interior cabinet, 51
interior glazed, 196
interior zone, 84, 101
interlock, 22
boiler control, 106
key, 199
intermittent, 22

intermittent problem, 236
internal combustion engine,
12, 13
cylinder, 11
International Standards Organization (ISO), 22,
137, 251
international system of
units, 34
internet, 137
intranet, 137
inverter, 138
invitation to bid, 199
ion, 114
ion exchange, 114
isolation joint, 199

J
jack, 138
jamb, 199
jockey pump, 51–52
joint, 199
broken, 183
butt, 184
control, 193
expansion, 193
isolation, 199
lap, 199
longitudinal, 201
miter cut, 202
tape, 219
tongue-and-groove, 221
joist, 199
jumper, 138
junction box, 138

K
keyed-alike cylinders, 199
key interlock, 199
kickplate, 199
kilovolt-ampere (kva), 138
kilowatt (kw), 138, 148
kilowatt-hour (kwh), 138–
139
knockout, 139

L
labor and material payment
bond, 199
labor bond, 199, 219
labyrinth, 22
labyrinth seal, 22
lagging, 22
laminar flow, 22
laminate, 199
lamination, 199
lamp, 139
electric heat, 130
fluorescent, 132, 146
gaseous, 133, 142, 153
halogen, 134, 149
high-intensity discharge,
135
high-pressure sodium, 135
incandescent, 136

The Institute of Real Estate Management

The Institute of Real Estate Management (IREM®) was founded in 1933 with the goals of establishing a Code of Ethics and standards of practice in real estate management as well as fostering knowledge, integrity, and efficiency among its practitioners. The Institute confers the CERTIFIED PROPERTY MANAGER® (CPM®) designation on individuals who meet specified criteria of education and experience in real estate management and subscribe to an established Code of Ethics. Real estate management firms that meet specific organizational and professional criteria are granted the status of ACCREDITED MANAGEMENT ORGANIZATION® (AMO®). Individuals who meet specified educational and professional requirements in residential site management and subscribe to a Code of Ethics are granted the status of ACCREDITED RESIDENTIAL MANAGER® (ARM®).

The Institute's membership includes more than 8,500 CPM members, approximately 3,800 ARM participants, and some 629 AMO firms. Among CPM members in the United states, nearly 45% manage conventionally financed multifamily rental housing properties, 15% manage federally assisted housing, and 18% manage condominium and cooperative ownership properties; approximately 54% manage office buildings, more than 39% manage shopping centers and retail strip stores, and roughly 28% manage industrial parks and warehouses.

Since 1933, IREM has been enhancing the prestige of property management through its activities and publications. The Institute offers a wide selection of courses and publications about real estate management and related topics. To obtain current information about IREM programs, write to the Institute of Real Estate Management, 430 North Michigan Avenue, P.O. Box 109025, Chicago, Illinois 60610-9025, or telephone 1-800-837-0706. Also visit our home page on the World Wide Web—http://www.irem.org.